THE FARMER'S BEDSIDE BOOK

The Farmer's

Bedside Book

COUNTRYWISE BOOKS

THE FARMER'S BEDSIDE BOOK

is published by

Countrywise Books: The Farmers Weekly

161/166 Fleet Street, London EC4

printed by Hazell, Watson & Viney Ltd

compiled by Suzanne Beedell

and designed by

Don Marshall

©

National Trade Press Ltd.

1964

COUNTRYWISE BOOKS

ARE EDITED BY

BARBARA HARGREAVES

Sole Distributors

Temple Press Books

❧ CONTENTS

5

7

9

❧ PREFACE

My task in making this book was one of exclusion rather than inclusion. Ten years' back numbers of the *Farmers Weekly* made a pile exactly ten feet tall and I had to get the essence of these into one book exactly one-and-a-quarter inches thick.

Barbara Hargreaves has been Editor of the Home Section during the whole of the ten years from 1953 to 1963 which the book covers, and there are many of her articles herein. I do not think that there is a subject on which she is not interesting and eminently readable. There are pieces from most of the regular contributors, both to the farming and home sections of the magazine; there are readers' letters, poems, competition entries, and stories.

The drawings have been selected from those which accompanied the original articles. They are an integral part of the *Farmers Weekly* without which no anthology from the magazine could be complete.

There is no particular order of time or subject about the contents; the book may be read from beginning to end, or dipped into as you wish. It is not intended specifically for male or female readers, but just for those who enjoy reading.

Many of the contributors are people who are by no means professional writers, yet they are so good that one wonders if any profession other than farming hides such talent. Or is it something about farming, something about living in the country, living in the wind and the sunshine, and the rain and the mud; knowing the meaning of hard work, and of birth and death, which stirs some creative force, some need for self expression in people which has resulted in the accumulation in ten years through one magazine, of enough material for half a dozen books such as this one.

SUZANNE BEEDELL

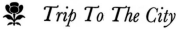

Could ambition plunder sorrow,
Then would I weep to light the faces
Of the people in the streets.
For in their eyes has never been the wild world,
Where a bird sings and the wind sweeps.
They've never seen the lacy damsons,
Etched against December skies,
Nor plucked at breath against a gale.
They've never seen the thin blue hummocks
Drift through autumn woods,
Nor seen the cloud dropped shadows
Slide along the hills,
They've never heard the almost silent sea
That whispers through the bracken on the cliffs.
Nor ever been so silent,
Nor ever been so still
To hear the gorse pods popping
To the quiet clouds.
Perhaps, when I am old,
I shall no longer care
From where the wind is blowing,
But be like them
With eyesight shortened,
Straitened by the city street,
O, let the warm soft mother wind blow from the hills,
And curl the jaws of lambs with yawns,
Turn up your collar, man in the street,
As you slipshod by with your aimless feet.
Turn up your collar, man in the street,
But listen to the wind.
And I? am less than a noise of twittering stars,
Or the shadows cast by the fluttering grass.

R. J.

🌺 SPRING

Whatever would happen, I wonder, if things didn't begin and end, come and go, rise and fall. If in the words of the negro song "there'd be no more crying, no more dying, no more striving". Heaven—they say. Would it, I wonder?

A life with no contrasts. A world all one colour. Roses all the year round and everyone smiling. We'd go dotty with the monotony. And if, in a state of bliss with the blossom a-bloom and the summer breeze on our brow, we exclaim, "If only this would go on for ever." What a monstrous lie we tell.

The warmth of the sun is more luxurious for giving back what its absence has taken away. A greeting more joyful for being reborn out of the parting with someone we love. Blossom more startling, born of a bare brown bough.

These are the contrasts which make up the balance of our lives, and add the colours—complementary one to the other—which turn everyday things into an exciting kaleidoscopic pattern of adventure.

And so, just as we're beginning to tire of the smell of wood-smoke and evenings by the fire which we welcomed at the turn of the year, we are ready to greet that recognisable something in the air which tells us it's spring.

Our hearts miss a beat—mine does anyway. For this is the signal to heave oneself out of the mental hibernation into which endless leaden skies and north-east winds are apt to drive one, on the last lap of winter.

I always think we must be a little less of the human being in the spring. A little closer to the earth. For that indefinable something which we are all aware of about now is akin, perhaps, to the supersonic sound to which only animal ears are sensitive?

Every year I say like the Irish, "Next year I'll not be feelin' it." But next year is here; and spring has struck again.

The dawn chorus which, if honest, one would admit to sounding like a lot of corks being twisted round in a number of bottles, is still (for me anyway) one of the sublime musical sounds. The little girl below our window who comes to pick pussy willow with her yellow hair tangled in the branches is still a scene as freshly sweet as it was five years ago when standing on tiptoe, she could just reach the bottom branch. And the furniture in our house looks just as preposterously arranged as it did ten springs ago.

Of course the piano should be on the opposite side of the room. Only idiots could have put the sofa so far from the light. How hideous that picture looks over the mantelpiece and why did we ever imagine anybody could work at a desk bang under the window?

Thus, with no reference to past upheavals I become, like my neighbours at the Rookery up the hill, all nest conscious and, with as much hullabaloo as they make, turn everything upside down.

This year, my spring sort-out was precipitated by a successful bid at a local auction sale. A portrait of a sloe-eyed gypsy boy with a bright blue scarf round his neck.

The artist had drawn him with bold black pencil strokes and the only colour he used was blue—a willow pattern blue—for his scarf. Curiously effective.

I know exactly where the picture should go. On a particular wall where the blue of that scarf would pick up the blue from a chinese bowl full of hyacinths on the table below.

I was right. It looked perfect. But as I stood there everything else looked just as hopelessly wrong.

This was late afternoon. By dusk with the family only half an hour from home I was sitting on top of the piano, one armchair stuck in the doorway, and another wedged between the sofa and the desk. I had failed to improve on last year's rearrangement or the year's before, and much too exhausted to start moving everything back in place. I was gazing at my gypsy in a daft sort of way and sniffing up the scent of the hyacinths.

But one thing spring does for you is to fatten up confidence in your own mood and, temporarily, take several inches off your conscience.

Heaven forbid the mood should last. I daren't think what havoc would be caused or what monotony would have to be endured if March hares and April fools met up with Midsummer madness. Let's keep them a fair way away from each other and preserve the pleasure of variety.

BARBARA HARGREAVES

TO SIT—OR TO SOW?

What makes the farmer so valuable to any nation is his ingrained belief that a man's first duty is to himself. This invites and obtains widespread criticism from the great majority of non-farming people who, incidentally, would be badly off if the farmer abandoned his natural habit and copied their example.

This marked difference between town and country was never more definitely illustrated than during the Cuba crisis. Granted, the average farmer worried in private about the possible outcome, but did he take part in any of the public protests? No. Why? Simply because he just hadn't time to spend demonstrating outside embassies, sitting on pavements, bothering the police and all the rest of it.

Instead he got on with his job. For instance, there was winter wheat to be sown before rain made such work impossible, cows to be milked, grain to be delivered, sugar beet to be lifted, and many other tasks that had to be done to time in order to keep faith with dozens of other people who depended on the farmer keeping his written or spoken word. And, above all there was his duty to that portion of the land of his own country that time and circumstance had placed in his keeping.

These thoughts came to me in connection with my own farming during that fateful week when Cuba filled the headlines and I was as sadly worried as were the great majority of British people. Ought I, as a farmer-journalist, to let the latter calling take pride of place and journey to London to find out what townsfolk were thinking and doing? Rightly or wrongly, I decided against that and, instead, got busy ensuring that all my winter wheat was sown before the rains came.

I think most British farmers did the same, according to the needs of their holdings. If mankind decided to be crazy enough to blow up the world and everybody in it, the fact that my wheat had been sown wouldn't make any difference to anybody. But if sanity prevailed, as it did, then my seed would be safely underground for the benefit of mankind, no matter whether I lived long enough to harvest it or not. By some standards a selfish narrow-minded attitude, by mine a much better one than either marching, rioting, or pavement-sitting. The basic idea, of course, is that if you can't help, don't hinder, but get on with your job.

A. G. STREET

A New Calf

Do you think at all, small boneless ones,
As you lie in the slime and straw,
That for you who didn't choose the change
The deal is somewhat raw?
Knowing the warmth of the homely womb,
The gentle sway of maternal walk,
Is it worth the cold, the air, the light,
To hear your mother talk?
As you kick and struggle and try to grow
In a medium new and unkind,
What puzzles and questions form themselves
In your baby bovine mind?
As the harsh tongue licks the slime away
And your lungs take in the strain
Of breathing a cold, unfriendly air,
Do you long for the dark again?
I watch and I wonder as there you lie
Kicking your legs and trying to rise,
Why you and every calf that's born,
Have such sadly enquiring eyes!

MRS. D. A. BUNNING

☙ ATMOSPHERIC PRESSURE!

It never rains but it pours—or so it seems here lately. We have had an abundance of apples (not one last year), a nice lot of plums on the few remaining trees, a gardenful of winter greens, a lovely lot of daddy-longlegs, moths, earwigs, wasps, harvesters, and small black flying beetles booming, buzzing and creeping into everything. We've had two sets of twins—or at least the cows have! And we've lost Gertie, an Ayrshire, from bloat. John has been on the "telly", in fact we've hardly had a dull moment.

Last week was dreadful. By 8 a.m. Monday after Dick, Jim and the schoolchildren had left the house, I felt as if I'd been run over by a steamroller (tho' I look quite the opposite).

It started on Friday. John suddenly shouted for me to bring some sharp knives quickly while he phoned for our vet. So I hurried as fast I am able at the moment, but before help came, poor Gertie was dead—bloat. What a loss—she did 1,500 gallons in her second lactation and was very popular despite her strong will and cabbage stealing.

But more was to follow. Jim, who has been helping our friends the Woodhouses, for several weeks at Oaksey, came home for the weekend to do some field-work for us. That fateful Friday evening he was driving the van when he skidded on a wet tricky corner in Bath and caught the tailend of a Rapier parked optimistically in a no parking area. The Rapier came off best—only smashed a rear light. The van was buckled on its near side along by the back wheel. The Rapier's owner would not exchange names and Jim in the excitement of the moment didn't take his number. The boys had gone to bed before their father came home late that night. Before breaking the bad news the next morning, I took up a strong sweet cuppa to him, and later put a specially good breakfast in front of him.

He received the news with a remarkable forbearance but with John feeling badly about Gertie, and Jim about the truck, the atmosphere sort of built up so that by Sunday evening, I somehow felt it was all my fault (tho' maybe I'm over-sensitive just now).

Even Charlie's eight passes in "O" level were brought into it. "Have you done anything about making Charlie organise himself to take maths again, Babs? Well, why not?" By the time John, frustrated in case the van would not now be repaired in time for him to do his last few trips across the Mendips, ironed me out a bit more by saying, "Have my sheets been sent to Shuttleworth yet?" Sam innocently carried on the good work by asking "have you re-footed my rugger socks yet, Mum?" I began to wish that Kirsten hadn't been away that weekend! But for Lynda coming to help, I should have been carried off in a padded, soundproof ambulance!

We might have lost another cow recently if Dick hadn't decided he would rather stay home that night and leave at 6 a.m. next day. He'd only been home long enough to have a meal and he told me he was going into the sitting room to do "homework" (for his job), adding briskly "If you are ready by 9 o'clock sharp I'll take you across to Wolverton."

Half an hour later the peace was shattered by Charlie coming to say that Bramble, who was calving, was in real trouble. Dick hurried down to the cowshed. A few minutes later he came puffing in tearing upstairs to change. "No hope of going out tonight now. Bramble's calf is just sitting inside her—all we can see is its rump." So I relaxed with some mending.

About forty minutes later the door burst open and there stood Dick with shirt held gingerly in his fingers saying, "It's another damn bull." Then seeing me he bellowed, "Aren't you ready yet Babs? I'm off in five minutes when I've washed—shan't wait for you if you aren't ready—they'll be closed." I answered, "Yes, dear," automatically as I boggled at the sight of my lord and master standing there in all his glory, muck up to his armpits, clad only in his socks and underpants. His trousers were a mucky grey heap on the floor.

An hour later, driving home up the lane, we saw the cowshed lights still on. "Whatever's happened now?" said my better half, but in a much more mellow mood. Charlie came out to meet us. "Bramble's had another one," he grinned. Twins! Sure enough there on the cowshed floor were two black and white calves with a bewildered Bramble looking on. Wonder if it's catching? We shall see!

BABS HONEY

🌹 CHRISTINA

A long, dark staircase with a small girl at the bottom of it wondering if she dare begin the frightening climb to the top . . . a voice from the doorway, saying, "Pop up and see Granny while I go and do some shopping" . . . the door banging and the dark becoming even darker. . . .

These memories came rushing back to me all at once when I opened the door of my mother's room yesterday and saw Christina sitting in the armchair smoking one of my mother's cigarettes and wearing a scarf round her head. She didn't look a day older in spite of the thirty odd years since I last saw her.

I see her again now, in my mind's eye, as I turned the corner of the third flight of stairs all those years ago. She was sitting in a bath-chair on the landing dressed in a red cloak with a hood . . . her hands folded demurely in her lap, her face . . . well, I was too scared to meet her eyes for more than a second, but in that glance I noticed extreme severity. And above all, an inhuman stillness.

I tore up the next flight and knocked hysterically on Granny's door with my small fist, still looking over my shoulder. Today's child would have burst into the room without knocking, but such was the convention in those days that one's manners halted even fear.

"You shouldn't have run all the way up the stairs like that, dear child," said Granny, as I stood panting at her bedside. "You'll tire yourself out."

A conventional piece of repartee, too, since most children of six could run up a dozen staircases without being the slightest bit fatigued.

It never occurred to me to ask my grandmother about Christina—who she was, what she was, why she was there.

Perhaps children kept things to themselves much more in those days. All that concerned me at the moment was how I could avoid her on my way down again.

I was offered my usual sweet, but it had no taste.

"Whatever's wrong with you this morning child?" asked my grandmother. "You're in a trance."

That was it. A trance. Some sort of magic had got me, for I had no idea what the word "trance" meant. If only I could break the spell perhaps Christina would vanish out of my life.

People who say they would like to go back to being a child with no worries don't know what they are talking about. A small mind is a miasma of unexplained mysteries. It seems that we inherit all the superstitions and folk-lore of primeval man, whatever teachings we have at mother's knee.

Pigeons came up to the window-sill in Granny's room to be fed with crumbs and on the days I visited her I was allowed to scatter them myself. How especially lovely that morning it was to see the big strong birds flying up and pecking away at the crumbs. If only I could fly down to the street like them, I thought; then I wouldn't have to descend that awful staircase past Christina.

Stuffed full of Grimm and Hans Andersen as I was, I could almost see the pigeons getting bigger, and bigger, or me getting small enough to fly away out of that dark house on one of their backs.

By the time my mother arrived to fetch me away I had worked out a plan to avoid Christina. As we descended the staircase I held on to the banisters with my left hand and my mother with my right hand. I shut my eyes and kept up a steady flow of chatter all the way down so that I wouldn't even feel or hear Christina's presence.

I counted the landings—third, second, first. Safe. I opened my eyes and saw the light streaming under the door into the dim hall. Never had it seemed so bright and inviting.

My mother never knew the agony of that descent until I told her the whole story yesterday—with Christina sitting there nonchalantly with a cigarette between her fingers.

"By the way," I said. "What is Christina doing here, anyway?"

"Granny says she's too old to paint now, and as Christina

is taking up room in her small flat she wants me to sell her. They are not making toy figures (artists' models) this size any more, so she should get a good price."

So poor old Christina was to be sold like a slave in the market place. It would be a revenge on my childhood fears to be glad of this news, but instead, I actually found myself asking my mother not to let her go. After all, perhaps it isn't often that one can look fear between the eyes and ask it to stay!

BARBARA HARGREAVES

🌸 HERB WINDOW BOX

This week I have been lifting my mint, thyme, parsley, borage and rue and planting them in a gaily painted window box, for my kitchen window-sill. Ordinary soil will do, keeping it moist. I shall then have a supply of herbs for the winter, even if you still have some in the garden it's often too wet or cold to run out. Incidentally, if your garden mint tends to run amok, to prevent it spreading you can dig a hole and sink a large tin or washing up bowl, leaving it slightly above the soil level, and if you transplant your mint to this it will stay put.

MRS. SANGSTER

🌸 ESSEX

I suppose the mention of "Essex" to most people conjures up visions of marshland, flat country, or ditches filled with sedges! But how misleading that description of Essex is!

As a child I lived near the village of Radwinter. I dream now of the delicious years I spent there; of hay-time, when we crawled about (crawling to escape the farmer's eye!) in search of luscious wild strawberries; my sisters packed theirs into jam jars, but I picked mine extravagantly on the stem, starry flowers and all because they were so pretty! I remember trimming my hat with them once or going jauntily home, all abob with strawberries! I must have been a curious child because I laboriously picked blackberries that way too, for the beauty of the sprays! Quite recently I nearly let my heart rule my head and almost blued the whole of my housekeeping money on a lovely white tea set I saw, simply because I was overcome by nostalgia at the sight of it, it was decorated with sprays of blackberries! I still hanker after it. . . .

There was a really "babbling brook" near our school, the edge was fringed with the lushest marsh marigolds. We paddled in the brook during our dinner hour and dried our feet on our dinner napkins. My mother could never understand how we made them so messy—often we would scamper off to a sunny corner in the churchyard to dry the mucky cloths on the headstones; they dried much quicker there until one day the nuns from nearby St. Julien reproved us! Woods which are now the property of the National Trust were then paradise to us, the rare and beautiful oxlips grew in profusion, sweet chestnuts making canopies to enchant, hazel nuts for the finding and beech nuts for industrious fingers. The surrounding meadows held such treasures as white and pink violets—myriads of them, ragged robins, ladies smocks, and even bee orchids. Oh yes, I knew where they all lived. We hung cowslip balls in our windows to scent the air, we made thick ropes of them to decorate wooden hoops, which we carried slung on beribboned poles, and went "a garlanding" on May Day singing a quaint little garland song, which I wish I could remember. My memory of that part of Essex is filled with gorgeous smells—particularly the smell of fat little bunches of white violets upon the school windowsills—held by rows of small paste pots!

The sharp tang of the clipped box hedges in the delightful Dutch Gardens given to Saffron Walden by Elizabeth Fry and missed by so many visitors to the lovely old town, because they do not know of its existence.

The smell of Saffron Walden's prideful possession—the museum—musty, but a dear old mustiness! More pungent, but still as dear, the smell of jars of green healing ointment, freshly made by an old lady I knew, from pure lard, and crushed greater celandine which grew abundantly in the watery lanes;

it was gathered for her by us children in return for which we received a small jar of the ointment to take home, it soothed away a sore knee! We gathered for the same old lady, fresh young green leaves of meadow sweet, she made a tea from them which did something "for the bowels dear!" I cannot remember whether it tightened or loosened them! But I loved squirming my nose into the heady cream foam of the flowers. The joyous fragrance of pheasant eye narcissus which grew so thickly, that we carried armsful to the church at Eastertide—the spicy breath of the wet yew as we filed in to the Children's Eucharist, haunts me still. The geraniumy smell of cut macro-carpo used to line the grave of a well-loved vicar—into which we were allowed to peep before the funeral, roses had been speared in amongst the evergreen, and I remember dropping hot tears into the beautiful grave, because it was all to be covered with earth! I also know another spot in Essex where heather grows and bracken and harebells, it is not all marsh-land and sea lavender, not by a long way.

I look back with pleasure on the memory of the long avenue of beech trees near Audley End, my name was carved with love and surrounded by hearts and the initials of the carver on one of the satiny branches; carved by one long since lost to me, but sweet to think of occasionally.

I have lived in lovely Worcestershire, cool Cambridgeshire, glorious Devon and others with equal claims to fame, but Essex for me will always be mine! I took my own children to see the marsh marigolds and the oxlips—they were enchanted, as I had been so it wasn't only me, was it? No, it was *Essex!*

MRS. RANKIN

ROSE-TRIMMED HAT

Daisy Spence sat between her parents in the pew in front of ours, the pews were old with high backs, but not so high that we couldn't see Daisy's hat. It was straw with pink roses all round the crown. We used to watch the Spence family coming into church, always late. Mrs. Spence, sharp pink nose quivering, Daisy with the roses abob on her hat looking like a suet duff with her puffy white face and little dark eyes, and then Mr. Spence, tall and thin with droopy moustaches and a sanctimonious expression.

"That man Spence," my Grandma Higgins was heard to remark, "that man Spence is so holy he makes my blood boil."

But we children were not concerned with Mr. Spence or, indeed, with any of the Spences, it was only Daisy's hat that fascinated us.

My sisters, Maud, she was 12, and Meg, 11, and me, I was 13, always wore the same. I don't only mean the same as each other, but the same kind of clothes, all the time. Navy blue serge skirts, white piqué blouses with sailor collars and hard sailor hats with navy ribbons round the crown. We each had two outfits, one for Sunday and one for weekdays. Our little brother, Albert, was always got up like a naval officer, and often when we were all out walking and real sailors passed us, they would grin and salute him.

Papa was in the Navy. Had been from a boy, Mam always said proudly. That was just it, she was so proud of Papa that everything that might please him was done, even to dressing the whole family in sailor's clothes all the time.

When I was younger I didn't mind so much. Maud and Meg didn't mind much anyway, but when I got older I did, I minded dreadfully. I longed to wear a muslin dress with roses at the waist and one of those big straw hats with red ribbons hanging down the back like the picture in my favourite book. I used to sit in church and hate Daisy Spence for her rose-trimmed straw, we all three used to sit and stare so hard at the back of Daisy's head, it's a wonder it didn't catch fire.

Of course I knew it was wrong to hate anyone so much just because you envied them their hat, especially in church. I used to squeeze my eyes tight and pray ever so hard to God not to let me go on being such a wicked sinful girl, but I expect he was too busy to hear because I just went on hating Daisy Spence harder than ever.

On Saturdays Mam would send we three girls into the little town for groceries and such like. Sometimes we had a copper or two to spend. Maud always gave hers to a beggar or the ragged children playing in the gutters. Meg spent hers on sweets which she ate all to herself, but I saved mine in a tin box hidden behind a loose brick in the back lavatory.

Every Sunday evening after we had finished singing hymns in the parlour, I'd go out and lock myself in and count my hoard. Of course Maud and Meg knew I was saving, but not why, that was my secret. I couldn't tell Mam either.

One Saturday Maud and Meg had colds and I was told to go to the town alone. My heart leapt, here was my chance. Before going out I visited my hoard and wrapped it up carefully in a paper bag. It was three shillings and eightpence halfpenny and a pearl button off my drawers.

Gorrage's was the only drapery shop in town. It was dim and smelt of camphor and damp, and they sold everything from ribbon, laces and boot buttons to calico, red flannel and ladies hats.

My hands were damp with nerves as I tried to mince nonchalantly past Mr. Gorrage's black figure washing its pale cold hands in invisible soap. I could feel the faint trickle of sweat at my hairline as I stepped into the hat department. The saleswoman in her severe black pursed her thin lips and said in a reedy voice, "Can I be of service?"

"Yes, please," my own lips were stiff with excitement. "I want to see some straw hats, with ribbons."

The next fifteen minutes were the most exciting of my life. A bewildering collection of hats were put on my head and to each one I remarked, "That's very nice," and waited for the next one. When some twelve or so hats had been tried on I inquired their prices. Alas, every one was a good deal more than three shillings and eightpence halfpenny and a pearl button. Greatly daring I rose and put on my prim sailor.

"Thank you very much," I said to the assistant, "I'll tell my mother and she will come and see you," and out I swept.

On the Sunday morning Mam called me into her room and I knew something was wrong. She only called us to her room if she was angry, or there was bad news. But it wasn't bad news this time, I could see by Mam's face she was angry.

"Sarah!" her voice was sharp, "What is this about you going trying hats in Gorrage's?" I might have known that in little place like Minsea my lovely secret wouldn't be mine long.

When Mam looked like that there was only one thing to do. Confess. So I did, sobbing out my story Mam's lavender-scented bosom; the pin of her fob watch scratched my cheek, but I was so upset I never noticed it till after.

I told her all about Daisy Spence's hat, and how I hated being dressed as a sailor, about the money and even its hiding place in the lavatory.

After I had done, Mam held me very tight and said, "Child, why did you not tell me all this before?"

"Oh I couldn't Mam!" I cried.

"Child," I looked up and her eyes were full of tears, "You are not afraid of me are you?"

"Oh no Mam!" I was as horrified as she was at the idea, "Only I didn't want to hurt you. About Papa and the Navy, you're so proud of him and so are we of course, but . . ." I trailed off lamely. Sensing a fresh outburst she laid a finger on my lips. "There child, it is all over. I see I have been very wrong."

On my fourteenth birthday I had a white muslin dress and a big straw hat with red ribbons hanging down the back. I think I was the happiest girl in the world the first time I wore it in church. I hardly glanced at Daisy Spence as she hurried in. I did just notice that her hat was rather faded and that the roses drooped. I remember wondering in an absent sort of way, why on earth I had ever coveted such an ugly hat.

PATRICIA GRAY

'Gilten Market'

There are still men, they say,
Who plant and plough according to a moon
Whose golden horns are plenty's promises
Or else the twin blades of a scything dearth . . .

For those who leave moons to astronomers
The runes are chalked on boards of world exchanges
Or scribbled on the earth by tractor tyres.
Yet, in forgotten corners of old barns,
The horseshoe still invokes a goddess luck,
While ancient sorceries
Hang on our trees
Toys of the bright moon's coinage
And men who needs must view a Christmas beast
As toil and money in live hundredweight
Will pause to gild its non-existent horns.

DONALD LAMBLE

🌹 SICK STORY!

More than twenty years ago I was at death's door. The doctor came upstairs and went away quickly and I knew my husband was waiting for the inevitable verdict. My husband—never a demonstrative one—came rushing upstairs and I thought now he will give me an encouraging farewell—perhaps tell me I have been a good wife. What he said was this.

"Of all the dirty tricks you have played on me, this is the worst. It was you who wanted these four children, not me, and now you are going off to peace and comfort to leave me to battle through life with them—it is not fair."—He went out and banged the door.

ANON

🌹 CAMPFIRE COOKERY

Barbecue was a term used by buccaneers for a framework on which large pieces of meat were roasted and in America today it is a name given to Alfresco feasts where food is cooked in this way. It has now become very popular in this country and I find it much the easiest method of making a camp fire.

We used a perforated tin drum, partly filled it with solid fuel and laying a few bits of paper and sticks at the bottom to help lighting. A piece of small mesh wire-netting is then fixed across the top for the food to lie on. A stronger grid can be used for boiling a kettle if Mum insists upon her "cuppa".

One or more drums can be used according to the number of people. No cooking utensils are required so the only things to be carried are the drums, fuel and food. In addition each person needs a fork or, better still, a skewer so that it does not matter if it is inadvertently dropped in the fire.

Any food which can be grilled is suitable, the most popular in our family being sausages and boned kippers. There are, however, many things which are quite easy to deal with but which are not often included in a menu of this kind.

For a rather more elaborate meal young pigeons split and rubbed with a little oil are excellent when barbecued and eaten cold, cooked legs of game, poultry, hare or rabbit can be similarly treated. Chops or steak should be first wrapped in thick kitchen paper which will eventually burn away but at the beginning it helps to retain the juices. Liver and bacon can also be cooked with great success and, of course, thick slices of bread can be toasted on the grid.

With a little imagination the fare can be varied almost endlessly and most attractive dishes prepared.

A great advantage of this type of fire is the almost total absence of smoke. There is also less risk of it spreading than with a loose fire. Even so, the greatest care must be taken in the selection of a site. If you have no suitable place on your own property, there is nearly always a friendly farmer who will allow you to go on his land if he is convinced that you will cause no damage. There are also numerous parts of commons and moors where a perfectly safe spot can be found.

The golden rules for choosing a site are that a fire must never be made in a wood or too close to a hedgerow, rick or building—especially a thatched one. It must be borne in mind, too, that the wind may quickly change and so endanger something which had appeared to be at a safe distance.

An enclosed fire, such as I have described, is excellent on the beach where there is a wind blowing.

A barbecue is a splendid way of entertaining the family's young friends and when the weather is not too hot it combines well with a sports party or a paper chase.

Actually, we often have a picnic of this kind on our own farm, without any guests, because we all thoroughly enjoy it. On these occasions the children make all the arrangements themselves. They get me to give them money to buy the food in the village shop and so give me a complete rest from catering at any rate for one meal.

In fact, if a benevolent uncle or god-parent has recently "weighed in", they sometimes insist upon using their own pocket money for their purchases and I am then their guest. Being somewhat sentimental, I am greatly touched.

When the meal is over we are careful to see that the fire is properly out. We have made a rule about all campfire parties

which I think is reasonable—that a grown-up must be present.

If the few simple precautions which I have mentioned are adhered to a barbecue makes a most enjoyable kind of picnic and—joy of joys—there is not so much as a sandwich tin to wash-up!

CHRISTIAN VERNON

🌹 WILTSHIRE

... Now, what of the Wiltshire people? To the outsider, some of us may appear slow and somewhat offhand, but let them come amongst us, and I am sure they will find that, "Ther be zummat bout they Wilsher Volk that thee cain't' bate em' no-were, zno!"

MRS. S. FISHER

31

🌹 THE MODERN CHATELAINE

In the days of the whimple, the lady of the house hooked on to her belt or girdle each day, a very useful and ornamental object called a chatelaine. It consisted of a number of silver hooks and chains from which were hung the keys of doors and boxes she wished to keep locked, but to which she needed frequent access. On other hooks there usually hung a pair of scissors, a thimble in a case, a pincushion, and a perfume bottle.

You can sometimes pick these chatelaines up in antique shops, for they went on being made up to Victorian times. I haven't seen one lately, and am told that soon after the war the Americans had a craze for them and took most of them back as presents for their wives or girl friends.

Going through a lot of old stuff in a chest the other day, I found one which had been given me long before the war and which I had forgotten I ever owned. Such a pretty thing, all silver with a chaste design of leaves and roses. The thimble had long since vanished from its little cup, but the sapphire-blue velvet pincushion—about the size of a sixpenny piece—still had the pins stuck in it.

And the little memorandum book with its real ivory pages still had three entries written inside it which read: Speak Cook Muriel luncheon. Buy Pink silk. Philip's white boots.

I hooked it through my leather belt and stood up jangling and, just as quickly, I put it back in the drawer. Nigger-brown corduroy was definitely not its background.

But what a good idea. To carry the tools of your trade round with you as you went about your housewifely duties.

I am sure I could compose a modern chatelaine for myself, of which the most advanced student of Time and Motion would approve. As I thought about it, my list of essential items got to such a length in my mind that had my chatelaine been more than a fantasy, I would have clanked round the house like a knight in armour.

However, by a severe process of elimination, I whittled

down my list to under a dozen items just to bring it nearer reality.

On the first count I had hooked on to my chatelaine every key to every door in this house just to keep the doors shut, but, on the second count settled for our bedroom and the spare room. The former to prevent my husband showing visitors the fine view over the river and at the same time a display of my most recently shed clothes. The latter in order to keep just one room in the house free from the muddy tracks of man and beast.

Instead of the pretty little velvet pincushions would hang a medium-sized magnet for collecting drawing pins, nails, kirbigrips and gramophone needles from every carpet and corner in the house. It might then be possible to keep a store of these things and dole them out when I'm asked, in place of threepences and sixpences for new lots.

Somebody told me once that she never bought hairpins. If she ran short of them she merely walked down the street with her eyes on the ground and within twenty-five yards she picked up enough to last her a month. She then took them home and boiled them for half an hour before using them.

Instead of the scissors, I would hang a screwdriver from my chatelaine, for apart from my kitchen spoon, it's a tool I reckon to use more than any other. If it's not a screw loose in a hinge, a door handle or a plug, then it's a fuse to be mended.

Fuses are constantly going in our house. It's nothing to find ourselves sitting down to supper and suddenly be plunged into total darkness. It doesn't surprise me in the least for I am sure we overload the generator or whatever it is by the amount of lights we have on at once in this house.

Lights, like doors, are the bane of my life, for I spend most of my time switching off the former and shutting the latter. And if I've been out and come home after switching-on time, I can recognise our house a mile away—it looks like a power station.

Fuse wire would also hang from my chatelaine, for however clever my hiding places, someone always manages to discover it, and use it for everything from hanging pictures to mending wire netting.

Also on my list would be a whistle, which I've discovered is far more effective for calling folk in for meals than any bell, gong, or clapper. A piercing note on a whistle is far more insistent than a bell which has too benevolent a voice. A whistle seems to say, "at once", whereas a bell says, "when you're ready".

The perfume bottle is the one old-fashioned item that I would keep on my modern chatelaine. Imagine being able to take great lungfuls of Chanel Number Five when you discovered the puppy had made a mess on the carpet, or the cabbage had boiled over, or the pig food was on the simmer. It would be like a swig from a brandy flask to a man stuck in a snowdrift.

And, lastly, I would hang from my chatelaine a pencil as big as a policeman's truncheon if I could find such a one. This Christmas I was given one a foot long. At last, I thought, this one will stay. Nobody can fit this one in bag or pocket.

But, believe it or not, yesterday it disappeared, and once more I found myself scratching a telephone number down with my nail.

BARBARA HARGREAVES

❧ A FLIGHT LINE

You can discover it by accident, of course. You are walking back in the early dark of an autumn or winter evening when suddenly, somewhere high above, you catch the quackle of duck talk. You look up and there, going like the clappers against the first star, is a wedge of mallard.

Having discovered these duck by accident you may dismiss their appearance as an accident, which would be a pity. For the betting is that if you stood in the same place, at the same time, every night for the next week you would see or hear duck on at least five of them. What's more the duck in question would be heading in the same direction each time.

You have blundered on what every coastal wildfowler, but I believe few inland shooting men, would immediately recognise as a flight line.

Duck, principally mallard and teal, find their way into the bag of every man with a gun who has shooting access to water meadows or river banks, and as such they're looked upon as a lucky entry under "Various" in the gamebook.

But the odd mallard killed in the water meadows in broad daylight is only part of the story. The story really begins with the age-old and fortunate habit that makes duck early risers, cautious sleepers and late diners.

This is the way of it: owing to the fact that duck got a bad fright at some time long past, practically the whole tribe now elects to feed at night and rest by day. Rumour has it that this was forced on them by the predatory behaviour of man. I personally doubt this very much. Man has only been harrowing duck on a large scale for a comparatively short time.

For daylight resting all duck prefer a large sheet of water in which they can settle, usually slap in the middle, tuck their heads back to front in that complacently contortionist way, and close at least one eye. Nothing pleases them better than to spend a day at sea if it is within reasonable range, say twenty miles.

The moment at which they leave to feed is governed by many things—the wind, the weather, the state of the moon, the roughness of the water on which they are squatting, the distance to the feeding ground, but most of all by the degree of light. All other conditions being agreeable to them, they will stay where they are until the light fades to a point at which they have no option but to take off.

Once airborne, they have one thought: to reach their grub as quickly as possible. The trip at sundown to feed is called "Evening Flight" and this is what you saw as you walked home in the dark. The reverse journey, or morning flight, will inevitably take place at around dawn and back over the same route.

Now all this is basic stuff. The point is how to exploit it. It's no good asking the average rough shooter whether he's noticed any good flight lines lately. I've asked them this on the west coast of Ireland, which is plainly teeming with wildfowl, only to be told that ducks don't behave like that in County Mayo. Of course they do. They behave like that everywhere from the Arkansas pine oak flats to the swamps of

35

the Nile Valley. What the Irish meant was that they themselves were never out and about and looking at the right time of day or night.

The same applies in most English inland districts where the shooting man considers the day is over when the first pheasant goes to roost.

Then the duck shooter's short moment of glory is just beginning. I believe that inland duck shooting should start on a one inch Ordnance Survey map. All river valleys should be noted, even those of quite small streams, for these are natural highways for flighting duck. Certainly every large sheet of water should be ringed, and I include the most uninteresting concrete reservoirs, for, in passing, let me record that in one morning at such a place I saw mergansers, goosanders, smew, goldeneye, widgeon, teal, mallard, shoveller, pintail, pochard and Canada geese.

Not all these are shootable, of course, and the reservoir was a bird sanctuary, but none of this dims the fact that they all had to go somewhere to eat at night. The question was, where? Back to the map again.

Look closely for sewage farms, not the nasty, modern hygienic kind but the good old smelly rural ones full of unspeakably plashy places. Ducks adore feeding amid these, and they'll taste all the better for it.

Reconnoitre on the ground all nearby lakes and ponds that the map discloses. Look for cover in the form of reeds but, even more important, find out whether there are shallows, for much of a duck's foraging is done by upending and taking stuff off the bottom.

Bear in mind also that seasonal feedings grounds will appear from time to time. The best of these are the fields of laid crops in the late summer, the stubble, particularly barley stubble, after harvest, also the winter flooded fields that make ideal pitching and paddling places for mallard and teal.

Now connect up on the map possible resting places with probable feeding grounds and invest some time in dawn or dusk reconnaissance of the flight lines so drawn. The practical certainty is that you will be rewarded with the far-off quack of mallard, the sighing of pinions, the crik-crak of teal, or even, in hard weather, the wee-oh of widgeon.

After that, with luck, and after suitable negotiation, comes the shooting. You may decide to intercept the duck along the flight path in which case be prepared for only a fleeting glimpse and a quick shot. For this reason pick nights when a gale is blowing into the ducks' faces: in wind or fog they'll fly low.

If you wait for them at the receiving end, which is far easier shooting, take note of the following. Don't fire at the first ones in. Let them settle and decoy others: once it gets dark even shooting will rarely disturb those that have found refuge. Duck, like pigeons, will land into the wind, so try to pick a stand at which they will pitch in over you. They will probably circle once and then come in fast and low. Don't be tempted to let drive while they're still way out. Decoys, either wooden or rubber ones, can help considerably, but choose the dozing kind with their heads well down: a head-up duck is a frightened duck. Above all, don't shoot the feeding point too often. Once a week is certainly enough.

You can, of course, produce a flight point by feeding a shallow flash of water with spoilt grain or potatoes. The pond you choose for this should be well out in the open with only reeds for cover. Duck don't like to feel crowded in by trees or bushes, especially if the water is a small one.

There are tricks about shooting flighting duck in half-light that can help to increase the size of the bag. Don't strain your eyes and keep looking round. Pick one priority arc and watch it like a hawk. Let your vision relax as much as possible and this is the best way I can put it—soak up the surrounding half-light. That way you'll notice anything shootable that comes into your field of vision at once. Start staring through the gloom and you'll be shooting at black spots on your eyeballs.

Listen! you can often hear duck, either their soft gabble or the sound of their wings, a great way off. If you have a dog, then watch him. He'll hear them coming before you do, and if his head begins to lift it's time to finger your safety catch.

You hear a lot of talk about the poetry of flight shooting at sun-up and sun-down and I'll grant you that this is a very strong element of the business. For my money, though, the greatest satisfaction is that you've worked the thing out for yourself, shot duck where few others suspected they existed,

37

alone or with a carefully chosen companion, and done it without the aid of dogs or beaters to put them into the air for you.

COLIN WILLOCK

🌸 THE SEA! THE SEA!

. . . we children used to shout as the car rounded the familiar bend in in the road. And there it lay stretching to nowhere—on good days misty blue, on windy ones grey, tipped all over with white, The colour mattered to us then for we were only allowed to bathe on blue days—grey days meant jerseys and not even a chance to paddle, for parents in those days were obsessed with the idea of "catching cold".

But as long as I could be by the sea, getting into it didn't concern me all that much, for no garden nook, climbable tree,

see-saw or swing compared with surf, sand and pebbles for me. I can remember so often standing in my grandmother's garden gazing at the South Downs, imagining the waves beating on the shore over the other side, longing for Sunday to come when I would be taken there again.

The sea at Brighton was the only sea I knew, and it is perhaps the most ordinary sort of coast in the whole of the British Isles. No inlet, no rock pools, no crags, no shape—just a straight unbroken line of water parallel to another stretch of concrete promenade. Sometimes at low tide a little sand appeared below the pebbles, which we fell upon with our wooden spades as if it was gold. Perhaps it was as well I did not know the sea in Cornwall in those days for the promenade sea I knew and loved would have seemed very dull by comparison.

I was thinking this last week as we drove down the steep road to the little Cornish cove where Bay and I were to spend a few days' holiday. If I had seen, as I saw now, at the turn of the road the blue-green circle of sea rolling gently in over the sand, lying as it were in the curve of a great arm of rock sloping up to the green fields above, I might have believed I had

entered another world—a world which I couldn't bear to have left.

We camped in a field overlooking the bay and went to sleep that night with the sound of the sea in our ears. Not the beating of waves on the shore but an endless drone like the sound you hear when you put a shell to your ear.

Surfing is the great sport in North Cornish seas and every little sweet and newspaper shop hires out surf boards. Some people appear to stay in the sea for hours just walking out and surfing back. It's a fascinating sport and not too difficult once you have the knack.

The cold water got the better of me and so I left Bay in and took rug, book and a picnic lunch on to the turfy cliff top where I had a perfect view of the whole bay and everyone in it. With nothing special to do and nothing much on one's mind watching other people on holiday is an ideal occupation. We all tend to behave the same way in the more trivial sphere of our human activities and it's amusing to watch the same scenes being played over again.

You know the sort of thing . . . Tommy builds a castle and Johnny knocks it down. Tommy bursts into tears and hits Johnny with a spade. Mummy makes peace and goes back to her book or her knitting, and the whole scene takes place over again.

Having tried so often to get dressed under the inadequate shelter of a towel it had never struck me, until I watched the same monkey contortions of a family below, that the only member of it who had adequate protection from its towel was the one who least needed it—a toddler of two. And after watching her father struggling hopelessly with the same sized towel it made me realise one should grade the family towels according to age, size and probably sex!

My eyes wandered . . . There was Bay striding back through the breakers for the hundredth time glistening like a seal in her black swim suit . . . there were two tiny little pantalooned babies staggering in the sand and falling down every other step . . . over there a colt of a boy bowling his father who was using a piece of driftwood as a bat and shrimping net as a wicket. . . .

Nobody was alone here. Everyone was part of a family group. Everyone looked brown, happy, shiny and well. Not a blonde, a beach ball or a bikini in sight, but no backcloth could have been more beautifully painted or the actors better cast for such a scene.

I read a little, dozed a little, gazed a little until Long Shanks came and dripped beside me on the rug demanding food.

BARBARA HARGREAVES

 *The Gate*

Seasons change; but still, beneath the trees
  Stands the old gate, astride the leafy path;
Silent sentinel o'er summer's ease,
  A fortress to the wiles of winter's wrath.

Timeless keeper of the ages past,
  Of secrets shy, and history unknown,
Forgotten, broken barrier, at last
  Keeps vigil in the dark, green gloom alone.

Lovers have wandered through there hand in hand,
  Horsemen taken wings to leap the bars,
Old men leaned there cherishing the land,
  And young men reached out there to touch the stars.

A thousand times its seasoned frame has swung,
  Brushing aside the spears of tangled grass,
Speeding shadowy forms of men unsung
  To other worlds, waiting for time to pass.

MRS. W. M. LERWILL

 Men

Why is it that
Men I despise
Hang around
Ignore my sighs?

But, when I sigh
In different tone,
Those I like
Leave me alone.

ANON

❧ TILL THE COWS COME HOME

We came upon him towards the end of the afternoon, when the heat of the day had reached its peak and remained motionless before descending into dusk.

As far as the eye could see the plain stretched without boundary of hedges, each field a neat patch cultivated to the last frugal foot. To the west a village stood, or rather grew as part of the earth, under a belt of solid limes heavy and still as the treees in a nursery frieze. Nearer, yet out of earshot, a row of bowed figures in peasant black with hats the colour of ripe wheat, worked in line across a family field, father, mother, one guessed, the grandparents and the older children.

Taut across the plain the railway lines unguarded by fence or embankment seemed to waver in the heat from the burning sky; and, within a few yards from where we had halted, in a small square of pasture, a herd of cows, tawny as the landscape, grazed up to the boundary of the lines.

Their guardian lay without shelter on the hard earth, head resting on paws, prick ears twitching in a cloud of flies, his eyes never leaving his charges. He raised his head as we climbed out of the car—avoiding with our hands the metal that seared the flesh at a touch—studied us with wise eyes, then settled down again to his vigil.

A cow detached herself from the rest, following her grazing towards the line. Instantly the dog was on his feet and quietly, without fuss, headed her back to the herd. I had time then to observe him closely.

A huge, sable Chien-loup, the guardian of the flocks of Europe, down countless centuries, against the wolf. His amber eyes, set in a broad brow, were too light and his coat too thick to stand comparison with the elegant Alsatians of the show-ring: but the loping, effortless gait of that low-slung body showed perfect angulation of the hind legs and the feet were round and compact, like a cat's.

The small square of his territory was bounded on each of three sides by cultivated ground. During the hour we waited,

43

fascinated by his intelligence, he was constantly on the alert, shepherding the straying herd from the temptation of the neighbours' growing crops.

There was no sign of water and not a scrap of food; yet, when we opened our picnic hamper within his sight and scent he never relaxed his concentration, made no plea.

I filled a tin with cold tea and placed this novel drink, for a French dog, a yard or so within his boundary, hoping that curiosity or a particularly delectable patch of grass would lure his charges towards it. My first intention had been to wrap up the remains of our meal and toss it to him as if he were an animal in a zoo. Now I walked round the square—although I felt no fear of the dog I had no desire to provoke his guardian powers by coming between him and his cattle—and placed the food gently by his side.

He accepted it gratefully, wolfing down the larger portions then frugally licking up every crumb. Madame Deniset, I thought, would for once be flattered by the formidable appetites of the so strange English, with their curious incapacity for doing full justice to her lavish idea of a light repast.

All around me rose the unforgettable, nostalgic smell of dusty French earth; that fertile soil of the battlefield of Europe. We stood there together, the dog and I, until I stooped and stroked the great, wise head. He acknowledged my presence with a courteously thumping tail, but made no move to follow me as I retraced my steps to the car.

We drove quietly away, anxious not to disturb him, and the dust from the unpaved road rose in a yellow, choking cloud behind us, blotting out herd and shepherd alike.

How long he had been there I do not know; when his vigil would end I could only guess.

Perhaps at dusk—the hour, as the French say, between dog and wolf—some distant signal, the thin, sweet bell from an ancient church would sound his freedom. He would gather his placid beasts, shepherding them gently in single file along the difficult and narrow path to rest and home.

KAY HILL

❀ TWEETIE PIES

"Have you got an airgun, dear?" It was my mother on the 'phone.

"Yes," I said, "I think there's one up in the attic among the bows and arrows and the hockey sticks. Why, for Heaven's sake, is Pa getting you down?"

"It's the sparrows," she replied. "They're driving me mad, and Jock (the chap who works for her) says the only way to get rid of them is with a gun."

"But you're not going to try and shoot them yourself," I said, astonished.

"I am," she replied, with a cocky note in her voice. "I'm getting absolutely ruthless about the brutes. They're ruining my garden and my nerves and I'm fed up."

I could hardly believe it. After a lifetime of turning her whole place into a bird sactuary. Of forbidding boys within miles for fear they were after eggs. Making life intolerable for any cat who dared show its whiskers inside the garden. After years of putting out the choicest mutton fat for the tits. Grating up bread crumbs finer than you would for bread sauce and laying a literal carpet of hemp on the lawn. (She even goes to local fairs to win them coconuts!) Our bird-crazed mother, to whom year after year we had given presents of the very latest in nesting boxes, was now referring to her darlings as brutes and threatening to discharge pellets into their downy little hearts.

"Of course, dear," she continued, "if you can find out if there's anything else which will get rid of them, fine. But nothing cruel, mind."

Well, I asked several people round about, and some said trap them, others said shoot 'em and the rest described their own pet theories all the way from the row of painted jam jars to strings of milk bottle tops.

A friend of ours in fact, given to highly ingenious devices of one sort and another, delivered himself of a very learned dissertation on the subject.

"Strange you should have asked me about this now," he said, settling back in one of our deck chairs and lighting his

45

pipe, "because this year I decided to launch a real blitz on the blighters—thought it was about time we kept a few cherries to ourselves.

"The key to it all," he said, "is never let them get used to one thing. I stuck feathers in a lot of spuds and hung 'em in the trees," he went on. "That held them for a bit, then I changed to a scarecrow, but directly I found 'em perching on that I went to town with the darnedest great cardboard cat you ever saw. That fairly got them, I can tell you."

"How big?" I asked. I was intrigued.

"Oh, big as a blooming elephant," he said, "Doris is the artist, she drew a beauty on three cardboard box lids. You know, head on one, body and tail on two more. Then we painted the lot black—took a whole lot of paint darned near—and strung 'em all together and hoisted the thing up on a pole into the tree."

"But what sort of cat?" I persisted, I was still intrigued.

"Oh, you know, round body, round head, curly tail, facing forwards," he said, describing it in circles with his pipe stem.

I was fascinated. I got a vivid picture of this black monster stuck up in the tree, just like the Cheshire Cat in "Alice in Wonderland". I couldn't wait to tell my Mother about it.

But as a matter of fact, I didn't tell her straight away because just after this I suddenly got wind of what sounded like the perfect answer to her problem—a magical device invented by a famous firm of electric-fence makers which they offered to let me try out.

I decided to put the thing to the test down the bottom end of the lawn where the thrushes, blackbirds, starlings, etc., all foregather on a second by second worm foray. I got the wire course all pinned out so it looked like some complicated new form of clock golf; switched on the battery and lay down behind a tree to watch the result.

When the first blackbird hopped on to the lawn my bird loving conscience scarcely pricked, and my heart was pounding. The hunt was on.

Click, click, click went the battery inside the little red box. Hoppity, hoppity hop went the little bird over the wire and picked up a nice juicy worm in its beak. Hoppity over the next wire, seizing another tasty morsel. Cocked its head one

46

side at the clicking sound. Decided it didn't come from the sort of beetle he was after, so hoppity skip over a couple more wires, one more worm for the sky and away he flew. Found some good grub on the end bit of the H's lawn he'd doubtless tell the others. "Can't miss it, look for the wires and listen for the beetle in the red box."

Desolate, I went to switch the thing off and jumped sky high myself, I must have put the whole contrivance on backwards or something to get a shock like that. Serves me right for leaving the instruction pamphlet behind.

I rang my mother. "Got any cardboard boxes?"

"Yes, dear, I think so, up in the attic. Whatever for?" It was her turn to be mystified.

"Well, cut out two circles . . . one three times as big as the other . . . I went round and round in the air with my left hand.

"Yes, of course it works." A little bird told me.

BARBARA HARGREAVES

 *A Hate Poem*

Whose misplaced creative power
First produced a plastic flower,
What clever devil had the sauce
To think this plastic tour-de-force
Could emulate the lovely rose
That, transient, buds and blooms and blows?

Winter's frost or summer's heat
Wither not this counterfeit,
Hygienic, scentless, boring-smug-
Unappetising to a slug;
Model of sterility,
Scorned by the self-respecting bee.

Yet people buy them every day,
They give good money for a spray,
Orchids and lilies, tailor-made,
In colours that can never fade,
I wonder which of us is crazy—
I'd rather have a living daisy.

MRS. M. SANSOM

❧ IN A LOWLY CATTLE SHED

It was Christmas eve. The weather till now had been damp, and a clammy fog was reluctant to leave the world each morning, and eager to return with the end of the short winter afternoon. But now, all strangely and suddenly the frost had come. Scintillating spears and stars lay on the paths and the windows had become fairy realms.

At last the work of the farm was finished. The pigs were bedded with clean straw and had eaten their fill.

In the field, the sheep had been counted, and were finding the shelter of hedges and buildings, the frost touching their thick fleeces with a faint lacing of white. Bright moonlight and a sky full of stars gave a bright clarity to the peaceful scene.

Yet, one creature stirred about the yard. A small cat moved restlessly from building to building. The doors were all shut and even the great stack in the yard would not afford her the warmth she needed on this icy night.

Methodically, she searched from place to place, lifting her feet daintily from the frosty ground; but all seemed impenetrable. Then, in desperation she saw that a piece of glass was missing from a window. By a devious route she reached the hole and jumped down into the warm darkness inside.

It was sweet-smelling in the shed, and the old cow lay quietly chewing the cud and allowing her eyelids to droop over her drowsy eyes. The only hay she had left had dropped into her trough and was formed into a nest shape by her exploring nose.

Stealthily the little cat crept to the low trough and pulled herself into it. Gratefully she sank down into its welcome softness; the old cow's breathing and chewing were the only sounds, and these mingled with and never broke the hush.

Early on Christmas morning the old cow felt a stiffness in her joints, and began to raise herself. While she was still on her knees she noticed a deep, rumbling, purring noise which came from the nest of hay in the trough. There lay the little mother cat with her four tiny babies snuggled among the hay.

For a moment the old cow paused, and in that moment time went back. Here she knelt as long ago her ancestors had knelt, to welcome the Son of God, laid in a manger. And Christ in His humanity, looked down on the scene—and smiled.

K. B. MAGER

DECOYS OF GRACE

The trouble about the decoys made by Bill Grace of Walderslade, near Rochester, Kent, is that they are almost too beautiful to use. Almost, but not quite, for you have only to see a pack of widgeon turn and whistle into them, paddles down and confident, or to watch wood pigeons clap out of the far-off trees and glide in, wings set, to realise that here, in Mr. Grace's work, you have a secret weapon in the shooting game.

Mr. Grace, an ex-RN submariner, has been turning out the finest decoys in the land since 1951. The decoy business hasn't brought him riches beyond a small car, a small house, and a small workshop, but he strikes you as being a man who is getting plenty out of life at that modest level.

He went into decoy making in the first place primarily because he liked working with his hands and, in his phrase "making things you can see and touch". He took over the business from a lifelong Kent wildfowler called Boddy and served six months' apprenticeship with him. He learnt the exact way in which old Boddy painted every feather on the wing of a mallard drake, and the peculiar white mottled pattern which he applied to the back of the cock widgeon. He learnt these things and sticks to them rigidly to this day, for Mr. Grace is not much of a one for change of any sort.

He carves his decoys out of western red cedar, cutting out the blanks to a template with a bandsaw and then finishing off with a spoke-shave and draw-knife. The heads he shapes separately from off-cuts and sticks them on with traditional carpenter's glue, though he admits that modern resin glues may be tougher. Every decoy gets three coats of paint, the best lead variety and the same brand that Mr. Boddy advised.

Grace is in his workshop most days from eight in the morning until the same hour at night. He says that if he could work continuously at a decoy, putting on one coat of paint after another, it would take him three and a half hours to finish. As it is, an order for 48 ducks is a fortnight's work, so you can see that there isn't a deal of profit in it.

"With timber the price it is, it's almost a shame to cut it. Still," he adds, "I wouldn't consider any lowering of standards. The wood I use will stand up to all the wear and tear it gets on its own. It doesn't really need one coat of paint, let alone three."

In everything he says, Bill Grace reveals the craftsman's approach. Show him some of his decoys that you bought you forget how many years ago, and he will most likely tell you the exact year; maybe there was a slight variation of paint quality at that time. "The makers aren't quite consistent, you know."

Though there can be only a loss in it for him he runs a hospital service for wounded decoys. "I get 'em back here in all conditions. Had a pigeon the other day that had caught a full shot-charge in its left wing. Had to rebuild the bird completely." His standard charge for removing odd pellets, filling in dents and repainting is 3s. 6d. per bird. "People like to keep their decoys looking nice," he says.

The only time in his business career when he remembers getting worked up is when a sportsman put in a special order for some curlew decoys and then ignored three of Grace's accounts. Grace went to see a lawyer about this. "It wasn't the money so much, which was only £8, but the point was I'd worked with my hands for it."

Being a most conservative man, Mr. Grace is not depressed by the thought of carving the same four or five shapes day in day out. He did break away recently and make a few miniature ducks because his wife said she'd like some. These miniatures, incidentally, should have a high sales value as decorations if put into one or two smart shops, but by and large, Grace doesn't care for fancy orders.

He'll build you a pinkfoot goose if you really want one, and he has made owls and even eagles for customers, though it's beyond him, and me, what they want them for. Possibly his happiest moment was when an order for 200 pheasant decoys fell through, possibly because the customer discovered at the last moment that you can't decoy pheasants.

Perhaps the strangest thing about Bill Grace is that he's never fired what he calls "a sporting rifle", meaning a shotgun, and far from being a bird watcher or wildfowler, regards crawling about on the muds after duck as lunatic. "I can't think," he says deliberately, "of a worse occupation."

If there is one criticism of Grace's work it is that the painted plumage of some of his ducks bears little resemblance to the real article.

This, however, is because the thing has become, without him knowing it, a sort of folk art in which he is reproducing traditional patterns simply because he accepts them as right and satisfying.

From the shooting point of view this doesn't, in my experience, matter at all. It is shape and attitude of a decoy that matters most. Ducks, at least, will work just as well if they are painted mat grey all over.

This is not Mr. Grace's method, though, and thank heaven for it. In the season his products can increase the size of one's bag no end. The rest of the year they are delightful things to have around the house. Here a word of warning. Don't let your wife get hold of them. Mr. Grace's ducks make magnificent and highly decorative door stops.

COLIN WILLOCK

🌹 HARVEST THANKSGIVING

She had come to church, as much as anything, to show the old cats that what they were watching for and hoping for was not to be.

There was old Miss Stott, for instance, kneeling alongside as good as gold and all the time peering through her fingers in their grey cotton gloves and as likely as not counting off the weeks on them as she prayed.

When you walked down to the bus on a Saturday night in your nylons and white peep-toe shoes, with your hair nicely curled and a bit of lipstick on, you could see the lace curtains in her cottage window waver and close, but never a sight of the old lady herself. She'd be watching still when the "picture" bus came back, and the boys and girls paired off in the dusk and crossed the bars of light falling across the road from the open windows and doors.

They said, in winter she stood in the shadows of her garden on the coldest nights, so that the lovers clinging for warmth in the porches up and down the street could only whisper all there was to say. Only Tom Bowes, that was always a laughing, good-hearted lad, but bold, had stopped his kissing his girl for a minute and called out, "Don't you wish you were here with me Miss Stott?" (And a lot of good it had done him, he'd got the sack within a month for making up to his boss's daughter, and the next thing he'd cleared off into the army, and come back as different as anything, they said on his last leave.)

54

It was nice to be standing up now after all that kneeling although folks were staring all the more—and everything from the smell of moth balls in the winter coats to the flowers and vegetables in the windows, was a reminder that the year was falling like the leaves off the trees.

There was nothing here of the harvest that had been all sun and gold, and the nights when she had stared up at that great moon while headlights went up and down the main road, and all around was the sharp sweet scent of corn.

It was a queer thing to be giving thanks for something that was over, when all the time you wanted it to go on for ever; and queerer still to think that it had started when she'd been wearing that old, faded blue frock, with her arms and legs all brown and scratched from the sheaves and her hair straight, and falling across her eyes.

She had carried the tea basket down to the field, and it had been heavy enough by the time she'd got there, with never a thought in her head except planning to get down to the cricket match when work was done, and perhaps wear her new dress at the dance in the village hall. When it had come to pouring his tea and stretching across to hand it to him, all of a sudden there were just two arms, his and hers, golden brown and dusty from the corn. They had not touched, but she had felt his arm a yard away, like white hot steel at the blacksmith's, and she'd gone on holding the cup, while he forgot to take it from her, and they had stared into each other's eyes until old Bob come along rattling his tin mug and complaining that there was work to be done.

To fall in love like that and with a student, as different as anything from the village lads, took a lot of accounting for. Some of the things he said were enough to make you laugh— that was at first before it began to hurt—and afterwards she remembered the words and didn't laugh any more.

That first evening he came to see the ten-acre field of red wheat that was standing as stiff and level as a table top so that it would have seemed no miracle to walk across it to the stream beyond. The sight seemed to take his breath away, and he started spouting something that seemed nonsense about immortal wheat that had never been sown and would never be reaped.

Well, you had to be kind to these townies, they knew nothing. They'd come bouncing on to the place in the mornings—when you'd been at it two hours or more. "Come on," they'd say, "when do we get cracking?" Then they'd start faster than anyone in their senses could go, forking the stuff up just anyhow at old Bob until he threatened to come down off the stack and go home. (If you could keep him soothed and quiet till after the dinner hour it would settle down, for by then they would be glad enough to work at the right pace.)

By four o'clock they'd be looking at their watches every other minute. "When do you knock off?" they would say.

Old Bob would straighten up for a while and look at the sun, feel the way of the wind and measure with his eye what was left in the field. "Nine o'clock," he'd say, "if things go right."

"My goodness," they would answer. "Five more hours of this?" And you would laugh to yourself to think a girl could beat them at it. But the next moment you would look round

Raynes

and see a couple of forks on the ground the wrong way round with the prongs sticking up, and a couple of figures climbing a distant fence on the quickest short cut to the local; and to make matters worse, climbing bang in the middle of the rails at the weakest spot instead of near the post.

Old Bob would stare and curse. "Ignorant!" he would say. "Plain ignorant. No education at all."

And the next morning a message would come up from the village. The gentlemen were too stiff, or their hands too blistered, to help today.

Well, this one had seemed no better, and she had laughed at him. "You'll know tomorrow," she had said, "who will reap this corn." And she could remember how silence had fallen, until the clanking of pails and the bark of a dog half a mile away had seemed right where they were standing.

Even then she had not guessed. She had just thought him a bit queer; but the next night and all the others, the things he said had not made sense but they were somehow wonderful, and they all came back word by word when he had gone.

"Freya," he said, "a goddess who was here when the first harvest was sown and will be here when the last is gathered. Some day I am going to write about you and you will be seventeen, and in love, for ever. Men will see you in every field of corn and forget to kiss their girls for dreaming of you."

Then he had done what he always did when she tried to look nice, like a film star. He had taken out his little pocket comb and unravelled the curls until her hair fell straight and soft again, and he could run his fingers through it, or strain it back and hold her face between his hands. If she wore her sparkling hair-slide or her bracelets he would slip them off and put them in his pocket until it was time to part.

There was never a word said about marriage. When she had asked him, pretending to joke, if he would send her some nice picture postcards from abroad, he had shaken his head. "This has been perfect, and it's going to stay perfect. Perhaps the only perfection we will know in all our lives."

Well, he may have been right but there was not much comfort in thinking about it now. Yet Lily and Jack, across the church, were standing there like strangers; and only a couple of years back they were walking the lanes entwined and silent as if there were no words good enough. Now, her blonde hair, that used to call up the wolf whistles from the boys on the bridge, was dragged and faded, and if Jack took a drop too much on the night it was that tractor of theirs bumping and fuming until he couldn't face his dinner at noon; and you could hear the names she called him right across the fields when he came home from work.

If that was marriage, what was she crying for? She had gathered the harvest as good as anyone, had been a part of it, and it was right to give thanks that all had come safely home.

Perhaps that very sheaf on the altar, bowing its head with the weight of the red grain, was one they had carried in, laughing and loving together.

Rising to leave at the sound of the organ, as was her custom in the cinema before the screen lovers sealed their story with the last kiss, she walked alone down the crowded church, triumphant, like a bride.

KAY HILL

"GONE SHARK FISHING"

"Come down—sea crawling with sharks. T & J." Finding this sort of message on a Monday morning just as you are bracing yourself to deal with the mountain on your desk is more than disturbing to a sense of duty. I weighed things up. It was imperative that I be back in the office by Wednesday. There might not be any more sharks till next year. The weather was perfect. I had waited for this chance ever since I was introduced to the sport by the senders of the telegram whom I met in Cornwall when the Bath and West was held there two years ago.

I started out at ten o'clock that night—the only way I could achieve things was by driving down to Cornwall that night and driving back the next. Little did I realise the scale of the operation I had embarked upon so lightly. The situation wasn't eased by the fact that I had none of the right clothes with me for this expedition; all I had in London was a tailored suit and a frilly sort of dress.

After a round of lunch-time calls I managed to achieve a more or less suitable wardrobe. A pair of old flannel trousers from a friend's husband reserved for cleaning out the boiler. A pair of shabby tennis shoes put aside for another's jumble collection (they have jumbles in London apparently). A shirt which had been thrown into the bottom of the wardrobe only that morning because it had got to the throttling stage (just my luck).

"Expect you early morning. Bring hat—alternative burnt face." the second telegram had read. And looking for this item proved the most difficult of all.

Woolworths were sold out of those cheap beach hats usually piled up on their counters by the score at this time of the year, so I found myself doing a quick dash round the big stores. From one beachwear department to another I rushed, getting hotter and more frustrated every second. Every 'hat' I tried seemed less and less equipped to do the job of protecting one's head than the one before. If it hadn't been for the fact that I was in such a tearing hurry it might have all been riotous fun. Such a bedazzlement of garments in these departments as I've ever seen—enough to outfit a clown for several circuses to come but hardly suitable, I thought, for the average female to wear for even the gentlest sunning on the beach. However, that's another article.

I failed to find even a slightly possible one, needless to say: either the crown was too pointed and the brim too narrow or if the crown was shallow the brim was a yard wide. Each variation providing the least resistance to sun or wind. As for the prices they were asking—I'd rather use a rhubarb leaf than pay them.

By ten o'clock that night I was on my way, leaving behind a somewhat unwifely sort of note on the table in the flat: "Back tomorrow, gone shark fishing . . ."

Soon after I set off thunderstorms broke and from then on I followed the fork lightning all the way west. Just as well, for it kept me awake. We are so used in this little country of ours to going short distances that we have no conception until we've covered over a hundred miles or so how tiring it can be. Certainly I had no idea just how soporific long stretches of black road could be until I tried doing this 260 miles at a stretch.

I ran out of petrol in a little village six miles from my destination. It was 5 a.m. and through my bleary eyes I spied a petrol pump at the corner of the street. Every bedroom curtain was close drawn so I hopped in the back of the car for a snooze until the village should wake up.

A rap on the car window awakened me and an old lady put her head in and asked me whether it was petrol I was wanting. She was quite used to finding cars waiting there in the early dawn, she told me.

"The little 'uns only get this far," she said, "tanks don't hold much, so I'm always up early for 'em."

I congratulated her on her business sense.

Half an hour later I was gobbling down bacon and eggs in my friends' cottage on the edge of Newlyn harbour.

No wonder artists plaster canvas after canvas with Cornish scenes. Those blue painted fishing boats lying in a blue-green harbour must be irresistible. I would gladly have spent a day wandering round that little port watching the fishermen at their nets and bringing in their catch. If I was to get me a shark, however, before I started back that night it was necessary to get a move on.

Armed with a bucket of mackerel for bait and two rods the size and strength of tent poles we set sail for the shark grounds forty minutes out to sea. The sky was overcast for the first time for days and there was an ugly looking chop starting on the sea. I felt apprehensive, for I'm probably the worst sailor alive.

Land was but a misty strip in the distance when we stopped the boat engine and prepared to fish. All the way our eyes had been scanning the water for a black fin. After a while the underside of each wave looked like a shark. Even the experts can't tell.

At this point they began to "dress" me for the occasion. First of all, a thick leather bodice, attached to which is the sort of harness you put on a baby to keep it anchored in its pram. Round my waist they tied a thick leather strap to which was fastened a kind of sporran. Actually, it reminded me of the thing I wore at a Girl Guide church ceremony many years ago when I had the job of carrying the colours. In this case the butt of the rod not the Union Jack lodged in it.

Our old fisherman baited my hook with a big fat mackerel. The hook was two inches long and nearly as thick as your baby finger. On one end of this you attach a piece of wire (brake cable wire—so you can imagine the strength of it). On the other end is nylon line about the thickness of bale string.

I threw out the bait and watched the silver fish slide down into the depths of the incredibly transparent water. Then we waited while my heart went bang bang.

I never expected the tug on the end of my line to come with such a gigantic bump. It nearly pulled me overboard. At the same time there was a shriek from my reel as the line streaked off it at about a hundred miles an hour.

"Hold on . . . let him go . . ." said my tall dark friend who knew the blue shark backwards. Thank heavens he was there for that moment I wasn't feeling at all confident of either getting my shark or remaining on board.

After I got used to the feeling of having a hurtling weight on the end of my line I began to enjoy myself. When the creature took a rest I reeled in a foot or two. And so we tussled.

Then I saw him just below the boat. Not a pleasant sight. Fat, white and wicked, just like the sharks you read about in books whose favourite food is sailors' legs.

Suddenly, just as I was steeling myself for a final bout with the brute I saw another one. Like a torpedo he came out of the blue. There was a thrash of tails, a thick froth on the water and then my line went limp. Below, the sea was translucent and calm—too innocent even to hold a starfish.

"What happened?" I almost wept with frustration.

"The other feller bit through the wire," was the reply. "Mistook it for a mackerel I'spect—it's happened before."

There isn't even an old pals act at work with sharks it seems—just like the ones on dry land, they're out to grab the other chap's loot from under his nose.

How many times I was told to "keep calm" I couldn't say, all I know is that that fight with the shark was worth every inch of the two-hundred-odd miles I had come.

BARBARA HARGREAVES

🌹 WESTMORLAND

... I have a store of memories of rides and walks, which I dip into at will, now that I no longer have such opportunities for exploration: I find that I can remember the very shapes of the hills whether of the rounded fells of the east of the county or the craggy walls of Langdale and the other glacial valleys of the west, and the very colours of the rocks, lichen and bracken. . . .

MRS. K. WALLING, Tregaron, Cards.

🌹 GOLF STORY

About twenty-five years ago a certain young man instituted time sheets for the employees on a large farming estate. One of these was an old-age pensioner, who received his cottage rent-free plus a small wage for in his own time keeping his eye on the estate golf course, and snaring any rabbits that were doing damage there.

His first sheet read as follows: "Monday, going round the golf course. Tuesday, going round and round the golf course. Wednesday, going round and round, and round the golf course. Thursday, going round, and round, and round, and round, the golf course. Friday, going round, and round, and round, and round, and round, the golf course. Saturday, felt giddy, fell over."

A. G. STREET

TAPE-RECORDED
TEATIME

"Is it teatime, Mummy?"

"Yes. Tell Jo and Richard."

"Richard. Rich....ard."

"Mummy. Richard's locked himself in the hut and he can't get out."

"Tell Jo to get his screwdriver and take the catch off the door."

"Jo, you've got to . . ."

"What is it for tea, Mummy?"

"Never mind what's for tea. Find the screwdriver that daddy gave you for your birthday and get the catch off the hut door. Richard's locked himself in."

"I can get in through the window. Shall I do it, Mummy?"

"Hullo, Richard. Going to have your tea now? It's sausages."

"I've brought a pet along to have tea with us."

"Let's see."

"Look what I got when I was locked in the hut."

"Well, put it back."

"It's a pet, Mummy."

"Don't be silly. Put it away."

"It's a spider, Mummy. If I put it down it will run away."

"Well, put it outside."

"What are sausages made of, Mummy?"

"Just meat."

"Jo says they're made of dogs. Are they, Mummy?"

"Of course not."

"Do worms have bosoms, Mummy."

"I don't know. Get on and eat your tea."

"Mummy. Richard has tipped all the sugar in his milk and there isn't any left for Jasmine and me. It isn't fair."

"Jasmine. You're not to give your sausages to Whizzo. Put him outside. Are you ready for cake?"

"What a super cake, Mummy. I want a piece with two cherries on it."

"Do I have to eat my cherries now, or can I save them?"

"Are these sausages girls or boys, Mummy?"

"Please, Jasmine, will you eat properly. You don't put all your fingers in your mouth with your bread."

"Eat your tea up, Richard, like a good boy."

"You shut up, Jasmine. You're not Mummy. You're Mrs. Knowall."

"Mummy, Richard had all the cherries off the cake."

"Sorry Mummy. I didn't mean to."

"Well, it's very naughty. You don't do things like that."

"Jasmine. Do you want a piece of cake?"

"No, thank you, Mummy . . . I'm going to be a Girl Guide when I grow up."

"I thought you were going to be a fairy."

"I'm going to be a Girl Guide first and then a fairy."

"Girl Guides are silly. Can I leave this sausage, Mummy? Giles Wilkins' father makes fireworks."

"Did you bring your football things home from school for me to wash?"

"No, Mummy. I forgot. Quigg II had his trousers ripped off at football this afternoon. I hope somebody rips mine soon. Super tea, Mummy. Can I get down now?"

GILLIAN HOLDEN

🌹 EVERY FISH HAS THE HEART OF A TIGER

For a fisherman the fact takes a bit of grasping; in Ireland there is an acre of water to every thirty-five acres of land, and this practically makes the place an archipelago. And, as everyone from Bord Failte (the Irish Tourist Board) to the man leaning over the bridge in Connemara will tell you, each one of those aqueous acres is packed gill to tail with enormous fish.

This promise was enough for my wife and myself. Nothing would do but we must go and thin them out. So, last spring, with more fishing rods than changes of clothing and all

John Cooper

somehow persuaded into a hired baby Fiat, we set out from Dublin to do just that thing.

Now if I die in a crash while driving on English roads it will be—or so my wife tells me—because I am looking out of the side window at a girl in a summer frock. That we escaped death in a head-on crash in Ireland at all was entirely due to the fact—or so my wife tells me—that there is never anything coming the other way. But it wasn't the girls I was looking at, although they are pretty enough. It was water, water, water, lakes, loughs, rivers, streams, trickles, tarns, meres—whole counties full of the stuff. Cavan especially appears to be only afloat.

The point was: where to start? For, the fishing in Ireland is not, as many British anglers seem to think, just one great glorious free for all. Most of it belongs to somebody, the more so since its value as a tourist asset is rapidly appreciating.

However, it's usually enough to ask the owner, and this is where the trouble began.

The first man we approached was a doctor. There was a queue outside his surgery, and it seemed rather cheek turning up when he was busy. The doctor took one look at the flies stuck in my hat, instantly put his entire water at our disposal, dreamily signed three prescriptions, opened the window, sniffed the breeze, opined that there would be a good hatch of mayfly shortly, took down his creel from behind the door and his rod from the wall. He said he rather thought he should come along to show us the water.

Then he shut the surgery door, reassured the queue of patients that he'd be back in a while, and away we went in a rackety Volkswagen. No one seemed surprised or resentful: in fact, one of the patients jumped in the back, saying that if the doctor didn't mind he'd stop for his rod on the way. I never did discover what was this man's complaint.

The length of an Irish "while" is indeterminate and indeterminable, for the country, as is well-known, exists in a space–time vacuum. In this instance it was five hours and a dozen trout later that the doctor looked at his watch and said: "Well, now, I'd clean forgot I've got a baby to deliver. I'd better be going."

He drove us back at the same terrible pace to the surgery where a different line of patients was sitting just as placidly as the first. In Ireland, during the mayfly season at least, the word "patient" takes on its true meaning.

The trout we caught that day were not exceptional for a mayfly water. As I remember, the biggest was a pound and a half and the average was about three-quarters, but on this river, as on every other water in the country, it was an article of local faith that the stream was full of fish of unequalled size and stamina.

Alas, the facts do not always bear out such optimism. After a time you get used to this and allow for it, but at first it can be disconcerting, and many fisherman who have heard great stories of Irish monsters go away disappointed.

Not that adjustment to the Irish sense of hyperbole is always easy. Consider the following case-history from our own tour.

We arrive at a remote pub in Co. Mayo. We have, we tell the landlord, heard great stories of the trout in the area.

"Ah, now," he says, "you would have. They've red spots on them the size of half-crowns, and every one of them has the heart of a tiger."

After about four thousand words of colourful descriptive matter and four whiskies, he admits that he doesn't care for the fishing himself. My wife asked whether we may try for these paragons.

"Sure, help yourselves," he says. "Where would be the best spot?" she asks.

"Sure, down the road a piece."

"How much a piece?" she asked.

"Oh, just keeping going till you reach the bridge."

"Which bridge?"

"Why the stone bridge, of course."

She points out that there are a number of stone bridges in the area. The landlord receives this piece of information gravely, and assesses it for some time. "That's right enough," he says at last, "but just ask. Anyone will tell you."

This is the key phrase: just ask, anyone will tell you.

They will, too.

We don't get away for another hour because the bar has filled up and everyone who comes in has his own four thousand words to do on the subject of the "b......y great trout" (the pronunciation is more like throut) that are to be found in the river in question.

Eventually we fight our way out into the courtyard, nearly blind with alcohol and misdirections.

We drive off down the road a piece to the bridge we can't miss, and sure enough we miss it and five others like it.

A man driving a cartload of turf approaches. We ask him the way. "You'd be after the trout," he says, "sure, just keep on a ways, you can't miss it."

An hour later, still driving around, we meet the same man coming back. "Did ye catch anything?" he wants to know. We tell him we haven't yet found the water. "Now that's a mysterious and mystical thing," he says, "and after I'd nearly led you to it."

By this time the whisky is wearing off and my wife is showing signs of stress. "We've already wasted two hours," she says irritably.

The turf man looks genuinely shocked. "Well," he says slowly, "that's no cause for worry. If you don't get there today the fish will still be biting tomorrow."

But lest you get the impression that the Irish gift for exaggeration is catching, let me tell you that though every word I have written so far is the truth, there are mighty big fish and they can be caught

The danger for the English visitor is that he expects to be instantaneously and spectacularly successful. Irish fish are no easier to catch than the fish back here. There are indifferent rivers and lakes as well as fruitful ones.

In exceptional waters such as Loughs Sheelin, Mask, Conn, and Corrib there are great trout, no doubt about that. Six-pound trout are fairly common, while fishermen scarcely bother to tell you that they have caught a thirty-pound pike, for they regard the event as an inconvenience.

For those who are interested in the rivers Suck and Erne, fifteen-pound bream are frequently caught. Big rudd are almost everywhere (there are a few true roach). Sea trout and salmon fishing can be had for a very few shillings. Forty-pound pike are landed on hand lines and forgotten within the month.

If you want to catch fish, go with a good map and an open mind. Don't necessarily accept the local advice or try the local methods, for the Irish are extraordinarily conservative in their angling. Often they will stay plugging away at a Lough with the wet-fly when a beautiful little river of chalkstream standard runs close by nearly unfished.

And, pray, do not be put off by stories of backwoods hotels. Tourism has produced cleanliness and hospitality, though not cuisine. The food can most charitably be described as "solid". In fact the things they cook best apart from bacon and eggs are salmon and trout. So if, for one Irish reason or another, you fail to connect with them at the river, you're bound sooner or later to catch up with them on a plate.

It's the one place you really can't miss them.

COLIN WILLOCK

🌹 THE PIT

Sometimes, living on a farm, there is so much to do in the way of making a living that your eyes are blind to the everyday things around you. That was how it was with the pond in our meadow, or the pit, as it is known in Norfolk.

We must have lived in our house nearly a year before winter came and with it the snow and a sharp frost. My husband and I were so busy lagging pipes that should have been lagged before, and generally keeping the taps flowing, we had almost forgotten we had children. So that when our son burst on us in the loft, scattering snow to left and right and yelling at the top of his not inconsiderable voice: "The pit's frozen! Can we skate?" he was greeted with a marked lack of interest.

I shivered, and said in a tone as icy as the blast that was coming at me through the gaps in the ancient tiles: "What pit?"

"That one in the front meadow!"

"But it's not big enough!"

"It is, Mummy! Do come and look!"

Of course my husband knew all about the pit. The horses drank out of it and the water for the pigs came from there. But he had never measured its depth nor thought, for one moment, that it could be used for anything other than pure utility.

I looked at my husband and he looked at me. Meekly we laid down the lagging and followed our son downstairs.

"Better go and see before they both get drowned," my husband said by way of excusing himself for having abandoned his job so readily.

And sure enough, when we got to the pit, the ice gleamed virgin white and enticing. Looked at in the light of a miniature ice rink it was almost ideal. A perfect circle, it was about thirty feet in diameter.

"Is it safe?" I asked with usual maternal caution.

"It was all right for us!" the children claimed.

But that wasn't good enough for me, so I sent Father across. And there wasn't a crack, not even a teeny creak.

"No one else's has frozen!" my daughter told me gleefully, jumping up and down in excitement.

It was true. Obviously this was not a deep pit and so had closed its surface in record time.

We mustered skates and we started. We had a glorious, exhausting week, parties for the children, headlight-lit parties for the grown-ups. We adults skated till midnight all week. Unlike everyone else round us the only reason we welcomed the thaw was that the excess of exercise had nearly laid us out.

But it had started us thinking.

"There are possibilities to that pit," my husband said.

And there were.

As soon as it was possible he waded in and carefully clomped all round. At no place was the depth more than four feet.

"Hmmm," he said, which meant he was thinking deeply.

The first thing that happened was that our son found his model yacht. One side of the pit had a decorative and very prolific bank of blackberries growing down to the water's edge. He had some worrying moments when the yacht became entangled in the prickles, but it didn't seem to matter. It all added to the fun.

Meanwhile, my husband had discovered one of the tractor drivers was a keen fisherman. Once a line of thought is moving it is easy to keep it going, so my husband asked the man if he could spare us a few fish with which to stock up the pit.

The tractor driver was marvellous. Every weekend he would appear with something. Perch, rudd, an old bream, all wriggled out of his clutches and into the water of our pit.

Then we saw an advertisement for a collapsible dinghy. A birthday was looming ahead so the boat was bought and produced on the appointed day.

I never remember anything being so successful. The pit became a desert island overnight. Or a Malayan swamp, or the Amazon. If imagination had run loose before, it was nothing to what happened now.

At first we made the children wear life jackets. But they are both good swimmers so that once they had mastered the art of rowing we did not worry. My son and his friends built harbours and extensive, unsafe jetties; my daughter discovered the bottom of the pit was clay and fashioned ash-trays and futuristic flower vases.

And, of course, after a year they fished. It is nothing for my husband to sit in the dinghy all evening solemnly catching fish, and just as solemnly putting them back. He says it soothes his nerves. Well, you know how it is. A woman never argues with a man when he says something like that.

Naturally, the children think it a good place to bathe in the summer. I'm not so sure of that when the horses use it as well. So the rule is heads out of the water or no bathing. I don't want anyone going down with an unnecessary germ.

"Hardly any need for going out these days," my son says, picking up his fishing rod.

He is all for throwing it open to the public and charging sixpence a head for doing whatever they choose.

But I put a stop to that. It wouldn't be quite the same somehow, commercialising the old pit. I'm just grateful to the farmer who years ago must have dig it out so symmetrically to get clay to patch up his buildings, little thinking that one day there would be folks like us who would enjoy the aftermath of his labours.

It was all there right in front of our eyes, just waiting to be noticed.

URSULA JOHNSTONE

🌹 *Logs To Burn*

Read these lines and generally learn
  The proper kind of logs to burn.
Oak logs will warm you well
  If they're old and dry.
Larch logs like pinewood smell,
  But the sparks will fly.
Beech logs for Christmas-time,
  Yew logs heat well.
"Scotch" logs it is a crime
  For anyone to sell.
Birch logs will burn too fast,
  Chestnut scarce at all.
Hawthorn logs are good to last
  If you cut them in the fall.
Holly logs will burn like wax,
  You should burn them green.
Elm logs like smouldering flax,
  No flames to be seen.
Pear logs and apple logs,
  They will scent your room.
Cherry logs across the dogs
  Will smell like flowers in bloom.
But ash logs, all smooth and grey,
  Burn them green or old;
Buy up all that comes your way,
  They're worth their weight in gold.

OLD WEST COUNTRY RHYME

☙ ONE UP ON GAGARIN

As one gets older, so I'm told by someone whose life work is studying human behaviour, one's senses gradually diminish, with the exception, he says, of our sense of taste, which will probably intensify.

According to his theory then, we shall cease to have the urge to go and gawp at the moon on a mid-summer night. Stop getting a tingle up our spine at the tall, dark and handsome, and tears eventually fail to come to our eyes when we come across a stretch of English landscape glistening in the special light you get between English showers.

In other words, as the years go by we shall gradually lower our sights till the only thing in focus will be that old armchair where, according to this boffin, we shall spend the rest of our days looking forward only to the next meal.

Well, I'm a good deal older than I was when all this theory was dished out and I'm still waiting for the first signs of wear in my sensibilities. I even wiggled my nose on an April morning this year to test whether the spring smell still made me feel like turning somersaults. It did.

And after last Saturday's experience I want to find that old theorist and tell him I went Gliding for the first time in my life. That I leapt at the chance. That it was the most wonderful sensation in the world, and that I'm thinking of joining a Gliding Club. AT MY AGE!

A friend of ours rang just as I was settling down to make tomato chutney. "Weather's just right for gliding this afternoon. Why don't you both come down for a turn round the sky?"

The tomatoes went back in the larder. I grabbed a sweater, scribbled a message for the children—Gone gliding, back for supper, ginger cake in shortbread tin in larder—and climbed into the car.

Ever seen those long trailers behind cars—looking rather like giant coffins? They're gliders shut up in boxes—the only sight I've had of one except when they've been pointed out to me in the sky.

On the airfield they look exactly like plastic toys—bright

red and yellow and propped up on the grass by one wing. Suddenly, without a sound, one of them whizzed into the air. Just like a stone out of a catapult. In fact this is just what happens, they are catapulted into the air.

My turn came. No coat, no hat, I just climbed into the cockpit, with some difficulty—as one might into one of Simon's friend's fiendish little sports cars.

The pilot, already buckled-in, also hatless, goggle-less, helped me on with my harness. "Ever done any gliding before?" he asked me. Obviously a routine question. "No." "Any flying?" "Yes."

Next minute we too were catapulted into the air. "There goes the rope," said the pilot. I looked over the edge and saw its little parachute floating down. So that's what a parachutist looks like from up here, I thought to myself. And there we were, hundreds of feet up in the air without an engine, drifting like a bird on the wing.

Except for the wind humming through the wings there wasn't a sound. The silence was the most dramatic thing about the whole experience. This was what one imagined flying was like when one was a child.

Aeroplanes give you no such sensation. What with passports, waiting-room, customs, etc., and being crowded into a long tube with lozenge-sized windows, the only sensation you get of being in the air is when you take off or when the Captain tells you how many thousand feet you are off the ground. The only view most of us get from the window is a few feet of wing. This isn't flying, it's a wonderful invention for getting you to your destination in the fastest time.

I looked over the side and saw the sea spread out like a bright blue puddle below. The hundreds of little sailing boats reminded me of the times I used to fill an old blue enamel washing-up bowl for my small son to sail his matchboxes with paper sails. These didn't seem from up there any more complicated in shape or rig. "We're up a thousand feet." The pilot spoke without raising his voice. It made me suddenly realise how loudly one has to talk to be heard above the clatter there is everywhere below.

"Like to loop?" he said. "Of course," I replied. I'm not altogether sure I wouldn't have climbed out and walked along the wing if he'd suggested it. The air is obviously intoxicating at that height.

My one concession to being a normally nervous person was to finger my harness for a moment. It did occur to me that this was the only thing which was going to prevent me from dropping out of this machine like a pebble out of a bucket when it turned upside down.

In a second we were upturned and there we hung with our heads pointing straight down to the sea—my hair falling over my face as if someone were tugging at it.

For all Gagarin's astonishing flight into space, I wonder if there was all that difference between our two sensations up there. "What a beautiful view," he said. "What a wonderful sight," I said.

He saw the curve of the Earth through a layer of space helmet and a buzz in his ears, but I saw the English Coast with the wind in my face and heard the silence in the sky.

BARBARA HARGREAVES

THE REAL ROMANCE OF WILLOW PATTERN

Have you ever wondered why there are so many versions of the Willow Pattern on your plates and dishes? Why, sometimes, there are only twenty-five apples on the tree—on others as many as fifty? And whereas the bridge usually has three figures on it, there are often only two or even one.

Here's the old rhyme about it:

> *Two pigeons flying high,*
> *A Chinese vessel sailing by;*
> *Weeping willow bending o'er*
> *Bridge of three men—if not four;*
> *Chinese temple there it stands*
> *Seems to take up all the land;*
> *An apple tree with apples on,*
> *A pretty fence to end my song.*

According to the legend there was once a Chinese mandarin living in the large pagoda. He had a beautiful daughter named Koong Shi, whom he had promised in marriage to a wealthy old merchant. But Koong Shi was in love with her father's secretary, a handsome young man named Chang. When the father discovered this he was furious. Locking her in her room overlooking the river, he pushed forward preparations for her marriage to the old merchant.

Chang, who had been banished from the house, wrote Koong Shi a farewell note declaring his undying love, and floated it down the river past the window, in a coconut shell; but Koong Shi, as determined as her father, sent a note back to Chang saying that she had already been a prisoner while the catkins were out on the willow trees; she hoped that before the peach blossoms appeared he would come and take her away. She reminded him of the old Chinese proverb that wise husbandmen gather their fruit while it is ripe instead of waiting for it to be stolen.

Overjoyed, Chang waited only for the eve of the wedding, and in the confusion of all the coming and going, he carried her off, together with her jewels in a little box. The mandarin discovered the elopement and gave chase; so in the normal "standard" design you have three figures on the bridge, Koong Shi carrying her distaff, Chang hanging on tightly to the jewel box, and the irate father behind brandishing a whip.

The lovers were apparently trying to reach Chang's home on the island at the head of the design. But they only got as far as the little house on the left before the mandarin caught them up. In a savage temper he burned the house to the ground, but just in time the kindly gods transformed the lovers into a pair of turtle doves, so that they could fly around the river for ever.

That's the legend. But I'm afraid that it doesn't exist in Chinese lore for the simple reason that this isn't really a Chinese pattern.

In case you feel dashed by this, let me tell you another story about the Willow Pattern, which happens to be true. In eighteenth-century England there was a young man named Thomas Turner. He was a doctor's son and probably much against his father's wishes apprenticed himself as a potter at the famous factory in Worcester. When he had served his time he set off on his travels as a journeyman potter. His way took him over the hills to Caughley, in Shropshire, where he found a job with an old potter named Gallimore, who made a rough sort of earthenware.

Now Mr. Gallimore had a daughter, and the young journeyman potter from Worcester took her eye. So they married, and Thomas eventually took over the pottery. Having learned to make fine porcelain at Worcester he put this knowledge to good use and so began to produce the lovely wares we now know as Caughley, or Salopian. The first version of the Willow Pattern was printed on this porcelain.

After a trip to Paris in search of new ideas for designs Thomas had come back with some Chinese motifs, which he had made up into a number of patterns. They weren't copies of Chinese patterns, but simply an arrangement of things seen on Chinese porcelain.

Well, that was the beginning. Then a designer at Caughley

named Thomas Minton—he afterwards founded the famous firm of that name—left to start on his own as a freelance. Having worked on the original copper plates from which the now very successful Willow Pattern was printed—by means of inked-paper transfers—he made different versions of it and sold them to potters like Adams, Davenport, Copeland, Wedgwood, and others. Each one had some difference: the position of the pagoda, or the bridge, the number of figures, the kind of trees, the number of apples, and so on.

These potters also shamelessly "lifted" each other's designs, so that unless a piece is marked with the potter's name it isn't easy to trace a variation to any particular factory.

Most modern pieces have settled down to a standard sort of pattern, so variations will usually be older pieces. These you can tell by their exceptional lightness, a shimmery look about the glaze and, usually, three little marks which you can feel by running your finger round the rim. These are stilt marks, made by the little spurs which were used in the old days to separate the plates in the kiln.

So if you love old china and earthenware, and want a quest which will keep you interested for many years, you could hardly do better than try to sort out the different versions of the Willow Pattern.

As for the legend, nobody seems to know when or by whom it was invented —probably by one of the manufacturers. Personally, I find that story about Thomas Turner and the potter's daughter of Caughley and the fact that the firm they founded has had a continuous existence right down to present-day Staffordshire, quite romantic enough in itself.

JANE DOUGLAS

... Daffodils that come before the swallow dares, and take the
winds of March with beauty

W. Shakespeare. The Winter's Tale

I am free to admit that I am the kind of man who would never notice
an oriole bird building a nest unless it came and built it in my hat . . .

Stephen Leacock

🌹 LIGHT UP THE WAX CANDLE

The scents of childhood are more memorable than its scenes. Perhaps because a fully developed sense of smell is something we're born with, whereas our eyes are constantly evolving a new look at familiar things.

Bruised laurels. I only have to squeeze a leaf between my fingers to conjure up those games of hide and seek in my grandmother's garden. Pass a bit of boggy ground where the duck have been paddling through the wild mint, to be back with my tiddler jar on a river's edge, my skirt tucked into my pants. Or catch the scent of a Mermaid rose on a June night to be sitting again on a garden seat against a trelliswork of roses dressed in my first low-backed dress.

And so it is with that strange pungent blend of scents-almost-not-English of fir trees and candlewax through which, for me, the whole spirit of my childhood Christmases were distilled. Preserved also in this spirit the magic of each successive year.

Our Christmas trees were so huge—or was I so small?—they seemed to reach the sky; with the fairy doll on the top looking down on us as from a cloud. The supernatural and the scriptures tended on such an occasion to get a bit mixed up.

I would gaze upwards. My eyes searching for the familiar objects: lavender bags, glass slippers, snow houses which were like resting places on the tinsel route to the star, placed as always on the bough immediately below the doll.

The candle-lighting ritual at teatime was to me the most important point in the day. Every hour from waking till then was a series of exciting preludes to this performance. Even the damp discomfort of newly scrubbed knees, scratchy organdie round the neck of my party dress and hair being untangled were glorious agonies of discomfort which brought the moment nearer.

"Why so serious, Poppet?" one of my fat uncles would say, as I stood watching my father light the long white taper in the fire, shelter the flame in the arc of his palm and convey it carefully to the first of the candles on the tree.

"Quite all right, thank you," I said with my mouth upcurved politely, praying he would say no more. Uncles were only boys grown up. Why should they understand?

Big trees were no longer possible in small houses; so when I had a home of my own, a very small home, the tree stood on the table. Down came the fairy doll from the clouds, with a philosophical sigh I bought a set of fairy lights and with the candles finally buried my magic.

Many years later; a couple of weeks before Christmas we arrived home late one night to an empty house and found a note from an elderly neighbour.

"How about cutting down six of my fir trees in exchange for the wood?"

I handed over the note. "Just the job," he said, "enough fencing stakes for that small paddock."

"Minus one Christmas tree," I thought to myself.

The one I chose was perfect. I mean perfect. It had grown straight up to the light and above the others so that its top end—the end I wanted—was evenly grown all round.

As I gazed up I was back once again in my mother's house. My dress scratching my neck, my scarlet slippered feet firmly apart, and my heart beating like a squirrel. . . .

I don't know what primitive, obstinate nonsense got into me at that moment, but I insisted on felling that tree myself and getting it every inch of the way into the house.

There was no Madam Hercules about it. I sizzled it through with the petrol saw to the last inch. It tottered and fell neatly between two of its still vertical sisters.

I measured nine feet down from the tip and zizzed through with the saw again. This tree was going to reach our ceiling, if it was the last Christmas tree I ever had.

It was a fight with the family every inch of the way. "Wasn't it foolish to have candles? The thing'll go up like a torch . . . A bit awkward taking up all this room . . . Be the dickens of a mess when it starts dropping. . . ." and so on.

At teatime on Christmas day amidst the chatter, giggles, cracker pulling I lit the first candle from a long white taper.

I turned out the light and there was the tree just as it had always been right up to the gap in the years. There was the familiar pungent smell. I hadn't expected the silence which

83

followed. This whole operation had been a selfish indulgence provoked by chance. Once the candles had been lit I wouldn't have minded at all if they had moved it out of the room. They were perfectly right, it took up a lot too much space.

"But Mummy, it's beautiful. Why haven't we always had candles?" This, from my daughter.

"I must say, it is a bit awe-inspiring," said one of the boys.

My eyes met my mother's across the room; and across the years. She smiled. The sort of smile that people who aren't in the secret, as was Mona Lisa, describe as inscrutable.

So when you are walking through your local store next Christmas, or even today if yours is still open, and you are a little sick at heart with the commercial smells of Christmas (spelt with an X), go home and light your tree with a pound of wax candles and treat yourself to a Magic Christmas Spell.

BARBARA HARGREAVES

 A TIME TO WORK...

When we first start altering the clock this innovation was called Daylight Saving. For some years now it has been known as Summer Time, and it is under this name that the Home Office has recently sent out a questionnaire to organisations representing touring, commerce and agriculture. The object of this inquiry is to find out what, if any, alterations in the present arrangements would be generally approved.

As far as I can make out there are three schools of thought in this matter. One, to which the majority of farming folk subscribe, wants no alteration, rather on the lines that sufficient for the day is the evil thereof. The second, which the holiday and tourist trade support, suggests extending Summer Time so that it lasts from March 1 to October 31. The third, which has more supporters than expected in both town and country, wants Summer Time all the year round in order to avoid the upsets inevitable in any chopping and changing.

For various reasons, I don't agree with any of these three

suggestions, and very definitely deplore the term "Daylight Saving". Instead, I look upon this clock altering business as "Daylight Using". Human beings can use daylight, but they cannot save it, any more than they can save yesterday's unused seats in a bus. The position of this island grants us varying amounts of daylight at different seasons of the year, and the aim should be to use those hours to the best advantage.

That is why I do not want to see all-the-year-round Summer Time, for the simple reason that this would be certain to bring a successful claim by many people for yet another hour's alteration in the clock during the summer months. Admittedly, we put up with that during the war years, 1941 to 1944, and many other silly things in addition. For example, we compelled farmers in most unsuitable wet districts to plough up grass and sow grain—fear engendered by war inevitably brings panic measures.

The purpose of what was then known as Double Summer Time was to save artificial lighting, and so enable people to do more work per day. In wartime it was possibly worth while. During peace the purpose would be to enable people to enjoy more daylight leisure, play more games, and so forth. In the majority of cases the result is that people play out of doors for two hours extra each day, and in consequence get up next morning too tired to do their work properly, knock-off over-tired and in a bad temper, and in a week or so either crock up or strike. The point is that there is a limit to the number of hours of daylight that the average human can use actively without undue strain on his or her mental and physical powers. Just think what would happen if in the Land of the Midnight Sun the people tried to work hard and play hard for twenty-four hours daily.

To extend the present Summer Time period at either end for a few weeks is just playing at the job—what is wanted is an entirely different approach to the problem. Instead of increased Summer Time during the summer, we should cancel it, and put the clock on during the dark winter months. I should like to see Summer Time of one hour begin on November 1 and end on January 31. I know that would mean many people going out to work in the dark, but it would also mean those same people, plus school children,

getting home in daylight, a much more valuable consideration.

Then the remaining nine months could be ruled by Green-
wich Time, which during that period would provide all the
daylight the great majority of people are capable of using
satisfactorily with no damaging effects on mind or body.

A. G. STREET

 Town Visitors

How lovely to live in the country
    On these bright, sunny days, they say.
What fun to help with the harvest
    And to ride home on the hay.
No thought of the rain and drifting snow,
    Of the mud and slush and icy toe,
Of cold east winds on hill-top high
    Or storm clouds racing in a blackened sky.

How lovely to make your own jelly,
    And from home-grown fruit; they say.
How much better beans and peas taste
    If gathered fresh that day;
No thought of the slugs and pecking birds
    Or of the weeds, in their idle words,
Of digging and hoeing and picking, too,
    The bottling I've really no time to do.

But what do you do in the winter,
    On the long dark evenings, they say,
Without pictures, dance floors or telly,
    And the village two miles away!
No thought of the games and family fun,
    Of the mending that waited till summer was done.
Of talk of next year's plans so vast,
    And the book I have time to read at last.

MRS. B. PATCHING

🌹 BEDFORDSHIRE

. . . Northerners say they find the county dull, flat and uninteresting, but I find delight in singing its praises. Lack of hills makes travelling easy and its undisputably fertile acres all the better to till.

Bordered by graceful willows the silent Ouse wends its quiet way by lush pasture and land that produces some of the best vegetables grown in England. . . .

. . . Bedfordshire has given the world: John Bunyan, the tinker of Elstow; John Howard, the great prison reformer; Thomas Tompion, the Ickwell blacksmith's son who became King's Clockmaker to James II. . . .

. . . Our county town of Bedford, busy on Saturday market day, rather sleepy other days. . . .

MRS. J. KING, *Roxton*

🌹 WED TO A WITCH

I have a secret suspicion I must have been a witch in one of my past incarnations, for I do have the most unfeminine liking for toads, tadpoles, mice and creepy crawlies of all kinds. For the feline species I have a very special regard and whole dynasties of them ebb and flow in our house.

Once when I was a child, exploring the dim and musty recesses of my grandfather's bookstore, I discovered a very ancient volume of witch lore, which looked curiously familiar. It told you how to put a murrain on your neighbour's cow, which was not very interesting, and how to bind a fairy to do your bidding, which I found very interesting indeed.

I longed to try out some of these spells, which were given in explicit detail, but the ingredients looked so terribly hard to obtain, not at all the sort of things you could find at an ordinary shop. How was I to procure a dried shrew mouse and grind it up? Or the blood of "ye white henne killed at ye full of ye moon"? As for the fairy, it seemed essential to have a "crystalle of Venice glasse" wherewith to bind it by a charmed thread. I just did not know where to look for this. There seemed to be a good many snags about these recipes. My reveries were interrupted by grandfather, who took the book from me and hid it away. "Not suitable for little girls," he said, and I never saw it again.

I have grown up to be most interested in astrology although I use it in a rather light-hearted way to guide my husband's farming policy. At least that is my story, I wonder what he'd say about it?

Now my husband is one of these Sceptical Scorpionic types who never used to care a fig for my Gypsies' Warnings when we were first married, but by now on those rare occasions when the Oracle speaks, he gives it, or rather me, a semi-reluctant ear. "After all," I say, "if you are married to a witch, you might as well take advantage of it," and he has learned to see the logic of this.

He is a restless farmer, liking nothing better than to dash about in the car on some farming business or other and is always in a great hurry, trying with great success to do a dozen different things all at the same time.

One morning he made for the door, cramming on his manury old farmer's hat, obviously off for the day but not telling me (typical Scorpio).

"Where are you going?" I asked, following him out.

"Off to Scotland to buy a bull," he replied, pecking my cheek and climbing in the car.

"But it's a terrible time to buy a bull! Couldn't you wait?"

"No other time possible. Expect me when you see me. Bye-bye, dear," said he jamming down the accelerator and was gone.

The little bull was beautiful, with a lengthy pedigree showing his aristocratic birth and, unfortunately, I could find no fault with him, so contented myself by muttering darkly, "You mark my words. There's a murrain on that bull." I am not quite sure what a murrain is, but it sounds good. Now six months later the little bull was found dead and the vet could find no satisfactory explanation of his decease, except to say that he might have been struck by lightning in the storm of the previous night.

I have always told him that cattle will never bring him luck, even though he is a good farmer with many progressive ideas. This has proved true, for though the land is by now fertile and luscious and the cows magnificently healthy and producing gallons of deliciously creamy clean milk, it has always been a hard struggle. The farm is high up in a hollow of the hills, there is a little arable land and the rainfall is unusually heavy, which brings me to my second little tale about hay-time 1955, which was one of the few years when we have not been making hay as late as October, on account of unbroken bad weather.

One morning at the end of June, my husband said to me, "Shall I start hay-time today?"

"Well," I replied, "considering what a bad time we had last year, I just think I'll look up to see if today is a good time to start!"

What I saw caused me to say, "Oh!" in an ominous tone.

"Don't start hay-time today, not till after tea anyway," I said.

"Can't I go to the Royal Show, then?"

"Certainly not. You might have an accident. You'd better stick to hoeing kale, I think, I can't see what possible harm could come to you just hoeing kale, do you? You might chop your wellingtons or trip over it, I suppose."

"Don't be silly," laughed my husband.

"Anyway," I went on, "for goodness sake don't start on the hay. You're in danger of accident from machinery and sharp tools and things like that."

I never saw my husband for the remainder of the morning, but shortly before lunch I found him, looking somewhat pale and shaken, bathing his head upstairs and asked him whatever was wrong.

"I've hurt my head," said he, "Whoever left that so-and-so hoe in the road ought to be shot. I was in the toolroom sharpening things up for hay-time, and when you called me for lunch, I hurried out and trod right on the business end of that hoe leaning against the wall as you go in. It knocked me flat and everything is still going round!"

This has become a family joke by now, and I must say that this way of being hurt by a hoe was a new one on me.

In the field of arable farming Astrology is rather a thorn in the flesh. "Is it a good day for sowing seeds?" I am asked. "Not bad," I may reply, "but Tuesday next week is the best day possible."

"What use is that to me?" is the reply. "Tuesday next week may be pouring down rain and today is just right. Have I got to wait and risk never getting the seeds sown at all?"

I have to admit that this hardly seems sensible.

I should have to do much experimental work to determine the relative effects of soil, climatic conditions, methods of cultivation and astrological conditions.

In my small vegetable garden I always follow the traditional rules just to be on the safe side. I plant the peas, beans and leafy green vegetables when the moon is waxing and in a water sign, and I plant the potatoes when there is a new moon in Taurus, and I must say my potatoes have always been prize specimens, except for the year before last when I did not follow this rule and the crop was half rotten. However, the rainfall was heavy, and the potatoes were not our usual variety, so who knows?

I should like to see carefully controlled agricultural experiments.

I wonder if all the traditional rules hold good, or if there is as much room for research as in other branches of Astrology.

ANON

 "IT NEVER RINGS FOR ME"

It's just struck ten p.m. as I write this and at midnight I shall change out of my comfortable sweater and woollen hose into a silk dress and nylons and go and fetch my two children from a dance.

Why change? Well, can one walk through a room full of fluffy frocks and accept a cup of coffee from the hostess, sit

and chat with her while the music does an hour's overtime in what I call sensible clothes but which others might describe as special to Mrs. H.

The only trouble is that having made this cold-blooded effort to change in the middle of the night even the tail-end

of a party brings you to life so that when Auld Lang Syne
pipes up I'm all set to make a night of it. And after driving
home a car load of kids, half of them dopey with sleep and the
other half prattling of the night's doings, you hang up the
silk dress in the dark and creep into bed just for a fleeting

moment you wish you were young again. Not young twenties, heaven forbid, but young teens for these are probably the golden years of one's life.

Every phase of childhood provides irritation, amusement and a certain amount of anxiety for parents. They're adorable when they're tiny but then there's teething, squealing and all those nappies. As toddlers they are chubby and charming but they swallow nails, wander off and exercise their self-will with excruciating sounds. At school age their personality begins to emerge, but so do wobbly bikes, shouting and bloody knees. But this teen-age has provided, for me anyway, the hardest work but also the greatest enjoyment.

According to the text books it's supposed to be anything but a comfortable time for parents. At this age they should be ill-mannered, dictatorial, moody, obnoxious, untidy and spotty.

They're untidy all right, but not by any special contrast to the rest of the family. Spotty—yes. But a large bottle of pink stuff does a good camouflage job for party going. They talk too much, they play the gramophone too loudly. They go to bed too late. They grow too fast. They eat too much. They waste time and indulge in harmless crazes. But these characteristics, and indulgences, excesses, call them what you will, seem to come well within range of normal coping.

Hard work they are indeed but nothing helps that along so easily as doing it in good company, and I find kids at this age extremely good company.

"But how can you stand the noise?" a friend of mine asked me as we sat chatting in the kitchen with the noise of Billy someone or other's band squealing from the other room. "I'd rather have that noise," I replied, "that a screaming baby or a two-year-old Mummying me around the house." "Besides, I rather like Billy So-and-so's band."

"Enjoy yourself, enjoy yourself—it's later than you think," goes the American song and you and I with teen-agers round the house should take these words to heart for in less time than it seems to take to sew on a couple of dozen name-tapes, they'll be out of the house and if not altogether out of your heart—you'll be sharing it with someone else!

Never again perhaps will they, nor you on their behalf,

be so free of care. For at this age they can discuss things like Love, Life and Religion with all the know-how in the world and no experience. Once they leave school, go to work and start becoming "normal" human beings, these subjects become matters of desperate importance, which they will discuss with everybody except you.

These days the telephone never rings for me but at least the conversation can be heard all over the house. Only too soon it will be conducted in undertones with the door shut and it will be a gamble whether utter misery or dreamy joy will emerge from the room at the end of it.

If the former, meals will be gloomy sessions helped along with "bright" conversation from Mother. If the latter then there'll be more telephone calls and more shirts to iron.

I am going to appreciate while I can the present situation where the owner of a billowy skirt and a new hair-do can go to bed without a worry in the world, and come down to breakfast next morning without caring a hang who sees her in her hair curlers.

I am indulging the fact that giggles instead of sighs come out of the telephone. That I have to listen to jokes, riddles and tongue twisters which must have been handed down from the time of Queen Anne; and that I'm greeted at the door by somebody with the colossal piece of news that Joan has broken off with John. Knowing that everybody including the said Joan and John are not losing much sleep over a partnership that began and ended during the Progressive Barn Dance.

And if you, like me, discover your broom cupboard empty one day and find the said items being used as partners for practising some new dance step, stop a moment and reflect how soon it will be when blondes replace brooms and how convinced you are going to be without being able to utter one word that she's not the right blonde.

It's midnight and I'm off to change for the dance delighted in spite of the wind and the rain outside, that my two are "too young to drive the car but too old to be carried into the house".

BARBARA HARGREAVES

Easter

I Got me flowers to straw Thy way,
  I got me boughs off many a tree;
But Thou wast up by break of day,
  And brought'st Thy sweets along with Thee.

Yet though my flowers be lost, they say
  A heart can never come too late;
Teach it to sing Thy praise this day,
  And then this day my life shall date.

GEORGE HERBERT

Easter

Oh, Mirth and Innocence! Oh, Milk and Water! Ye happy mixtures of more happy days.

Byron, Beppo

✿ FIVE, SIX, PICK UP STICKS

I have a friend who cannot walk through a wood or coppice without peering at each upspringing hazel for the long, smooth spears that will make him a walking stick. It is painful for him to walk through someone else's property without permission to search out, and cut, sticks.

Another friend of mine, a Major Muir, began at the age of 60 (and in spite of having only one arm through war-disablement) to carve the most exquisite heads of animals on long holly poles, suitable for use in jumping the most recalcitrant of country streams. These poles are a real achievement. I asked Major Muir to reveal the tricks of the trade. This is what he told me:

The first essential is—find your stick!

Search in the woods where badger earths delve deeply into the sandy ridges, or where badger and fox roam when all is still, for your long straight stems in the old holly bushes. With a small folding saw, as used for pruning fruit trees, cut through the cross branch an inch or two on each side of the straight stem. Then, with a sharp knife, or secateurs, cut off all the side twigs and the thin end of the stem. Your pole should now be five feet long, about an inch thick, with a short T handle.

Experience and experiment taught Major Muir to cut his sticks only between late summer and Christmas, when there is very little sap in the wood.

Holly wood, as everyone knows, is extremely strong and durable. Ash, blackthorn and hazel are quite good but you will find that holly is the most satisfactory.

When you have found a number, place them, thick end down, in a water butt in a shady corner and leave them for a month or so. They will shrink considerably, but are less liable to split. At the end of this period, allow them to dry out for a few days, and then work can begin on the carving, before stripping the bark.

A vice clamped to a bench, a few inches of rubber wrapped round the stick to prevent it being crushed, good photographs of the animal one wishes to carve, and a small junior hacksaw with removable blades and very fine teeth—these are the initial "tools for the job".

A cabinet-maker's half-round rasp is very satisfactory for finishing; a small gouge and chisel, glass paper, glue, a little common stain, complete the requirements of the carver.

The eyes on Major Muir's sticks are particularly interesting, I think. This is how he does it. Cut round the eyeball (after marking the place with a pencil) with a tiny clockmaker's screwdriver. These can be bought for about five shillings for a set of five, and may be sharpened on a carborundum stone into tiny chisels. A touch of Indian ink soon makes a dog's eyes black, and when dry a spot of waterproof glue (or nail varnish) makes a brilliant, shining eye.

Most of the sticks are stained with one or two coats of ordinary floor stain and are considered better left unvarnished. A little brass or rubber ferrule should be fixed to the bottom of the stick to prevent wear and tear when it is in use. Steel is best left alone as it is liable to rust.

So there you are. Follow the instructions carefully and the stick is made.

Imagination may be set to work to think up new designs. Badgers, otters, dogs, a fox, a cat, one's dearest friend or most disliked enemy. . . . The cherubic baby or the hoary old man . . . all may be carved on the end of a pole. Caricature may step in and take charge, as sometimes happens in more conventional mediums of art, and the result prove both illuminating and amusing.

The most difficult part of the job will be to find—lawfully and not illicitly—the straight, strong poles. But keen eyes, ardent spirits and a body suitably garbed must probe thicket and spinney for them.

PHYLLIS M. WADSWORTH

On Shearing Sheep

Should you smile—oh so politely
As you grip it—oh so tightly
And then throw it with a grunt onto the ground;
Or can you show your grinding teeth
And add your hard won spoil to the ever growing mound?

Do you tip it on its nose
While clipping round its toes—
Or do you hang it like a lantern in mid-air?
Do you help it to its feet
Or leave it there to bleat
When you've whipped away its wool and left it bare?

Should you ask if it enjoys
All the bustle and the noise,
And, if it answers that it doesn't do at all,
Should you whisper in its ear
"I'm going to shear you, dear"
As you carefully place a cushion to break a heavy fall?

Or is this un-necessary,
Do you need to be so wary,
Can you shout and rave and clip away at will?
Do the sheep's feelings matter
Or the quantity of clatter
As you vainly try to make the blessed thing lie still.

MRS. J. A. WOOD

TAKE A PECK OF SNAILS

Are you unduly troubled with snails?

Are the tender green shoots you carefully nurture in your garden eaten off in the damp darkness, and does your husband worry because of husk among his cows?

Then don't follow the general example and keep ducks—follow my example and eat snails.

I know your immediate reaction will be revulsion, though I cannot understand why. You eat winkles—sea snails—what is so different about land snails that such fierce abhorrence has grown up in England against them?

It was a Frenchwoman who interested me in the idea—the French eat 600,000,000 snails every year! My love of food and curiosity for anything new and unusual made me an easy convert.

Gardening one afternoon, I picked up two large brown snails which I handed to my son for the poultry. My French visitor screamed with delight. "Ah, des escargots," and snatched them from beneath my child's crushing foot.

She held them tenderly, regarded them lovingly, and asked where she could find more. I waved an all-embracing hand round the garden and she spent the next few hours searching diligently in every nook and cranny, finding about sixty snails of all ages and sizes.

Only the brown are edible; the brown and white striped ones were discarded; but the common English brown snail is similar to the French petit gris considered by gourmets as more sweet and tender than the large white snail.

The preparation and cooking is a tedious business, typical of French Cordon Bleu methods, so generally unacceptable to English housewives impatient with these culinary airs and graces.

After collecting the snails—at least two dozen per person—they must be left without food for at least twenty-four hours to eliminate excreta. As snails hibernate during the winter, living on food stored in their livers, they can be kept several weeks without food if necessary. In this way sufficient can be collected over a period.

But be warned by my experience. Do see that they are kept in an escape-proof container. I put about fifty snails inside a plant-pot with another inverted over and left them in my husband's office. His early morning temper was not improved when he found they had escaped overnight, leaving trails of silvery slime over papers, furniture, books and veterinary equipment with equal disregard. As he does not share my gastronomic enthusiasm I was commanded to collect up the blank blanks and make sure I removed them all.

Despite my truly diligent efforts some eluded me and the odd snail would pop up in the middle of his desk weeks later.

After the necessary period of starvation the snails must be left to steep in salt for twenty-four hours. This kills them. Here again I slipped up, putting snails and salt in a leaky bowl in the larder where the resulting slimy residue trickled green and smelly over the floor.

The most nauseating part of this generally unpleasant preparation now follows. Each snail must be put under cold running water and the green slime that has collected in the shell opening washed away!

Now simmer in water, to which a little salt and garlic has been added, for six hours. The pleasant dull tinkle as the shells simmer together makes unusual kitchen music.

After cooking remove each snail from its shell with a knitting needle or skewer, discard the back portion and replace the remaining edible part in the shell.

Now for the pièce de résistance. A typically French sauce. Pound 6 large cloves of garlic, mix with 3 tablespoonsful of chopped fresh parsley and 2 oz. of butter. Fill up the snail shells with this mixture, place in a moderate oven for 15 minutes and serve hot with brown bread and butter.

If you have no lobster pick with which to eat your snails, a fine steel knitting needle serves as well.

The flavour of the snail is impossible to define, the sauce—you must like garlic—is delicious!

LEE HUDSON

🌺 THE WEATHER I'D LIKE

I noticed the official records show that February, 1960 granted us much more than the average number of hours of sunshine. No doubt that is true, but I seem to have missed most of them. Anyway, hereabout there was hardly one day last month without some rain, and my farm has remained a more or less glorious mudpond for some four months now.

Which means that instead of having my spring sowing at least half done, it is now only just begun. Thanks to Leap year I did do half a day's drilling in February—to be precise on February the twenty-ninth. By using spring-tined cultivators instead of disc harrows this was just possible, but even so I cannot write that "well begun means half done". And of course it rained again on March 1, so that's that for a while.

It is curious how yet another implement, popular some forty or fifty years ago, has now come back into favour. For twenty years at least I have done all my spring and autumn cultivations prior to drilling with disc harrows, and deemed the cultivator a back number. Now, in common with the majority of my neighbours, I use discs on land ploughed out of ley or turf, but for fallowed-up stubbles the new light spring-tined harrows not only make a better job, but are much quicker in doing it.

One result of my last week's notes on the difference between yields on the chalk in very wet and very dry summers has been a request from a reader that I should set down the actual weather during the next twelve months that would best suit me and my farming. So, although it must be at least a million to one against my preferences coming to pass, here they are, but I doubt if many other farmers will agree with them.

March, dry and dusty—this year should suit everybody, even if the temperature is on the low side. April, a mixture of fine days and wet ones, spaced nicely to give, say, four fine days in succession and then a wet one with half an inch of rain. Temperature a trifle warmer than average for the time of year.

May, of course, is the key month, its weather largely determining the yield of almost every crop in Britain. For myself I prefer May to be very wet and very warm, in other words, to produce bowler's wickets rather than batsman's. A cold and dry May is the very devil, the only way to minimise its harmful effects is to be generous with nitrogen to keep the crops going and growing during such a barren time.

Then, having had my lovely wet warm May—a minimum of four inches of rain, and better with a half as much again—from then on I am on the side of all my town friends. June can be dry and sunny on every one of its thirty days as they would like it to be for their leisure and their games; I shall be able to fish in comfort and make some good hay.

For myself, I should never grumble if July copied my ideal June; but, as I realise that every farmer isn't mainly a grain-grower, I shall have no objections to one or possibly two inches of rain this month, always provided this amount falls very steadily and thunderstorms don't happen.

August should be a replica of June, dry and sunny from beginning to end, so that I can harvest cheaply and in first-class condition the heavy crops a wet warm May will have produced for me. By the end of this month after summer weather such as I have outlined my grain harvest will be finished, so I can do with a moderate fall of rain during September, enough to set the plough doing a good job.

October should be like September, a helpful mixture of wet and dry weather. Enough rain to enable autumn sowing to proceed at speed, and the sown crops to come away to a good regular plant; but not enough rain to make sugar beet harvesting a muddy trial for everybody concerned. November and December want to be as dry as they can possibly be in our climate, for this not only helps every type of farming, it also adds to the pleasure of shooting—last year I got wet through at least twice a week during these months.

I noticed that up to date I have not even mentioned frost and snow, for the simple reason that to me both are expensive and uncomfortable nuisances. Some people assure me that snow is wonderful manure; I prefer to buy mine in a bag. Again, frost is a wonderful cultivator of arable land. I agree, but I don't want to see much of it before the New Year, nor after February 1. However, I can put up with a modicum of frost in January, always provided February is dry and warm, and snow gives me and mine a complete miss.

Altogether that tots up to a very interesting speculation; and, as one can refer back to the written word, one year from now anybody will be able to check my wishes with what actually has happened. Which will be very different. Already March has come in like a lion—admittedly, a half-drowned lion. Whether he goes out like a lamb is immaterial to me provided both the lion's skin and the lamb's fleece are dry as dust.

But if the wet weather continues much longer I shall have to quote a remark an old-age pensioner friend of mine made to me some twenty-odd years ago during a similar sort of spring. "I tell 'ee wot 'tis Maister, if thease weather don't soon alter thic cuckoo'll 'ave to come awver web-vooted thease round."

A. G. STREET

✿ A GOOD STORY

The best farming story that has come my way for some time. The other day a general, red tabs and all, was explaining to a farm foreman why he and his companions had ignored the notices stating that this particular farm was out of bounds to troops.

"We are on a tactical exercise without troops, my man. That means we have to imagine that all the bridges over the river have been blown up, and so we have to come round over this land."

"I see," said the foreman. "Well, suppose you now imagine those bridges have all been repaired and shove off the way you came." According to my informant the army retired in some disorder.

A. G. STREET

🌹 OT ON THE TRAIL

We're all very fond of Cindy and there are lamentations when she has to go away twice a year to kennels. It's I who have always insisted on the banishment, knowing it's the only safeguard against a lot of little unwanted spaniels when you've got a family who are incapable of shutting a door.

But this time I weakened. The idea of not having to write another cheque attracted me enormously after the shock of school bills. And then the firmest of firm oaths the family made to shut doors, combined with my own silly affection for the animal, finally achieved the repeal of her three-week sentence.

It took one weekend to regret undeniably the folly of my decision.

As a matter of fact, nothing nor nobody could have got me to weaken had I known the unabashed pertinacity of her most ardent suitor. One Othello, a black spaniel given to the proprietor of "The King's Head" by a Colonel So-and-So because it wouldn't retrieve. Othello was black as night, powerful as his Shakespearian origin and known by his master and friends as Ot.

Ot was the father of Cindy's last litter so one couldn't help but reluctantly commend such faithfulness in any creature as fickle as all big black spaniels are intended by nature to be.

Towards the end of the weekend Ot and I were about equal where outwitting each other was concerned. By Monday, he had won his round, with me driving to the kennels muttering infuriated never agains under my breath, with the object of my wrath in the back of the car with a silly smile on her face.

It'll all be quite simple I had said to myself and the family, as long as everyone keeps all the doors shut. If you want to keep Cindy here you've just all got to co-operate. "Yes, yes, of course," they said with the look which means how you do go on so.

But long years of leaving doors on the jar had left its mark in spite of their good intentions. And so, this weekend they left behind them, as usual, a trail of half-opened doors—car, stable, barn, wherever they went.

Ot, like all cunning types with an eye to the main chance, in this case our Cindy, was quick to size up who were his allies and who his opponents. When he saw me coming he'd bolt but he trailed round after the boys for a chance to get his paw inside the first door they left open.

After a series of nick-of-time rescues I decided the only safe place was the car. Ot realising that his hopes were momentarily dashed curled up in the yard alongside the car and went to sleep.

Whether to protect his beloved from other interested parties or to be on the spot should some other clot leave the car door open I wasn't sure, until a friend of mine walked into the house holding on to the back of her skirt with an agonised look on her face. I thought she'd broken a zip or something until she said in an extremely cross voice, "Where the heck did you pick up that beastly black dog?"

Ot had obviously marked her down as another woman out to frustrate his love life and had given her a good nip for her pains.

I made her a cup of coffee and let her go on with her "the-trouble-with-you's," "why-don't-you's" and "if-I-was-you's" until I felt she'd worked off her resentment and we were friendly again.

Ot was beginning to get me down. The only solution of letting poor Cindy out seemed to be to get somewhere where Ot couldn't follow. I decided to do my shopping and come back via the common.

"Ha, ha," I said out loud to Ot, as I put on my coat, "foiled again my boy." But unfortunately, when I opened the car door to put my shopping basket on the back seat, Ot jumped in, too. With shrieks of "get out Ot" to the world at large, I flung him from the car by the scruff of the neck with the sort of superhuman strength one acquires in these situations.

The town seemed very peaceful and on the common there wasn't a dog in sight. We had a lovely walk and returned home having successfully hoodwinked old Ot. So I thought.

But I had left the window open. Only a few inches. And going out into the yard for something was just in time to find Cindy with all but her back end out of the window with Ot watching hopefully.

By this time, I was seeing black dogs everywhere. On the ceiling, on the walls, in the kitchen sink.

Only that night with Cindy shut up in the kitchen and everybody in bed did I relax.

Much later on, in the middle of the night, something woke me up. I turned on the light and with my heart going bangedy bang I watched the door slowly opening. Just like one reads in cheap thrillers. And there, big, black, with his eyes gleaming like the Hound of the Baskervilles, stood Ot in all his impertinent, infuriating glory.

Downstairs the front door was wide open. But if it had been shut, and I still don't know who had been sleepwalking, it wouldn't have surprised me for by that time I felt pretty sure that Ot was capable of getting through the keyhole.

Next day I took Cindy and my cheque book to the kennels.

BARBARA HARGREAVES

🌹 BERKSHIRE

The Royal County: of the many lovely counties of England, to my mind Berkshire stands out as Queen of the lot. I was born there and have lived there the whole of my life and I love it! I can think of only one thing we have not got and that is the sea, but we do not need that while we have our River Thames flowing right through the county from the extreme north near Oxford to Windsor on the eastern boundary. Our scenery is varied and beautiful. There are the rolling Downs, overlooking the fertile Berkshire Vale and the distant Oxford spires; the peaceful valleys of the Kennet and Lambourn; the coppices (where the noted Berkshire hurdles are made) which in springtime are carpeted with primroses, anemones, and bluebells; acres of heather covered commons to provide honey for the bees; and very varying farm land from sand to heavy clay, the farms in size from smallholdings to very large arable ones.

🌹 *Bullocks In Autumn*

Now here's to the bullock that grazes our field—
No worries about solids, or calvings, or yield.
If he's got a flat back and plenty of thigh,
You can keep all your dairy cows—so say I!

We don't have to milk him each morning and eve
Since he just feeds himself until he's a beeve.
It sounds very simple—but really it's not,
For the crux of the matter's the size of his bot.

So we send for the cake bags and also the grains
And put some good hay out in case of the rains,
Make sure he's not limping, and dose him for husk
And see that he's bedded down nicely at dusk.
On thinking it over, it comes to me now,
There's more work to a bullock than there is to a cow.

Contributed "with much feeling," he says, by
E. B. FOSTER-MOORE

✿ WAKE UP FELLOW HEDGEHOGS—IT'S SPRING

Every year I think it will have gone. Perhaps like our bodies the arteries of our souls harden and the old enchantment eventually vanishes, leaving just a memory of that curious exhilaration one experiences on the first day of Spring.

A day when the sun permeates the dampness and penetrates the clammy niches and gives the whole atmosphere that inimitable odour which rouses every hedgehog from his bed of leaves, and gives hope to the melancholy.

I suppose in all of us there are still traces of a primitive reaction to something or other—particularly temperature. How often do we put tummies or headaches down to a change in the weather. Normally tough as nails, an east wind can reduce me to something fit for the rag bag. Every job is an effort, my eyes start drooping, and all I want to do is to curl up and sleep.

Perhaps I am always in a state of semi-hibernation during the winter which would account for that remarkable feeling of coming to life in spring. That spontaneous reaction to the first whiff of it in the air, the curious feeling of elation quite unlike any other sensation which from year to year I feel sure I can't recapture.

But one day last week I woke up and knew it was there again and as I jumped out of bed I gave a comradely shout to hedgehogs and dormice and all other fellow hibernators. "Come on, you lot, we can start living again."

On such a day I like to take a long, long stroll. A kind of tour of inspection right round familiar ground. During the winter there's shooting, sawing wood or short sharp walks with one's head down against the wind. In the summer there's the garden and the river bank or a wander up the hill. But directly it's Spring I like to take in all the territory with time to stop and gaze.

I start along the river bank. A pair of duck fly up from the reeds. Good, that means they'll be nesting there again. Each year I wonder if the foxes or my nosy terrier will put them off. The watercress is just showing green above the water. I must get the children down to picking it these holidays. Suppose I shall have to bribe them.

There's a sudden fluty note above me and I smile to myself as one does in a sort of lunatic way on these solitary walks, for this means the redshank with the one leg has survived the winter and in spite of his disability is not to go unloved, for I see two of them fly over my head.

Each winter I watch that redshank with his one leg stumping about the marsh like Long John Silver and wonder whether he will either make a quick snack for a fox or remain a bachelor next spring.

There goes a hare up the hill with my terrier in pursuit. Her ears are still pricked so she's not hurrying, just taking a little gentle exercise. I'm rather glad I no longer have my whippet, there was always the chance she'd nab a hare at this time of the year when love takes the edge off their caution.

As I get up to the edge of the wood my terrier comes out with her tongue almost trailing on the ground. Silly girl, with those stumps for legs you hadn't a chance.

If I was a nature study teacher I'd bring the children out of the classrooms on such a day as this and sit them down on camp stools in the middle of the wood. For at no other time of the year can one see vegetation growing almost as you watch it. To heck with bean shoots and cress on blotting paper, bend down, my darlings, and watch that fern frond uncurling, and look how the bluebell spikes are pushing the leaves aside. Take out your books and mark off those familiar names as you see them now at the very start of their lives.

Up past the gamekeeper's cottage which hasn't housed a gamekeeper for many a long year. And out of it tumble a variety of grubby, cheerful children, looking just like all the illustrations outside cottage doors for a hundred years.

Every spring I look to see if the pram out in the garden contains yet another sleeping addition to the family. It does!

Once again I smile as I notice that the washing on the line is still off white, which among other things makes local gossip. But I've never passed this cottage without hearing sounds of merriment nor seen one of the brood looking anything but blooming, so if a not too careful washer can bring about this I'm not sure off-white (all Blue-Dazzers please forgive) is such a bad colour.

Out of the wood and along the beech avenue. Slow old things, beeches, it'll be another month before they stir. Meanwhile they line the avenue like two rows of elephants. The texture and colour is identical. Wonder why I'd never noticed it before.

Down on to the other bank of the river. Gracious, they've actually sawn up that old elm. I thought that upturned tree was there for all time.

Surely the kingcups are early this year. But then I remember I always think this as I catch a glimpse of that gold buried among the brown. Once I dug up some kingcups and they thrived beautifully in a great blue and white bowl on the window-sill, so long as I remembered to keep them going with pints of water.

I got back as the pheasants started their fussing and fretting over which is whose perch for the night. I always know it's getting late when I hear that.

There had been nothing to report except the sawn-up elm and the redshank being still with us. Everything was the same as last Spring and the Spring before.

And so was the enchantment. Thank God.

BARBARA HARGREAVES

❧ THE RUNNING OF THE DEER . . .

Deer are widely distributed throughout Britain, apart from a few counties in Wales, yet we know surprisingly little about them, partly because they choose remote country or thick cover and also because they are most active at night. They often roam near farmland and sooner or later, may damage crops.

Red deer, the largest, are found only in Scotland, parts of the West Country, Norfolk and Suffolk, the extreme north of England and occasionally elsewhere. The stags weigh up to thirty stone and occasionally more, though usually much less in the north. Red deer are easily distinguishable by their size and colour, which is bright red in summer and a darker red-brown or mousy-brown in winter.

The stags have formidable antlers which they cast in early spring and grow again during spring and summer. These usually become larger and show more points each successive year, but growth is largely governed by diet, and calcium and other minerals in the soil. The female, or hind, is smaller than the stag and follows the same colour changes but carries no antlers. The calves are almost always single and are dropped in June.

Red deer like to roam extensive areas of forest, moorland, or open hill. They are principally grazers but also browse on tree leaves and bushes. If they find root crops they can cause a tremendous amount of damage.

All deer are very shy and hard to approach but a short, sharp lesson delivered before they begin to come regularly will usually keep them off a crop. There is no need to exterminate the herd; the loss of one or two will usually persuade the rest to move on, and gives an appreciable quantity of excellent venison when shot at the right time of year. But try not to shoot stags between the end of September and the end of July or hinds between the end of February and the end of October.

The actual shooting is the most difficult part. A shotgun is quite useless, and its use is unforgivable because it seldom kills and causes endless suffering or maiming. Likewise a .22 rifle is equally ineffective. You must use the right weapon and then take the shot where a miss or ricochet will not be dangerous.

A rule of thumb guide is never to use a rifle under .250 calibre. Even then the bullet will travel a long way and a miss or ricochet will be lethal for a great distance, so a good background of thick woodland or rising ground must be found.

Although few farmers possess such a weapon, there is usually someone in the district who has a high-powered rifle and who has experience of deer and safety in shooting. A shot, even from a high-powered rifle, will not kill unless the bullet hits a vital part. Roughly speaking, these are in the forward half of the body, so aim either for the heart or lung area which is just behind the shoulder, or for the neck. Deer will often run a long way after receiving the former shot and a follow up should always be made.

Fallow deer are next in size and more common in England. They are not indigenous but were introduced centuries ago and are often completely wild, though many have escaped from parks and gone feral. They are considerably smaller than red deer, a big buck probably weighing around twelve stone.

Fallow deer vary widely in colour. The commonest pattern is a reddish coat, liberally sprinkled with white spots the size of a penny, but some are pure white, others almost jet black and they can be practically any shade between. The bucks carry antlers quite unlike those of the red deer; the upper part is palmated or flat, with the points going backwards from the palm. The same seasons for shooting apply though bucks may be shot up to the end of October.

They feed by night and inhabit much denser cover, so usually are seen only in late evening or very early morning. They also have a marked taste for root crops, especially sugar beet, and by their tendency to herd, can cause a great deal more damage than red deer.

Roe deer, the other of the commonly found species, are seldom seen in groups of more than four or five. These graceful little animals are not often a menace to crops. The bucks rarely weigh more than sixty pound or stand higher than three feet at the shoulder; they have neat heads which carry six points at maturity with one point on each antler at the front of the main beam and one at the back. The doe is very slender and frequently produces twin kids.

Roe are bright, almost startling, red in summer and mousy-brown in winter. The kids are spotted with white when born but lose the spots with their first winter coat.

They are chiefly browsers but like lush growth, such as

young corn and roots, and are very fond of lucerne. They also like to live in standing crops and are more difficult to dislodge because they do not wander far away.

This habit can lead to their undoing, as a careful approach to a favoured spot at first light often puts them in range. A lighter rifle can be used and a .22 Hornet—not .22 rim fire—is ideal because its high-speed bullet seldom goes clean through and almost always disintegrates on striking an object which would ricochet a larger bullet. Shotguns should not be used, but if circumstances do not allow the use of a rifle, it is just permissible to use a shotgun provided that a shotgun ball is used and not game-shot.

A firearms certificate is needed for ball cartridges but this is seldom refused for a good purpose. Roe bucks are in season from early May to late September and does from the beginning of November to the end of February.

Owners of plantations and extensive woodlands have their own problem and the ideal solution is never to let the deer population get out of hand. This can be accomplished by yearly selective shooting—a somewhat specialised business. But if an owner is not fairly experienced, it is best to obtain expert advice from one of the numerous sporting organisations whose members are dedicated to the welfare of deer and whose experience is at anyone's disposal.

These people can tell quickly what kind of deer are about by studying the slots or footprints and damage done, and they know what to do with the carcass, which can be spoiled if not handled properly.

There are other methods of keeping deer off crops and they may enjoy temporary success but deer are intelligent animals and will soon find a way round them. Ordinary crow scarers can be used at night and are probably the best method. Tins tied on a rope or wire as a trip wire are temporarily effective but, unless their position is frequently changed, deer soon learn to avoid them. The same applies to rags soaked in strong smelling fluids, though provided no gaps are left and the rags are treated frequently they may do the job.

But deer should be left unmolested if they are not causing damage, unless wanted for meat or a bit of sport.

K. C. G. MORRISON

Thoughts From The Stove

Blood of the bramble richly spills
Over the apple's snow;
Ice of the sugar swiftly melts,
Strongly the bubbles grow,
Swelling to burst with elfin plops
All over the seething pan.
Throughout the house the fragrance floats
Gladd'ning the heart of man.
Autumn's harvest of hedgerow fruit
For winter will soon be stored,
Many more jars of luscious jam
Will swell the housewife's hoard.

SYLVIA FISHER

❧ SPORT!

One farming luxury I do indulge in, and shall continue so to do whilst health and pocket permit, is shooting. As most countrymen expected, our climate has recently been reducing 1959's rain deficit at speed. Anyway I got properly wet through at least twice weekly during November, admittedly not at work but at play. But what is the shooting host to do when the chosen day dawns in a downpour? To cancel the day by telephone, relying on a wet weather forecast, almost invariably brings a fine day; so the better bet is to carry on with the arrangements, and go shooting in the hope that the weather will change for the better.

Incidentally, how difficult it is to explain to overseas Commonwealth friends, much less to foreigners, the paramount importance of sport in Britain. If one lies to such people, saying that one has a business engagement for any particular day, they understand, and try to fix up another one; but if, as I did the other day, one pleads shooting an excuse, they just don't get it. The only way is to be quite honest, and to explain that you can steal an English countryman's money and he will forgive you; that even if you run away with his wife he may forgive you; but that if you upset his sport he will never forgive you. The weather's bad enough without one's friends' interference.

A. G. STREET

❧ SNIFF AND SNIP GARDEN

For many country housewives the kitchen garden becomes a trying necessity rather than a pleasure, while the flowers must be for ever weeded and dead-headed in order to provide us with a few summer vases. Many women are, however, discovering the joys of a cooking-garden, a combination of flowers, vegetables and herbs known to the French as "Jardin Potager" and to the Americans as a "Sniff and Snip Garden".

Such a garden, even when tiny, will provide delicious foods to tempt the palate as well as delicate scents to please the nose and a mass of colour to feast the eyes.

The garden is designed for ease of working, and a large area is not necessary. 10 × 10 feet is ideal; even 10 × 5 feet is possible. A square or rectangular plot is not necessary, though easier for the amateur to plan. A semi-circular plot is perhaps the most attractive, particularly with a wall or high fence used as the background, indeed such a fence is an attractive background to any shaped plot you may choose. Preferably the plot should be very near the kitchen.

A sunny spot is essential, but the quality of soil is not too important as many herbs do not need good soil, and the vegetables and flowers can be helped along with fertiliser. Before planting, the garden should of course be well dug and raked, and the rows carefully planned, preferably on paper.

Beds should be small, with short rows to make work easier, and these short rows will be quite adequate for the types of herbs and quickly matured crops which will form the basis of this garden. A square or rectangular plot can be divided into four equal-sized beds with paths between. A semi-circular plot can be divided into four by paths.

Edge the paths with plants of alpine strawberries, pinks and dwarf lavender. Use the back wall or fence for supporting runner beans, the unusual blue Coco beans and tall-growing

tomatoes, including the plum, cherry, currant and yellow varieties. Arrange the plants symmetrically, with the beans on the outer edges and tomatoes towards the centre of the wall.

For flowers, try mignonette, mixed candytuft, dwarf nasturtiums, calendulas and zinnias. When selecting herbs, choose some of the old favourites, parsley, thyme (including the lemon variety), applemint, pineapple mint and spearmint. Experiment with feathery dill, fennel and chervil, savory, basil, marjoram and blue-flowered borage.

For taller plants, try rosemary and rose geraniums (the leaves are useful for flavouring apple jelly and sponge cakes). Plant one or two rows of carrots, beetroot and spinach, to be grown quickly and eaten young, and some varieties of radish, including Black Spanish.

This is the place to experiment with lettuce, including a reddish-tinged variety and the decorative and useful Salad Bowl type. Plan the garden with an eye to succession sowing, alternating root crops with leafy ones, for many of the crops will mature quickly. Finish the garden with decorative tubs for growing strawberries and trailing cucumbers.

For the first planting, try the following plan, dividing the garden into four sections.

In one section plant a row of basil, followed by two thickly planted rows of zinnias; then three rows of calendulas and a row of mint.

In the second section, try chervil, red-tinted lettuce, cos lettuce, spring onions, radishes and chives.

The third section can contain thyme, love-in-the-mist, dill, tarragon, savory, fennel, borage, and parsley.

In the fourth section, have nasturtiums, candytuft, mignonette, rose-geraniums. Quantities can of course be varied to

suit the needs of the family, but flowers are most effective when grown in thickly sown rows which will not look sparse when cut frequently.

The profusion of herbs thus introduced into the kitchen garden can be used in many unusual ways. The herbs should be gathered on a dry sunny day when the flowers are mature but not old. They should be spread thinly on papers or tied lightly in bunches and put in a dry airy room, preferably in the dark to keep their colour and flavour. They can alternatively be spread on trays and dried in a fairly fast oven. The leaves can be rubbed free of the stems and put in glass bottles for storage, but they keep their flavour better if left on the stalks in airtight bottles.

To make the best of the scented herbs, mix equal quantities of rosemary, thyme and bay leaves and put them in muslin bags to scent the household linen. To keep moths at bay, mix two parts of powdered mint and rosemary with one part each of thyme, tansy and powdered cloves.

In the kitchen a sprig of thyme and parsley and a bay leaf makes the classic "bouquet garni" for soups and stews. For omelettes, a selection of fine herbs should contain chervil, tarragon, chives and parsley. Mint should not only be used for cooking new peas and potatoes and making sauce, but also for enhancing the flavour of fresh sliced tomatoes or fresh fruit salad.

Chives mix with cream cheese, go in stews and open sandwhiches. Dill is an old favourite in Scandinavia, Austria and Germany, for fish, cucumber dishes and old or new potatoes. Marjoram is good with lamb, in potato soup and pease pudding and with insipid marrows and turnips. Rosemary is good for roasting chicken, for mushroom dishes, beef stews, spaghetti sauce and fish. Tansy is delicious in salads, and is an essential ingredient in a veal stuffing. Parsley, rich in vitamins, may be used in salads, sauces and soups, and as the filling for wholemeal bread sandwiches.

Sage, commonly used for poultry stuffing, has important digestive qualities, in the same way as fennel, used to counter-act the oiliness of fish. The field for experiment is almost limitless when you start a "Sniff and Snip" garden.

MARY NORWAK

 BUTTERFLIES AROUND YOUR FARM

Practically every farm in England provides winter quarters for butterflies and when you see the first small Tortoiseshell hungrily sucking nectar from the early spring flowers you can be pretty sure that it has just woken up from a long sleep in one of your sheds or barns.

It is not only snug quarters among dark beams that attract these colourful butterflies; the nettles growing in sunny corners are just as important. You may do your best to get rid of them, but for both the Tortoiseshells and the lovely Peacocks, who conduct their elaborate courtship flights round the farm yard, nettles are vitally important. Each female lays a big batch of green eggs on the underside of a nettle leaf and later you can find the "nest" of squirming, spiny caterpillars stripping the nettles down to bare stalks before they crawl away to pupate on some fence or wall, or nearby undergrowth.

Later in the summer you may notice a Red Admiral taking an interest in your nettles as well. Velvety-black, marked with white dots and with bright scarlet bands across its wings, this butterfly comes to us from the Continent, crossing the Channel in big swarms in favourable weather.

The Painted Lady is another traveller from abroad. She is much lighter in colour, pink, brown and cream, and thistles or

burdock are the plants for breeding. Like the Red Admiral she can't resist a buddleia in flower and there is no better way of attracting butterflies than to plant a bush at the corner of the house.

We have seventy-odd butterflies on the British list and only two of them ever did any harm. There is no doubt that the large and small Cabbage White are pests, but the pretty little Green-veined White, who is perfectly innocent, is often wrongly suspected. It will come into the garden to visit flowers, but is really more at home in the lane just round the corner. Here it will dance along in the sunshine together with the Orange-Tip and lay its eggs on hedge-mustard and other wild plants of the same family.

The male Orange-Tip is very conspicuous with the vivid orange tips on its forewings but you might easily mistake the demure female for just another white, unless you looked at her closely when she had settled on a flowerhead and saw the beautiful mosaic of green and white which covers the under-surface of her wings.

The original "butter-fly", the butter-yellow Brimstone, often wakes up very early in the spring, long before there are any flowers about, and you may catch sight of it chasing along the hedgerows while the twigs are still brown and bare.

The Brimstone scorns the comfort of man-made winter shelter and prefers to hibernate in a clump of ivy or a thick holly bush. The females, which are parchment coloured, seem to have more sense than the males and you never see them on the wing until the weather is really warming up. Then they get down to business and fly for miles searching out the buck-thorn bushes on which they lay their eggs.

The Speckled Wood is one butterfly that you are more likely to catch sight of in the coppice or in a shady sunken lane than in full sunshine. Its brown wings are dappled with creamy spots, like sunlight falling through leaves, and it likes to flit from sun to shade and back again, stopping now and then to fit a creamy-white egg to a curving blade of grass.

The Comma is a woodland butterfly too, a wild, ragged looking creature with deeply serrated edges to its brown and tawny wings. In the autumn, when the Michaelmas daisies are in bloom, it will sometimes come into the garden, but when

the time for feasting has passed it disappears again and finds itself winter quarters among the branches of some gnarled old oak in the woods.

England without hedgerows would be unthinkable and there is a whole group of butterflies which I always classify in my mind as "hedgerow flitters". Along the hedges they find shelter, flowers to provide nectar, and food plants for their larvae. The well-sprayed corn field, and the grazing land that grows grass only is barren country to a butterfly, and nowadays it is, in many places, only the hedgerows and the steep banks of sunken lanes that provide the conditions they need.

In places like this, or on some odd piece of waste ground, a jungle of flowering weeds, you can watch the Hedge Brown, or Gatekeeper to give it its old name, with its orange-brown wings and prominent white-centred eye-spots. I know a farm in Devon where a special local race of Hedge Browns has its headquarters. Here the butterflies have much larger spots than normal and are highly prized by collectors.

The black and creamy-white Marbled White and the Large Skipper, the Wall Butterfly and the Large Meadow Brown, with its slow floppy flight, are all butterflies which you may find in odd corners of fields and meadows where some little oasis has been left to nature.

The clover and lucerne fields have their own special butter-fly, the Clouded Yellow, a lovely rich golden-yellow insect with almost black borders round the edges of all four wings. You cannot be sure of seeing it every summer, however, because it is only a migrant and sometimes several years go by before we get a "Clouded Yellow" season. When they do come they often arrive in vast numbers, and if you farm near the coast you may awake one morning to find the fields alive with butterflies, and when they settle down at dusk the insects look like large gold coins hanging from the clover.

If you own some woodland or coppice you will probably be giving shelter to at least some of the family of Fritillaries. In the spring the Pearl-bordered and the small Pearl Fritillaries succeed each other on the wing when bluebells and purple bugle are in bloom. In July you may see the Silver-washed Fritillary darting and gliding over the bracken.

None of our butterflies are prettier than the blues, and if

you have a patch of bird's foot trefoil the Common Blue may even breed in your own garden; it does in mine. But to see the really brilliant Adonis Blue or the silvery-blue Chalk-Hill Blue you must get right out on to open downs. These butterflies like the short turf, the fresh breezes and the open sky which seems to be reflected in their wings.

L. HUGH NEWMAN

EARTHA AND HER KITS

I must tell you about Eartha, our little grey cat. In the winter she goes to bed with us, choosing any bed to sleep on; if it's cold she gets under the eiderdown. One night she beat us all to it, we found her in bed. In the middle of a double bed, her head just showing on the pillow, her paws on the sheet. The look of sheer bliss on her face told us the rest. Yes, her toes were on the hot water bottle!

A month ago she had kittens in a box in the kitchen. A fortnight later we put the box in the hay barn. All was well until one morning a cold gale force wind decided Eartha to bring them indoors again. We saw her go up the steps and across to the barn, she came out carrying one kitten. Taking a short cut she came along the side of the barn on to a wall. We ran out saying she is never going to jump down. We might have credited her with more sense. An old tractor was beside the wall. Eartha stepped under the mudguard, on to the wheel; using the spade lugs as stairs, she came down daintily and brought the kitten across into the house. Needless to say we saved her the second journey.

MRS. B. E. ROGERS

❧ CURTAINS UP!

When Uncle Abelard left me £20, I knew exactly what I'd do with it.

"I'm going to buy some gimmicky curtains for the parlour," I said to Husband. And I did.

Bold black and yellow horizontal stripes.

I hung them up at the tall windows, and smirked with pleasure. Against the misty-green walls, dark green carpet and pale leather chairs they looked dramatic.

I placed our fat scarlet pouffe in just the right place to accent the room: and rang up my best enemy.

"Come to tea dear," I purred.

She came. She stood at the parlour door. I waited proudly.

She opened her eyes very wide and said:

"Oh my dear; isn't it just like a clearing in a jungle; where the zebras come down to drink!"

Touching the virile looking pouffe, I said:

"Isn't this attractive, don't you think?"

She considered it for a moment, and said:

"Well . . . isn't it just a thought like a hunk of raw meat; something the tigers have left behind, perhaps!"

I gave her rather a plain tea; in the dining room.

She quickly circulated her description of our room round the village.

"Like a water-hole, honestly, my dears."

We had many callers in the next few days; and they all left a glistening trail of wit behind them.

Even my own Wolf-Cub son eyed me from the corner of a beady eye and sighed, "Moughli once slept here!"

I gave my zebras one despairing look, and to my son I said:

"Help Mummy get our old curtains out of the 'jumble sale box'. "

Now my kitchen table cloths and cushion covers are bold black and yellow stripes. A new neighbour prowling round while I made coffee, fingered them and said:

"I say, what smashing material! Wouldn't some curtains of it be absolutely it?"

JOAN COWLEY

❧ "PRETTY GUTSY, MUM"

Old sayings can be a terrible bore, but there's no doubting the truth of them. For instance, "a prophet has no honour in his own land". How many of us know this to be a bit of truth as bang up to date as it was when somebody wrote it on a piece of goat skin? "Familiarity breeds contempt." What a smasher of a remark that must have been when it was first uttered. Would have stopped him dead in his tracks. Today it explains its own ineffectualness—so familiar a saying we don't even hear it.

But forget it as an aphorism and re-examine it as a statement and you find the truth in it. "Contempt" is a stronger word perhaps than we'd use in such a context today. It could mean lack of respect, but familiarity shouldn't breed lack of respect. If it does then it's not the closeness of the relationship which is at fault but the actual relationship of the people themselves.

No. I think "apprehension" is a truer interpretation today. Familiarity breeds apprehension about the ability of our children for instance. We try not to show it but it takes quite a bit of effort to realise that the chap at the steering wheel is actually capable of taking us safely down the main road when it seems only yesterday that we strapped him firmly into his pushchair to stop him jumping out. Or to believe that when the little girl whose hair you were plaiting only yesterday plants you firmly down to set your hair you won't end up looking like the Wizard of Oz.

One of the most frightening experiences of my life was when Simon first took me through a crowded town in a pony trap. I thought I was presenting a calm exterior in spite of clenching my teeth and gripping the seat. But he knew. "Keep calm, Mum, I can manage O.K." I hate to have to admit that if someone else's fifteen year old-boy had been driving I wouldn't have had such jitters—familiarity, yes?

But I've improved since those days. Either through sheer practice on my part or maturity on his. Nevertheless, when he said to me the other weekend, "Lovely day for a sail, Mum, want to come," a picture of me splashing around mid-ocean, I'm ashamed to say, didn't fail to conjure itself up in my mind.

I had to go. If it had been anyone else's invitation I could

have easily said, "What, and me drown?" But how can you allow a boy who thinks he's a man to think he's still a boy!

"A fine day for a sail" means, of course, there's plenty of wind; which in turn means waves. And of these I saw far too many as we approached the open sea from the river mouth.

The trouble with growing older is losing one's sense of bravado. The sort of dare devilishness one has when younger. As a girl when I got on a horse it never occurred to me I'd fall off. Nowadays, I feel the bump before I hit the ground. It was the same that day. The moment I saw those waves I felt the cold water down my neck. And if that wasn't enough I had to remember two friends of mine, who, several years ago, had nearly drowned in the Solent!

The land seemed an awful long way away. Once I ventured to remark with a forced chirpiness in my voice that the other side of the boat was almost in the water. The answer, "Oh, I'm just testing out how far she'll go," wasn't encouraging.

Luckily I had something to do. I was in charge of the smaller of the two sails and my job was to keep it filled (billowing like a pillow-case on the line) by pulling on the rope—will I ever remember to call them sheets?

Was I clumsy. I barged about that boat like a donkey in a wheelbarrow. Pulling the sheet in either too much or too little. Simon kept issuing orders quietly and tolerantly.

After we'd been going like this for some time I suddenly realised I wasn't worrying any more about his ability to keep us from capsizing, but only concerned with being a bit nimbler on my pins and not all fumbs and fingers. It's incredible how you suddenly catch up with your real age when you're out in this sort of situation with the young.

Just as I was beginning to feel depressed and wondering if I really had better go and get myself a set of lavender and old lace, Simon made his only remark of the voyage.

"Pretty gutsy, your coming along, Mum—it's quite a sea."

Lavender and lace be damned. There's life in the old girl yet, as I've just remembered my own mother used to say to me!

BARBARA HARGREAVES

❦ PIGEONS WITH LONG TAILS

Why should anyone want to feed a wild, free bird, capable of finding its own grist, and being shot from—almost—any bedroom window? Ah, why indeed, ladies.

Of course, I should have seen the shadow on the skyline, when my husband halted us, just as we were skylarking down that little tongue of land adjacent to the shoot of our respected neighbour, with a peremptory "Bring them darned children and dogs away from Devil's Pudding Basin! Old Markover is rearing down there this year!"

But the reason for this tender solicitude wasn't at all obvious, till the other chilly Sunday morning, in the "I'll get the mussus up to get me a cup of tea" era, when my nice but nattered dreams were rudely shattered.

"There goes another, and another, and another!" my husband roared, reaching for his trousers. "He may be your cousin, but if he takes his damn dog for a walk on Ferny Bank again, and frightens my pheasants, I'll shoot the buzzard! Just got a dozen of 'em ticed up there nicely out of Devil's Pudding Basin . . . Been feeding 'em every day . . . Oh, I'll plaster that biscuit's carcass on the nearest wall!"

Feeding them? Cramming them more likely. This occupation has ranked much higher than feeding the rest of the livestock, not excluding himself. Every single day he's staggered up to this ruin of withered brake, this focal point of The Shoot, in which he and some other local diehards are interested, to act the goddess of peace and plenty.

And this isn't the end of the disgraceful affair. They're all at it! There's Who'sit of a rival shoot, chucking a bit down for them in his beet, just two fields off, and Who'sit's neighbour of yet another combination, busily salting his kale in the field beyond that, and old Filostem an' all, with his bit of business in the top spinney. . . . While those finicky and pampered polly-birds waddle around from pillar to post eating the bread out of the mouths of the hens, which have gone into a moult.

And this vile seduction, this wicked wheedleation, from right behind the rightful owner's backside, isn't just a matter of a bit of rough barley. Oh no! Very carefully, my husband drew a small greasy bottle labelled "Scotch Whisky" from the depths of his shooting bag, and held it to the light.

"Aha," said I. "Going to get them drunk, then clonk 'em on the head. Save a lot of bother. . . ."

He stiffened at the very idea. "This," he said indignantly, is my very special and secret recipe . . . just mix a couple of drops with the barley, and the smell u'll draw 'em for miles!

"But I didn't think they could smell!"

"Smell! Smell!" he declaimed. "They've got noses—er—beaks like bloodhounds!"

There are many, it seems, who hatch not, neither do they rear, and yet the late King George the Fifth—at the height of the shooting season—was not provided like one of these. On our last town-trip I got the low-down.

"A jewel!" my husband exclaimed, gesturing ecstatically towards a daggly coppice. "A little jewel! There's Lordie rearing on one side of it, and old Blastem turning 'em down on the other! You couldn't half tice 'em there!"

Letting go the wheel of the car he made a gesture as if to embrace a scrofulous and sodden hillock.

"Diddleum's Shoot!" he announced impressively. "He let it go for £35 last year, he's asking £70 this. You see, Jacky Flashback, who's got the shoot next door, is rearing this year!

"Got 'em feeding nicely down there!" he enthuses, careering towards a clay-bound copse. "Make a right good do of it! Come a full moon, there's old Doublebore 'Bang Bang' up the top of it, and young Whizzer going 'Phizang, Phizang' at the bottom. Then there's Skinem, who does a bit of keepering for them, cornered the pheasant market, they reckon. Smart as mustard. Mrs. Turkey was all behopeful when she got two or three feeding with her hens, but he soon put paid to that from behind the nearest hedge!"

And do those who so steadfastly feed and tice, always feast where they fatten?

This morning—this calculated day, so artfully sandwiched in, after the day of: "Them dabbers from down the bottom who'll just scare 'em up here nicely," and before the day of: "Them baskets from up the top, who'll blow everything to bits," my husband and his co-partners set out to Shoot the Shoot.

Shuddering in the splintering sleet, I watched them move jubilantly towards Ferny Bank, guns acock, dogs—more or less—under control. Now at last will my dear one reap the reward of sore labour. Now will our pantries bulge with fatted Smithfield birds. Now will our willing teeth. . . .

Well I am sure I hope so, but I can't help feeling just a bit doubtful. You see, Dead-eye Dickie, who gets around this district quite a lot, shooting—er—pigeons for farmers, watched them go too. And I couldn't help overhearing him in the Post Office afterwards:

"They wunna do much," he said very, very dryly. "Me and me brother was through all that little lot, the day before yesterday!"

KAY TARRANT

Handyman's Handicap

No Union calls a strike for me.
There's none to "see me right."
So doing jobs that others scorn,
I'm slaving day and night.

I mended all Ma Boscombe's fence,
Then painted it like new.
But Ma lives in a pre-war dream,
And paid what she thought due.

Old Farmer Jopp wants me to hedge,
And there's a rick to thatch.
Someone has forced the school house door,
So can I mend the latch?

I wish I'd stuck to just one trade,
Or run away to sea.
I wish I'd come up on the pools.
I wish I wasn't me.

BERYL M. RALPH

✿ THE WASP

He flew in briskly through the bedroom window, swooping towards the bed with a barely audible buzz, and it was not until he alighted on the breakfast tray perched on my legs, that I realised he was a little tipsy.

He was undoubtedly a fine figure of a wasp, as gaily striped as any awning and with a devil-may-care awareness of the beauty of the morning. In the misty garden, beyond the window, the pears were hanging golden in a moisture-laden stillness and I felt sure that it was upon these that my wasp had made himself a trifle ridiculous.

He propped himself up against the edge of the shallow bowl of marmalade and gazed at me speculatively as if to coax me to invite him to have some.

"Go away," I said as I reached for another slice of toast. Perhaps I had spoken too sharply, for he seemed to flinch and mumble something as he hauled himself off the tray into unwilling flight. Peering at me as he sailed past my face, he gave me the distinct impression that he was affronted and was on the point of making a somewhat hurt, if dignified, departure.

Unfortunately, he was in no state to do that. As he turned at the casement, he swayed in the air, missed the opening and thumped against the window frame.

From the sill, he gazed mournfully across at me and then must have realised I was seeing how stupid he looked. He pulled himself together, drew his antenna across his face like an experienced inebriate and obviously decided to show me a thing or two.

I swear that in the next minute and a half, he carried out an aerial display deliberately calculated to impress me. I felt like an observer at an insect Farnborough as he flexed his legs and made an almost vertical take-off. Round and round and about he flew, darting, hovering and swooping in mock low level attacks across the foot of my bed, over the coverlet, at toast height above my tray and finally past the end of my nose with a leer which, even with my vision distorted, was utterly triumphant.

The breathtaking performance could not last for ever and I had an idea that he might settle somewhere near to receive my approbation if not actually a prize in the shape of a shred of marmalade. Surely enough, he timed his landing perfectly, touching down on my plate with a flutter of his wings.

"Bravo," I said, "You've obviously flown before." He fixed me with a peevish stare which plainly indicated that flattery was insufficient and then he began arching his back and shambling forward towards my marmalade. With his reward so close, he paused to see if anything was to be done about it. It was: I raised by hand to whisk him away and the cream jug slithered towards the edge of the tray, leaving a pale rivulet on the polished wood.

My wasp rose in astonishment at the clatter. He looked at me once more and then, because, I suppose, it was on use flying over spilt milk, he departed in leisurely flight towards the dressing shelf.

As I righted my tray and munched the final piece of toast I thankfully observed that he was absorbed in his examination of the powders, paints and perfumes.

Was he filled with resentment at my having just witnessed his waspish weakness? Or could it have been that he had reached the mature conclusion that I had been a meany over the marmalade? I could not hope to know to what it was he took such a sudden and violent exception. But he did.

Without a sound he left the dressing shelf and came at me as purposefully as with a fixed bayonet and instinctively I felt that he was about to do me an injury. Hastily I made to ease the tray off my legs, the better to defend myself.

He didn't sting me, of course, they hardly ever do, but I was sufficiently alarmed to spring out of bed with complete abandonment of dignity.

My wasp, sober and alert now to the strong possibility of retribution for the disturbance he had caused, made for the window and, for all I know, went straight to the pear tree to celebrate his victory.

PATRICIA CAMERON

135

❧ DEVON

... If, and when I retire it will be still North Devon, somewhere not too far from the sea and on the south side of a hill with a lovely view.

I think it is all these lovely views one is always seeing that really capture one's heart. This is what I mean. While motoring along a quiet country lane at the top of the hill, it is always, "Oh, look," and what do we see? Fields, like patchwork quilts, streams with birds of every kind and colour, woods, dark green firs and the lighter greens of beech, oak and willow and the little villages with their church towers and more hills all around. All we have to do then is to motor on around the next bend and the scene is quite different, a river winding its way down to the sea, passing a little town with the fishing boats by the harbour wall. ...

MRS. R. J. SAUNDERS, *Ilfracombe*

❧ THE ONE THAT GETS AWAY

In the good—or maybe the bad—old days when Edwardian shooters slew 3,000 pheasants a day and reckoned it only an average bag, it was a favourite game among the editors of sporting magazines to invite crack shots to name what was, in their expert opinion, the most difficult bird to kill.

Almost without exception they named the high, gliding, curling pheasants, for high, gliding, curling pheasants were what the giant battues of the period were designed to produce. And if the experts missed one or two of these "tall" birds they were likely to remember the occasion.

Mind you, these gentry didn't miss much, for game shooting was almost a profession with them. At Holkham, Blenheim and Sandringham in those days you met such performers as the Marquess of Ripon and Lord Walsingham. Of these two it is reliably reported that, with the aid of a pair of guns and a loader apiece, they demolished a complete covey of eight partridges, getting two each in front and two each behind.

The thing worth remarking about this story is not that they both had two rights and lefts—you'd expect that—but that their shooting manners were so perfect and instinctive that neither took the other's bird. I mention this just to establish the kind of shooters the editor of the *Badminton Magazine* was dealing with when, in 1905, he asked his first fifteen-a-side that included Ripon, Walsingham, Prince Victor Duleep Singh and the Marquess of Granby—which was the hardest shot.

Fourteen out of fifteen top marksmen voted for the pheasant, most of them for high pheasants, and a good many of them for pheasants gliding with motionless wings. A Mr. R. G. Hargreaves plumped for the second barrel at a flock of teal well on the wing, but then I suspect he was just trying to be different.

Now move forward in time 56 seasons to a day when big bags are numbered in hundreds, when small-scale rearing is all the thing, when wildfowling is the common sportsman's joy, and when pigeon shooting has become a specialist's job—to 1961, in fact. What answers do we get then? I asked a widely different team of modern crack shots which bird they missed most frequently. Their selections and the reasons they give are so varied and full of shooting wisdom that I believe they are worth quoting at length.

First Major Archie Coats, professional pigeon-shooter on Lord Rank's and other big Hampshire estates. Coats started off in the traditional manner.

"My first choice," he told me, "must be the very high cock pheasant which has reached the zenith of its rise and is planing down. For a number of reasons you may have failed to take this bird in front and have to shoot it either over your head or even behind. The main reason why this bird is so difficult is because you have to depress your gun to allow for its descending glide, as opposed to elevating for most normal driven shots.

"Number two on my list is the pigeon coming straight at you when you are standing in tall beeches in a high wind. He looks simple, but in fact he's lilting about all over the place.

The wind catches him and lifts him across the tree tops."

Archie Coats adds: "I asked some of the regulars I take out pigeon shooting with me. They are all first-class shots. Their answers included: a single low partridge going downhill. You are standing on a slope and have to take it behind. You tend to shoot over it. . . . A single driven snipe when you are shooting pheasants in marshy ground. Complete difference of pace fools you. . . ."

Next, Aubrey Buxton who wrote that excellent book, *The King in His Country*, the story of George VI's shooting days. Buxton modestly says that he'd rate himself as a fair reserve for a Norfolk gameshooter's first eleven. He professes that he is often beaten by a low fast bird at maximum game-shooting range and well out on the flank, especially when it's a grouse following the contours of a hill. A keen and accomplished wild-fowler, Buxton tells me that a duck skimming the marsh at long range often fools him in the same way. He shoots below it and believes that the fall-off trajectory has something to do with this. One is tempted to say that the remedy is either to use long range cartridges or bigger shot, but Buxton is such an experienced hand that I am sure he has taken this into consideration.

Tim Sedgewick is probably the high priest of wildfowlers, for the magazine he edits, *The Shooting Times*, caters very much for the marshmen. Tim was a gamekeeper for many years before he took up the pen, and his easy misses are a delightfully mixed bag, as one would expect.

"A bird that takes a lot of hitting," he begins, "is a sparrow-hawk dropping from her nest and vanishing quickly among tree trunks." He goes on, "But my own preference, when it comes to hard shots, is a fast curlew with the wind up its tail flashing over a gunner who is lying behind a shingle bank. It takes more hitting than any game bird. Ditto a single red-shank dashing low across drowned saltings when you are shooting on top of, or just at the base of, a sea wall. Shank seem to be able to duck the flash. I used to shoot up to ten thousand cartridges a season but I'd say all round that this redshank is the hardest shot in the book."

Another great wildfowler, Mackenzie Thorpe of Sutton Bridge, probably the greatest living expert on calling and shooting grey geese, voted for the curlew too. Kenzie says: "I reckon an old curlew takes a lot of beating, particularly going downwind. The wing beat looks lazy but they're shifting all right. And jink! You've only got to move a finger and they swing away."

What of the men who hear most of the shooting confessions of the worst as well as the best shots in the country. I mean the coaches at the West London Shooting Grounds at Northolt. They spend their working lives ironing out the errors of both cracks and duffers as they blast away at claybirds.

Smithy, the head coach, says: "It's the dropping bird that fools most of them. Guns seem to shoot over it (compare Archie Coats here). This is either because they imagine it's on a level course or because they never get the gun up to the cheek. They tend to put the head down to the stock and this makes them miss low. You really want to pull as you blot the bird out."

Percy Stanbury, assistant manager at West London, refused to name the most difficult species of bird, maintaining that any shot was a question of sound basic technique and that shooting technique started with the feet. Stance was the answer to a clean kill on any target, but he conceded: "If I must name a type of shot I'd say the bird directly overhead that has to be taken behind, and possibly the incoming bird off the right or left shoulder."

So much for the experts. What, finally, of the average performers? This is where I step in. After rejecting all the shamefully easy birds I miss I have no difficulty in picking out the target to which my gun invariably gives a safe conduct.

This is the mallard or teal dropping out of a clear, half-lit sky at evening flight when it means to pitch directly behind you. It is late and is going straight in without any preliminary orbit. Its wings are half closed and it is whiffling from side to side with undercarriage and airbrakes down. It may not be travelling very fast but it is dropping like a lift. I feel even Lord Walsingham might miss a few of those.

COLIN WILLOCK

🌹 BOXING DAY "MEET"

My father only comes to stay with us once a year—at Christmas. His single-minded passion is shooting, consequently, there's quite a palaver goes on about arranging to get him some good sport on Boxing Day.

On our old shoot, which is a fairly rough mixture of everything including coots and carrion crows, we go down there at weekends and take what comes. Some Saturdays we return in a lordly way with several brace of pheasants for the pot. Another time it'll be nothing or the odd rook.

But my father—so my husband thinks—mustn't be subjected to this "slumming"—as he calls it. And must be shown some "interesting" sport.

Personally, I find nothing so interesting as the occasional rat or magpie cropping up between the pheasants, but for the sake of the syndicate's pride, pa-in-law must have the opportunity of some "high birds" or "driven partridges."

And so, a couple of weeks before this Boxing Day shoot, there's always a lot of talk about beaters, working out the route, and all that; while I do my little bit by packing up a suitably interesting lunch with turkey sandwiches, cold plum pudding and a Thermos full of hot rum punch!

For the past five years this BD shoot routine has followed its usual course and up till now my father has managed to go home with at least two brace of something "interesting" in the boot of his car. There was no reason to think, therefore, that the sixth year shouldn't produce the same results.

We went through the first wood. Nothing. Over the next couple of fields. No sign of life. Through a small copse, usually fairly productive. Not a sniff, not a flutter. We could have been on the moon.

For myself, I didn't care two hoots. I was thoroughly enjoying my walk with the dogs. My father too, striding along pink in the face and cheerful, seemed quite unperturbed by not having to move his gun from his shoulder. Only the hosts were looking at each other anxiously and agreeing it was "darned unusual".

We came to the big wood known as Oak Piece. "This is

where the devils must be hiding," said my husband. "Funny how you never can tell from one week to another where they'll be." We spread out across the width of the wood and started through.

In spite of the beating up noises we were making, bashing trees, prodding bramble bushes and see 'em out encouragements to the dogs, I felt sure I heard a familiar tune coming from somewhere. Twice I stopped to listen, wondering if it was my imagination or the echoes of last night's gramophone music. The third time it was unmistakable. Somebody, and not so far away at that, was blowing a hunting horn.

I don't remember very clearly what happened after that. Except that everything seemed to happen at once.

I think it must have been the hare that started it. All I know is I saw it cross the ride in front of me. Then there was a bang, sundry other loud noises and the next moment, though I had to blink twice to be sure I wasn't dreaming, there were a couple of foxhounds, our spaniels and somebody's terrier, all in a heap in the middle of the ride.

Then a horse appeared through the trees. Then another. Then several more came crashing through and landed in the ride. Whips were cracking. The horn kept blowing. The dogs were barking and squeaking and everybody's steam was rising up in great swirls as if the Flying Scot was about to take off for the North.

I made a grab for my dog and nearly got swallowed by a hound. My father was producing a sort of melancholy background moan. "What in heaven's name happened, what on earth. . . ." And my husband somewhere still hidden in the trees was swearing at his retriever, buried under a pile of hounds.

It was interesting to stand back in the role of spectator in a situation where the female had no possible reason for interfering. This was no conflab or political parley which one could break up by announcing that food was on the table. Nor was it the sort of squabble where frenzied Mum lays in and knocks a couple of heads together.

This was man against man and the enjoyment of having absolutely nothing to do with it quite made up for any embarrassment the situation was causing. Besides, I was becoming increasingly aware of the fascinating fact that here we all were creating a scene which was actually taking place, and wasn't a drawing in the Christmas number of *Punch*.

All we awaited now was the inevitable meeting of the two party leaders.

Unarmed though he was the MFH looked a great deal more belligerent than his opponent with a gun. What their respective private feelings were I could guess but never print. What they actually said to each other was strictly in the tradition of British sportsmen, even if the words did emerge through clenched teeth.

It was all over in a couple of sentences—"my chap" didn't get hold of "your chap" and "not surprising we didn't get a fox/bird." And then hats were raised and both parties retreated.

There are times when I find this civilised behaviour the weeniest bit of a bore. In spite of goodwill to all men and that sort of thing I would have enjoyed hearing an exchange of good Anglo-Saxon words or even a spot of gun waving or crop-wagging.

Nobody could say we had failed to give my father an interesting day, even if it wasn't the sort of interesting stuff he could put in the boot of his car.

BARBARA HARGREAVES

🌹 SHE SELLS SEAWEED— OFF THE SEASHORE

The stuff on my plate looked like cowdung, but tasted unmistakably of the tang of the tide with the faintest hint of something medicinal thrown in. And my grinning farmer host assured me it was a first-class pick-me-up after a glassy night, which made it almost a prescription. This was laverbread.

I learnt that the laver or porphyra—which is what it was—

had been got from Miss Audrey Hicks, doyenne of the free-lances that used to scour the translucent laver weed from rocks of Freshwater West, and sell it for the table.

I found her at Angle in South Pembrokeshire where she has been earning a living from laver gathering for forty years, ever since as an independent school-leaver she opted for self-employment from the sea. She is a quiet determined person whose words take wing when she talks of the sea.

The sea is Audrey Hicks' boss, her working hours are de-termined by its moods and movements, by the wind, tide, sun and moon. For laver, the chocolate-coloured sea-weed that grows like a membrane on the rocks in the tidal pools, must be picked by day or moonlit night as and when the tides permit.

Her harvesting may take her for miles along the rocks that are her meadows, which flush and wane with crop like a far-mer's fields. After winter dormancy, the laver begins to move in February and reaches its peak in mid-April when a good week's harvesting with up to five hours daily between tides might yield three hundredweights or more. At the end she may be hurried back by the tide, carrying a sacked hundred-weight across her shoulder.

Her laver is a favourite dish in South Wales, served with the breakfast bacon. It has been popular in many parts of Britain, especially in the West Country, but all Miss Hicks' supplies go to South Wales.

She brings her day's or night's haul back to her little sedge-thatched hut, strongly built with massive driftwood beyond the pound of tide. Here it is dried for a week, turned daily on a floor of sand that takes seven years to grow the bacterial flora for perfect curing. The dried laver is then sacked and sent by rail to Swansea.

Harvesting porphyra for a living, apart from storm and tide hazards and the economic insecurity that haunts a livelihood dependent on the sea, is not always peaceful. There have been macabre experiences with dead mariners and queer ship-wrecked cargoes, strafings by aircraft during the war, good laver pickings from unexploded mines, arguments with irate C.O.s about rights to work her trade in restricted areas. And on one evening she was pinned down behind some rocks by a madman with a purloined rifle who wanted some live target practice. And got it.

Preparing laver for the table is a ritual of washing and boiling done mostly now in small cottage factories where large piles of the dried frond are reduced by long boiling to a dark pulp. But laver is eagerly sought and bought by the ton in South Wales, sprinkled with oatmeal and fried with breakfast bacon as bara lawr, both for its flavour and its reputed medicinal properties.

For the connoisseur of esoteric recipes it can be heated with butter, gravy, lemon juice and pepper in an aluminium saucepan—there is a fetish against iron—and eaten as the "natural" sauce of mutton and lamb grazed and fattened on saltings that are themselves washed and flavoured by the sea.

J. L. JONES

Hill Farm Garden On Christmas Eve

There's an awareness over the hill—
A hushed awaiting, all calm and still
In the darkening wood no creatures call
Cattle are quiet, in shed and stall.
On a jasmine spray hang stars near bright,
As that which wise men followed one night.
From purple darkness comes drifting hence
A strange sweet fragrance like frankincense.
Cradled in leaves, so white on dark earth
Christmas roses, hail the Holy Birth.

MRS. M. J. DAWSON

Shrimp

I'm a sheep dog puppy, and alas
I'm rather small,
But is it my fault that I never
Grow at all?

He'll never make a sheep dog, I have
Heard them say,
He's like a little lamb himself . . . then
I run away.

It gives a chap a complex, always
Being told,
That Brother Tim was almost trained, at
Ten months old.

They call me SHRIMP, *which doesn't help*
Morale at all,
So I act as if I'm stupid when I
Hear them call.

In fact, all my markings are real
True pedigree,
I'm not related to the Poodle
Family.

Poor Shrimp, they say, he'd panic, he'd soon
Turn tail and creep
Back into his kennel, if looked at
By a sheep.

I said to my Mother, who is kind
And very wise,
Do you think I'm always going to
Be this size?

She said, Don't worry if you're small
And rather odd,
There are too many of us like peas
In a pod.

KAY TURNER

❧ LOOKING FOR
A COWBELL

After travelling many hundreds of miles across the face of France, it dawned on me that French cows lead the most extraordinary lives.

To begin with, they seldom or never have fields, and if they do these fields have no hedges.

The great, big-boned, dun-coloured cows with soft brown eyes and long eyelashes, graze in placid rings, their necks collared in deep leather straps, their lives dedicated, one hopes, to the production of those huge cartwheels of decorated butter adorning the stalls in country markets.

The cows in fields, miles from anywhere, apparently confining themselves by will-power to a small unfenced piece of land surrounded by tempting crops, invariably turned out to be fiercely guarded by a small lone child, or a formidable, even lonelier dog. Unfenced railway lines ran relentlessly across the landscape. Such, one imagined, listening to the aimless, timeless singing of a small girl, was the solitude that nurtured the shepherd saints of France.

The road that led to the Pyrenees also led to cows with untrammelled lives. All night long, high up in the cold air, a torrent of rushing mountain water sweeping through the clean streets of the little town, a thousand lights burning as proof of the cheapness of electricity, the small clamour of cowbells on the mountain slopes sounded above the ever present menace of distant thunder. Tink, tonk—then a pause; then yet a third note. Sometimes clashing like a carillon, sometimes widely separated, with a fourth and fifth note added or subtracted, leading a sleepless listener to evolve a mental betting list on the next sequence.

After a few nights the possession of a single, genuine cowbell, as against the elaborate polished brass affairs on sale to tourists, became an obsession.

"I must have a cowbell."

"But what on earth for? You can't expect a respectable English cow to go tinkling round the countryside."

"Well, I could ring it to bring people in to meals. Tink, tonk, Come and get it."

"One hearty yell from you would bring the cattle home across the sands of Dee; and in any case there is no time now."

"I must have a cowbell."

In silence we whirled down mountain passes; and the plain below, obviously without a cowbell for thousands of miles, appeared and vanished like a dizzy carpet through gaps in the rocks. The last mountain town slowed us down to a crawl, and there under torrential thunder rain, swaggering beneath a cape, self-confident, gay, sunburned, arrogant, was a modern musketeer, my image of D'Artagnan, in control of the traffic in the little market square. He brought us, nonchalantly, to a halt. Here was my last chance.

"Where," I asked in French, leaning out of the car, "can I buy a cowbell?"

He looked at me for a moment, then burst into great gusts of uncontrollable laughter, slapping his knees, doubling up, straightening himself only to become helplessly involved in his enormous joke.

"Say it again," he said, when he could speak.

I repeated it, word for word. The traffic began pulling up all around, Gallic hoots of impatience breaking out from every car. Again the roars of laughter above the mounting rage of the motor horns, as with tears in his eyes he directed us to a nearby ironmonger's shop; where, as things turned out I was promptly, politely, unsmilingly served with a genuine, un-polished cowbell in a soft golden bronze metal marked with a cross—and this in answer to the identical question.

What had I said? I will never know. What he said was more to the point.

As he waved us across the market square he had, like most policeman after a holdup, the last word, and in this case, shouted for the whole town to hear.

"Oh, oh, oh, la jolie petite Anglaise!"

I consider myself neither little nor pretty, though certainly English, but oh boy, to be told so in a single sentence certainly rang that bell!

KAY HILL

❀ THE BAD
AND THE SCARED

A bunch of taut-limbed horses, fresh from the mountains, milled nervously around my neighbour's yard. A solid, glisten-ing nugget of horse-flesh jutted up out of the mob, compact and without blemish. A twitch of muscle sent the gelding's smooth skin rippling as when a pebble is cast into a red pool.

That was the first time I saw him.

The next occasion was when we were gathering sheep on my part of the hill not long afterwards. My middle-aged

neighbour was riding him out for the first time. All day this violent-spirited animal had been erupting; another rider, passing too close, left a piece of sleeve between its slashing teeth, another horse got kicked on the hock. But disaster didn't descend until we were near the fences of a sheep-fold. The gelding reared viciously and with almost cool deliberation fell back to crash against the heavy larch rails. I can still recall wondering whether the splintering noise was that of cracking timber or the hillman's ribs. It was both.

A few days later it attacked a farm-hand. The man had a few stitches and a fright, and just missed being awarded a bed next to his boss in the local hospital.

That was six months ago. I saw the horse again last week. It was being ridden by the same man. This time it was as quiet and relaxed as a child's first pony.

"Hosses is like folks," my neighbour explained, "some be born bad, some gits to be sinners through wrong company, and other'n be bad 'cos they'm affeared, I reck'n."

His success with the animal obviously confirmed his diagnosis, but it takes sound horsemastership to detect the difference.

Up here in the hills, where the horse business has had such a come-back, we are beginning to realise that it pays to turn out more schooled animals than we have been doing previously. Fortunately, there is no lack of skill; horses had retained their importance here as a means of transport, for even the spread of mechanisation could do nothing to assist the mountain shepherd who is still dependent on his pony.

Sooner or later we inevitably meet with a dangerous horse—one that is either mad or bad. The former is comparatively rare among the wild, native stock. Unlike lowland horse breeding, nature still makes its own selection to a considerable extent in these wild herds.

Unfortunately, there is only one thing to do with a really mad horse—or bull, or dog, for that matter.

Outlaws and animals which have temperaments scarred and embittered in some way are not quite so uncommon. Though the worst horses in my experience have been those which have been produced by external factors, there is no doubt that heredity can play a large part.

St. Simon, the unbeaten wonder horse, is a striking example.

In-breeding to this temperamental tyrant produced an un-ending line of excitable descendants. When it is known that there are inherited tendencies to temperamental instability a horse master can expect a long, continuing struggle. Rarely in such an animal's lifetime can caution and vigilance be re-laxed.

Happily such horses are few. By far the greater number of problem horse are those which are made so.

The latter are often easier to deal with. We ride them hard, without saddle and with saddle, with a bucking rope and without. These are the brawling, brash mounts which are the delight of all the young rough riders in these hills. They like the task because it is a straight-forward, no-waiting one, de-monstrating who's boss. Real western stuff, this.

But here, again, is where the recognition of the cause of aggressiveness is so vital. It would be seeking trouble to rough-ride an animal which has become sour-spirited from past mishandling, or which is throwing a panic attack out of ex-treme fear.

Unlike a man, a horse lives by experience alone. He knows only what he has felt, seen, suffered. He has no vision of the future, no starry promise to enthuse his soul; he possesses only the sense of present well-being, or of the pain and bitterness of the past. And this he knows and remembers with all his hard, clear-seeing mind.

I own a pretty bay mare, which, until recently was a prob-lem horse. She was a quiet ride, with gentle, affectionate manners—outside her stable. When in her loose box she was utterly and determinedly homicidal.

The first time I discovered it she nearly ripped my arm off. To anyone approaching her in the box she was a fury of teeth and hooves.

Last spring I visited her original owner, who had broken her. His wife directed me to the stables. It was only a small low-roofed building and though the doors were closed I could clearly hear the torrent of colourful Celtic expletives which was coming from it.

The door was opened to my call and I went in. A small, sweaty, wild-eyed gelding stood bridled in the corner. It was bitted in a viciously tight curb. A small stream of blood hung from each side of its mouth like scarlet icicles and the bridle tinkled continuously as the animal trembled.

I realised what had been happening. In the dim, confined space of this shed the gelding was being backed for the first time. The animal was probably quite fresh from the hills and had never been indoors before in its life.

It would hardly forget its first experience of it. Such is the way one kind of problem horse is created . . . and perhaps the most dangerous. A runaway which forms the habit of bolting blindly in sheer panic risks injuring itself as well as its rider; a bully in which is a vice does at least remain in control of itself and is sure of what it is doing and where it is going.

Finally, the courageous defiance of an intelligent, independent spirited animal should not be mistaken for the aggression of a bully. The former, with tact and patience, will frequently develop into the finest, most exhilarating ride of them all.

There's much mellifluous nonsense written about horse-breaking.

"I heard of somebody sayin' that they tamed wild 'uns by breathin' into the hosses noses," commented my assistant the other day, and added, "if you'd tried with some of the rum 'uns I've seen they'd have breathed back right quick and pruned your nose clean off'n your face into the bargain."

I think I've seen practised most of the usual—and unusual—methods of handling a dangerous horse, all the gypsy tricks and all the semi-superstitious manoeuvres one finds in a remote countryside, but ultimately it isn't merely the method—it's the man.

Two miles up the mountain track from me, living with his father in the bleakest sheep farm in these parts, is a teen-age youth who is sought out by his neighbours when they've got an outlaw to be tamed.

He is a great gangling lad with clumsy hands and big feet. He would probably be considered a borderline mental defective by most in this arrogant t.v.o.-and-diploma age; like a few others up here, he can't read or write, he's apparently clueless and almost incoherent in speech. But one night I heard him talk—to a snarling devil of a horse—and his voice was as low and sweet as the croon of the pigeons in the evening pines behind the farm.

When he stretched out his thick-fingered hands they were quiet and calm; their movement was without suddenness or threat. Within moments he had that flat-eared, white-eyed animal standing relaxed and stripped of aggression.

"Glyn," I said, "how do you manage in a few minutes what would take the rest of us as many weeks? Do you talk horse language or something?"

"Dunno 'bout that," he said, with an owlish grin, "but mebbe I thinks like 'un."

HUW MEREDITH

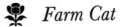 *Farm Cat*

I'm a tough cat, and a rough cat,
I'm a barn cat,
They give me milk from a tin bowl,
I don't get fat.

On that, so I'm always prowling,
Looking for meat,
Even a barn cat wants something
Solid to eat.

There's a house cat, she sleeps in,
She ignores me,
If I meet her outside, she will
Leap up a tree.

I know she has two meals a day,
And fish for tea,
I crept inside once and took it,
No one saw me.

So after that I was sleeping
For two whole days,
But I wouldn't be a house cat,
With sissy ways.

One day I had a nasty scrap
With a stranger,
A ginger chap, I laid him low
In a manger.

The house cat watched the first half,
But when the blood
Flew out, she disappeared, you see
She Is a dud.

I'm wasted in this barn, so why
Dilly Dally,
I'll go and be a gang leader
In Cats' Alley!

KAY TURNER

♣ THE COTTAGE LILY

"The Lily is an herbe with a white flower; and though the leaves of the flower be whit, yet within shineth the likenesse of gold." This beautiful word-picture of the Madonna Lily (*Lilium Candidum*) was penned in the thirteenth century by the great scholar, Bartholomaeus Anglicus. No writer, I think, has since bettered it, and every summer, when these lovely flowers fill the air with their delightful fragrance, his words come to mind.

The origins of the Madonna Lily are lost, but it is acknowledged to be one of the oldest cultivated lilies in existence, and is wrapped in historical and religious significance. With the years, many flowers have changed almost out of recognition, but it pleases me to think that the Madonna Lilies growing in my garden today are not appreciably different from those which probably flourished here many centuries ago.

Some people think that this lily is difficult to grow successfully, but it will grow for most of us provided a few basic rules are observed.

First, buy your bulbs from lily specialists, even if it means paying a little more. They will supply you with firm fresh bulbs whose vital basal roots are intact and alive. The bulbs are best obtained during August or early September and should be planted immediately upon receipt. Within a matter of weeks they will throw up a rosette of basal leaves which show that the bulbs are healthily active. Further growth is not made until spring, but these basal leaves will remain green all winter.

When planting, choose a site which is reasonably sunny, sheltered and well-drained. The soil may be enriched with a little well-rotted manure and a sprinkling of lime. As a precaution against disease dust the bulbs with sulphur powder before planting, and to prevent moisture collecting in the scales tilt them a little to one side. The bulbs should be buried with the top just under the ground.

It is often said that Madonna Lilies thrive to perfection in an old cottage garden where they receive but scant attention, and there may be more than a grain of truth in this because they really do resent disturbance and once planted should be left alone. Also, cottage gardens are usually on the small side, and (as in my own case) the borders are packed with plants. This, too, suits the Madonna Lily, because the other subjects give a certain amount of shelter against rough winds, and during hot weather provide the cool root which all lilies appreciate so much.

One appeal, when planting your lily bulbs, do not dot them here and there. Plant them in groups.

LEE DENNY

A GHOSTLY GLOAMING

One of these days, I've been saying to myself, I must go and find out just what the attraction is in duck-shooting that will get a man—a lover of his comforts—out of bed at dawn in the middle of winter for pleasure.

Unfortunately for me I couldn't have chosen a worse day to satisfy my curiosity—or, for that matter, a worse place, except perhaps the Caucasus Mountains, for we were staying with my sister and her husband in the far north of Scotland in the middle of the most severe freeze-up this island has known for 135 years. It hadn't started when I set out and I wasn't fully aware of it when I got back for I just imagined it was usual to return from this crazy spot in a semi-glacial condition.

As a novice, I was spared the dawn flight. Instead we would "take it easy" with the evening flight. Perhaps it was the Peter Scott pictures all over the walls of my sister's house which inspired me; perhaps it was the rarefied air of the Highlands that went to my head. Whatever it was that inspired me to make this fatal trip, I should, by now, know my limitations as a sportswoman. I should have known that once I stop moving about outdoors after October my extremities cool to such a low temperature that I cease to think about anything else.

To bag a duck or a goose successfully, as you may know,

involves sitting (or preferably lying) dead still, not just while it flies over your head but several hours before. Just in case their big bird brains conclude that if you've been there more than two hours you're not there at all.

As a duck-flighter's wife, I'm quite reconciled to welcoming home happy, muddy souls full of stories of not a duck in sight. My mental menus never go so far as to include roast duck or goose unless firmly labelled "Sainsbury". Either they didn't fly in or they flew too high, or they flew the other way. Imagine, therefore, my surprise when on arriving at the appointed area, to see six wild geese walking about the field as calmly as farmyard birds.

Things happened fast after that. The man with the gun fell on his face as if he'd been shot in the back, and with tremendous hissings under his breath, and vigorous circular motions of his arms, I concluded that I was to bend double and go about a mile round to shoo them his way.

I found this enjoyable. As a child I loved cowboys and Indian games, lying in ambush and jumping out on people, and as I bent my head almost to my knees and took long, stealthy strides round the hedges and peered through gaps to see if the birds were still there, I recaptured some of the old thrill of my tomboy days.

When I reached a place for a favourable shoo they were still there, pecking away at the grass. Funny, I thought, if they turn out to be only farmyard geese and run away when I clap my hands.

However, they flew—but in the wrong direction: away from the gun. For once I began to believe the stories that came home to me so often, for here was a case where if the shooer had had a gun and the gun had done the shooing, we might have put a couple in the bag.

We walked down to the beach and straight away I got an eyeful of Peter Scott, for there, swimming about, were hundreds of widgeon, teal, pochard etc.—and duck, the names of which I can't remember. We were both in a fair state of excitement, for neither of us expected to see such a crowd all at once cruising about in full view, like the sort you feed in the Municipal Gardens with old crusts.

"A wildfowler's feast," my husband kept saying, with his

eyes glued to the binoculars. On the East Coast, where he usually indulges this sport, you never see them except coming in on the wing or miles out like so many blobs.

Naturally, of course, they all flew off the moment we got within camera or gun range but, as my husband said: "We're not ready for them yet."

I looked at my watch. It was two o'clock. Dusk was at five-ish. We had three whole hours to "get ready" for those duck.

The wind was getting up, the Firth looked cold and grey and the sky was the same colour. I pulled my coat closer and turned the collar up round my ears. Well, I had asked for it, and now I was going to get it.

I borrowed the binoculars and walked about a bit, looking at things, and when I came back I found my husband digging what looked like his own grave, with some pieces of old tin can of the sort you find among the flotsam on a beach.

He dug until he came to water while I gazed, fascinated. Was he really proposing to spend the next three hours in this terrible pit?

Gently, he lowered himself down into it till only his hat showed above the edge. Rapidly I took photographs. I might at least get some good laughs out of this in the comfort of my own home.

"You know," he said, kindly but firmly, "I really think it's about time you went and hid yourself or we shan't see a thing."

Wildly I looked round for some sort of rude hut, a few sticks—anything but a cold grave.

There were two hungry-looking gorse bushes in the distance. Miserably, I made my way towards them. In moderate temperatures I can think of nothing pleasanter than to sit and gaze round the countryside for hours on end; there's always something to look at, think about, and the odd forty winks enhance the pleasure. But in winter temperatures, to sit for more than a moment is torture. If only one's limbs would go solid it wouldn't be so bad, but instead, for some reason, one's shoes and gloves become full of little sharp knives.

I could draw you a detailed plan of the view from those gorse bushes and every stick and stone within reach. I know intimately the shape of every river, road and tree. I know the times of every train between 2 p.m. and 5 p.m. and when the lights go on in the carriages.

It was the longest twilight of my life. At one point I looked at the sky and convinced myself that there was to be no night. Every now and again I looked the other way, but there wasn't a duck in sight. "When they fly in," I said to myself, "it'll make up for all this."

And still I gazed at the sky and still no duck and no dark.

I must have gone to sleep, for I woke up in pitch dark with a familiar voice hollering at me across the fields.

Tottering to my frozen feet, I hobbled back to where I could see the lights of the car. After all that, I thought, I went to sleep on the wretched birds.

But they had never been. Perhaps a little bird told them where we were. . . .

BARBARA HARGREAVES

I never saw a Purple Cow;
 I never hope to see one;
But I can tell you, Anyhow;
 I'd rather see than Be One.

Horse and Foal

Horse and Foal

"Round-hoof'd, Short-jointed, fetlocks shag and long,
Broad breast, full eye, small head and nostril wide,
High crest, short ears, straight legs and passing strong,
Thin mane, thick tail, broad buttock, tender hide:
Look, what a horse should have he did not lack,
Save a proud rider on so proud a back".

W. SHAKESPEARE
Venus and Adonis

🌹 LUCKLESS, DUCKLESS, GUTLESS

Oh my clever Cambells, my cute and comical Khakis, thou art lost and gone for ever, and I'm dreadful sorry! Your pens are pulled down to patch up the pigsties, and the lingering echo of your ceremonial quack is just the wind wiffling across your wasted runs. No more can I look from my window and see you dibbling in the dabbles, or bustling bright-eyed about your business.

When you were mine, I never needed sleeping-pills, only a bucket of water or a collapsible bed. Mornings were heavy; so heavy that I rarely got more than half an eye open before hearing the improving saws of the disapproving postman float in through my bedroom window. But nights—nights were all my own. I was one with the owl, the ghost-moth, and the courting couples. I was one also with the trout, the water-rat, and the—er—caddisworm.

Drive you to the water? Never! But where you drove me was another matter. Many an impromptu paddle—and worse —I had at midnight, as you ducked and splashed in the chequered moonlight, as imperturbable under my shower of missiles as Londoners under the Luftwaffe. And on damp, bright, high-snailing nights, you'd be six fields away fanning out on the lush new ley, oblivious of my frantic "widdy-waddying" and conscious only of the glorious squelch and slime and slither of fine fat slugs. Nowadays these vile molluscs are multiplying unchecked and will soon ruin the lot of us!

Unlike some that squat and boothug and cockadoodle round the farm, you were true aristocrats—courtly but kingly. Never, never could you forget that you were only forty or fifty generations off a wild, free and independent mallard. Those that felt the call of the blood most strongly, would disappear down the brook on a long portage, deserting the home that knew them, living off the country, and laying where they listed. Sometimes these conquistadors returned, sometimes they left their bleached bones on a foreign shore—for Mr. Fox always did fancy a fat duck!

Nor did you fall into mauve-combed declines, or wobbly wilts—you were ever too busy filling the bucket to kick it! Only at harvest-time did you become undone, unducked, and flop about like leaking feather-beds, forgetting your daily—or twice daily—duty. Overnight the eggs blossomed like mushrooms in the mud—er litter—of your runs. Eggs, sea-blue, jade-green, and pearly-white; eggs so fine and large, with marigold yokes; eggs for connoisseurs so subtly flavoured in the wild garlic season; eggs to make all other eggs taste like an afterthought.

You were career girls to the last quack! I only ever knew one of you—an eccentric, no doubt—who took upon herself the time-wasting lot of female-kind and stole her nest, brooded, and brought forth two, which she tried to rear Spartan-fashion on unlimited water and walking, and soon abandoned to the care of the local authority.

Sometimes—particularly when I cut my hand on yet another tin of corned beef—my thoughts fly back to your snow-white cousins and I am seized with an entirely different nostalgia. Was there ever any quicker way of growing delicious flesh, which melted so sweetly on the tongue at the green-pea season? Not, of course, dear girls, that I always had green peas when I had you. In this there was considerable and stimulating rivalry between us—while we planted, you plotted; while you plundered, I pondered. Your persistence and perseverance in these matters was an example to all of us. There was that time when you—with a gourmand's delicacy of taste which we quite failed to appreciate—decided that you would eat your corn green. To foil you in this end we laid all our available netting round the hedge of the cornfield; that we hadn't quite enough to surround the top of the field didn't worry us—this, we considered, would be quite beyond your reach. And then, feeling rather bucked, we stood at the window to gloat. You moved up the lane in an aggravated yet determined file headed by "Percy Bysshe", a drake of infinite resource, who repeatedly, and unsuccessfully, probed the wired hedge-bottom, and tailed, well in the rear, by "Bumble-foot Anne".

Then you did something which wiped the silly grins from our faces. Still undaunted and still probing, you rounded the

corner of the lane and passed on to the high-road, where cars—normally so frightening to a duck of delicate nerves—whizzed by; but your dander was up, you were not to be scared by mere man-made contraptions. Rooted to the spot like a couple of gabies; we watched your thin, unbroken khaki line move boldly up half a mile of that road, till Percy's probing found the first gap beyond the netting, and you passed in a queue to paradise.

I always did prefer a chap who pulled his chair to the table with a hearty scrape and fell to with a will. Everything—no matter what—greencorn and slugs, potatoes and fish-waste, slid down the gullet like the Boa's goat. Nor did we ever need to reach for our coats; just when things were beginning to hum, with wretched, mumbled excuses about "lights for the dear little chuckies" or "supper for the darling hens." Night, light, half-light, it was all one to you. When I swayed up the lane with your buckets, in the pitch dark—going only on a wing and a prayer—you did not question or quiz like an awakened wife, but side-stepped my blundering feet and fell to.

Ah what a paradise we lived in then! Your lovely eggs queued up in buckets waiting to be washed, while each partner eyed the other expectantly; great tottering battlements of egg-boxes threatened to brain us; the cheques poured in; the bank manager raised his hat; the corn-merchant rushed to greet us with outstretched arms. Then came the earthquake—duck eggs, it seemed, were poisonous.

Suddenly all over the country everyone's aunt knew someone's cousin who had passed on of a surfeit of duck eggs. Boil all duck eggs 15 minutes, declared august medical opinion. Boil a duck egg 15 minutes and what have you? Just a nasty woolly taste in the mouth. Soon no one wanted your priceless treasures. Like lambs, you went to slaughter.

I should have taken up my keenest pen to fight for the purity of duck eggs—from healthy ducks, on clean water. I should have organised the duck-keepers and lusty nonagenarian duck-egg-eaters of Britain (these hearty grandads would need no bathchairs) and, placarded and shouting suitable slogans, we should have marched on the capital. There might have been two duck eggs on every plate every morning, and ducks we could turn to on every pool, lake, and river in Britain. But —I did nothing at all—nothing whatever. Now for ever I am condemned to be just a luckless, duckless, joyless, keeper of hens.

KAY TARRANT

🌼 WATER BABY

I had a letter recently from an old aunt of mine who lives in a little croft on the banks of Loch Ness. She is supposed to have the second sight and has a wonderful power over birds and animals. There was always some invalid being nursed in her house, a bird with a broken wing or a cat or dog or even a fox with a damaged leg.

According to her letter, she had taken up another interest, underwater creatures. "You'll never guess what has happened," she wrote, "I have seen our local phenomenon, the Loch Ness monster, or Nessie, as she is affectionately called. And what's more, I have made friends with her."

I wasn't really very surprised at this. Lots of people have claimed to have seen Nessie, so why not Aunt Mairi? But her next letter contained a bit of a shock.

"Nessie now comes to see me regularly," she wrote. "I have been feeding her and she is now quite tame. She tells me what I had actually begun to suspect, that she is now with young. This is the result of a visit to an old friend who lives in a Norwegian fjord. Isn't this most interesting?"

Indeed it was. I began to think I should go and pay a visit to Aunt Mairi. I wondered if she had been talking and how long it would be before the Press got on to the story. What a boost for tourism in Scotland! I could just imagine the headlines—"NESSIE APPEARS AGAIN! NOW A MOTHER! THE WORLD'S GREATEST WONDER—HER BABY MONSTER!"

All was still quiet, however, when I reached Loch Ness, the water dark green and calm, reflecting the tree-clad hills. I was soon approaching Aunt Mairi's little croft and there she was at the door to meet me. Her red hair shone, her blue eyes smiled. She was greatly excited.

"You're too late!" she cried. "Oh, if you had only been here last night such happenings! Nessie had her baby!"

Her keen eyes swept the loch, then she clutched my arm and pointed "Look, there she goes!"

I turned and scanned the water. Far out were dark ripples . . . and beyond? Was there something long and dark making down the loch, with an infinitesimal dot following behind?

I turned back. Aunt Mairi had a proud smile on her lips. "Ah, well," she said, "she'll be back. Come away in now and we'll have a cup of tea."

MARY SMITH

"I'M NO DIANA!"

Following the hunt has never been my cup of tea; not even by car. I'm terrified of horses, indifferent to the fate of foxes, and anti-social re the wired fence. Neither have I sentiment for Pink coats and England's glory; and the Speaking of Hounds does nothing for me. In all, I'm no Diana.

But Husbands and children differ. Something in their blood bubbles to roisterous life with words like hound, fox or covert; and hepcatting teenagers were never more truly "SENT" than are mine by the Music of the Horn.

So Saturday's dawn wakens me with a weight like the Taj Mahal on my chest and a certainty of impending doom.

I rise. I'd rather not, of course. I'd prefer to lie there and let the next few hours gallop across me. But then the hens would smash their eggs or might even resort to cannibalism and, hunting aside, I care about such things. So I plunge kitchen-wards, and wade across a sea of saddlery to the sink.

Achieving a space on the kitchen table I lay breakfast. I cook breakfast, but no one cares. They care only whether the going will be Good, Soft or Tacky. Five minutes before they set out they will recognise some emptiness within them and beseech me for sandwiches, but it's too early for that yet.

Two hours hence, there is no discernible progress. A strap is lost, a buckle bent, a jodhpur split. A mount will have developed a mysterious cut/blister/lameness. My youngest born has started to turn green with pre-hunting nerves and reminds me that she will need at least four aspirins this morning to calm her down. I give her two, and bully her into drinking a cup of hot milk whilst we stoically ignore her elder sister's taunt of "Ninny" and her father's impatient mumblings re dope for nerves.

Sneakingly I agree, but am goaded to defiant "So What?" Doesn't a certain local huntress admit to four double brandies to encourage her into the saddle, plus a refuelling at a stiff fence? Surely aspirin and hot milk for a jittery little twelve-year-old are innocuous! Although my common sense tells me it would be far more practical to dope the horse! They are away at last, and now it is I who need the aspirin.

My body returns to the house, but the rest of me goes hunting with them. In my imagination I am at every fence, every ditch; galloping over every slippery hollow, every cunningly concealed rabbit warren. I am decapitated by low-hanging branches, impaled on sharp hedge-stakes, and mangled by plunging horses. And I am not even alone in this, for it's happening to my children too—right, left and centre—(as they say in "The Archers"). "Why don't you follow us in the car?" my husband says when I admit to this torment. "You'd see then how little danger there is and it would do you a power of good."

But I don't want doing a power of good. And I'm convinced that my following the Hunt would no nothing for their necks; it might only endanger my own! In any case, should it be that my loved ones ARE ever surrendered by the Chase, prone on a five-barred gate, then let me receive them with a bed and h & c to hand, and not on some lonely windswept wold.

Long after I've resigned myself to a kinless old age they return. Mud-caked, irritable, disillusioned and hungry. And do I receive them with opens arms? Not I!

Limp from my diet of aspirin and anxiety I flounder among them, reviling, denouncing and ridiculing as I prepare a meal.

"It's so silly," I storm. "Why can't they shoot the fox, poison the fox, hang the fox? Don't they realise how stupid they look—hordes of walloping great people tearing after one tiny fox?"

And meek now; and rosy and sleepy and bursting with soup and sausage they smile slyly and do not argue, realising, half sorrowfully, that I shall never know what I am missing in the glory and excitement of the Chase.

I can actually *Feel* their sympathy!

CHRISTABEL RANDELL

... As Good As A Rest

Scintillating conversation oscillating all around,
But the farmer's contribution,
"That's a roughish piece of ground."

Waving palms and golden beaches, sparkling water flecked with foam,
But the holidaying farmer
Cannot help but think of home.

'Will the bailiff really manage?—"Garçon, one more cognac, please."
'Will the rooks be at the taties,
Pigeons eating all the peas?'

"Yes, my dear, the view is lovely"—'Wouldn't like to plough that field.
Hope old Primrose hasn't calved yet,
—Though her milk would help the yield.'

'Clever things, these mountain railways—missus wouldn't ride in it.
Mebbe we could run a rail
Of sorts to our old silage pit.'

'Wonder if Bill's weighed that litter—reckon they're fair due to go.
Should grade well—' "Highest peak?
Must be yon with all the snow."

"What my dear? The farm's all right, and am I really worrying?
Nonsense, dear, MY holiday's
To get away from everything."

Z. M. S.

🌹 ONE LAST LOOK

This weather reminds me of something my old nurse said to me once when I was about six. I can remember the moment as clearly as if it was now. The tears were pouring down my face and I was clinging on the pram with one small paw, and half running, half walking to keep up with the woman striding on ahead with exasperation. The reason for my tears I have no idea, but there was a fresh outburst when she said—her voice had a tool-sharp edge—"I'll give you a chocolate the day I fail to get tears out of you."

In these more enlightened days, continual sobs would indicate something wrong with the child's health or upbringing and we would try to discover the cause. But then, children who cried were boobies and cry-babies. And even now, if things build up to the sort of frustrating pitch where a jolly good cry would relieve my feelings and would do nobody or myself any harm, I fight back the tears as if they were something disgusting like being sick in public.

And so, like my exasperated old nurse, as the rain never fails to fall, however encouragingly bright the dawn, I was beginning to believe that no day would ever end without rain.

But yesterday the barometer needle suddenly flew up. The sun came out and stayed out till a full moon took over. Rivers sank to a reasonable level, puddles shrank and looking out at the garden from the kitchen seemed less like gazing into an aquarium.

In the spring I like to make a sort of tour of inspection through the marsh, woods and fields and up the hills to watch the countryside coming to life again. In the autumn I like to take a last look at things before the long, cold sleep.

This year, my tour has been delayed by almost a month because of the rain and I was beginning to think the leaves would all be off the trees before I'd get a chance to get round. But about teatime yesterday, when the sun was just going down on the first dry day for months, I said to the children: "You can toast your own crumpets today, dears," picked up my stick, shouted the dogs and was off.

As a girl, I found this time of the year depressing. When my

170

elders were raving about the autumn tints I was regretting the shorter days, and the colder weather with no more picnics, tennis and bare legs. Now I'm older, the first brown leaf tells me that soon I can stop working late in the garden and come in to a tea by the fire with plenty of time for my book before bedtime.

Up the hill the rain-filled stubble stalks sprayed little cold jets of water into my boots, and the finches made off with little squeaks of protest ahead of us. The hedges were still full of berries on branches elongated by months of rain. Some of them curved up and over just like weeping willows. The Old Man's Beard looked sadly in need of the hair-drier and the blackberries, saturated with wet, looked plump and lush but tasted of nothing. Only the hips with their plastic jackets and the spindles, pert and pink and pretty, seemed to have effectively resisted this incredible weather. The crab apples were lying soggy in the mud and I thought to myself, "No apple jelly this year." Nor sloe either, for that matter, for like the blackberries they too were saturated, with their grapy bloom all gone.

Pigeons flew out above my head. Why do they always fly out the other side when you have a gun? Ahead of me the dogs put out a squawking pheasant. The sun shining through the yellow leaves made them look like chinese silk and the wind, which sprang up every now and again, scattered them to the ground, so that it looked as if someone had chucked a handful of golden lockets into the air.

Up by the cottages on the edge of the wood the everlasting pram was still at anchor outside the back door, but the baby, who in spring lay meaningless and asleep in its shawl, was leaning on its harness like a fat little trap pony going up hill, and bawling baby abominations out of its chocolate-rimmed mouth.

In the wood, only the nettles were still green and they stung like vipers even through my troussers. Why are they so much more virulent when wet? The pigeons flapped about in the topmost branches and a robin sang. No, you couldn't call it singing, "pronounced" perhaps, that strange melancholy little phrase which always spells winter to me. Perhaps because one doesn't hear it above the richer notes of the spring and summer birds at other times of the year.

On the other side of the wood I came out on to a broad field of plough and stubble. The moon was coming up on my left, the sun was sinking on my right. A hare got up under my feet and leapt back into the wood. My terrier followed yapping, and while I waited for her to come out I leant against the fencing post with wise old Cindy, who has grown out of chasing hares. The family think training has achieved this but she and I knew better.

She has merely learnt in the wisdom of her old age the pointlessness of chasing after something you know you can't have.

I looked up and around me. The autumn twilights are the loveliest of the year. They last much longer and there's that peculiar half blue, half yellow luminosity about the sky which so defines the shapes of things that buildings, trees and hills look as if they were cut out with a pair of scissors and stuck on the background. Dusk comes very slowly and it's dark before you're fully aware of it. I could only just see my terrier emerging from the wood by the white bits on her chest and back.

We walked back by the river with a moon reflected in the water all the way; just as if we were kicking a big white ball along in front of us. Every now and again there was a splash in the reeds below the bank as a dabchick or a water rat dived out of our way, and sometimes a swish of wings and a quack as the duck are disturbed at their evening meal. A mist was rising off the surface of the water and the wind dropped as we rounded the curve in the river and came upon six swans lying in midriver, like a tiny fleet at anchor.

With their white forms against the dark willows and the mist round them like a gossamer veil, I thought for a moment I was seeing a scene from Swan Lake, or a picture from my Hans Andersen. I stood watching them for a while and then went in to the warm realistic noisy midst of my household. It had been a dramatic curtain to the last act of the season.

BARBARA HARGREAVES

🌺 THE BEE ON THE BUS

Let's face it; I don't like travelling by bus and I don't like having to go to town on business, but on this particularly glorious summer day, when bus travel seemed even more repellent than usual, I had to bow to the Fates, and needless to say I did it with a bad grace. So eventually I found myself on the top deck of our hourly bus, congratulating myself that at least someone liked fresh air and had opened the windows.

As I settled myself in my seat and prepared to fill my pipe I made my usual guarded inspection of the bus, from the "send your parcels by country bus" notice to the most vociferous of the passengers, a group of roughish looking town lads of about fourteen years of age, obviously returning from some jaunt in the country. There they were, sitting in the front seats, smoking away like chimneys, wearing what looked like odds and ends of their elder brothers' cast off Teddy clothing, guffawing in their half-broken voices and generally behaving in a way that made some of the female travellers purse their lips, nod their heads and give vent to that expression of aggravation known to writers as "tut!"

When I came to sit behind these boys they were having a great argument over the relative merits of spending their remaining pocket money on ice-cream or cigarettes and their leader, in a worse for wear gold-threaded jacket, respectfully referred to by the others as "Slug", made the outcome pretty clear by pocketing all their money and growling "Fags er nuffink!"

I was just calculating in my mind how long it would be before he would find himself enjoying the hospitality of an approved school when a great big striped-jerseyed bumble-bee blundered in through the open window and began its crazed efforts to fly out again, through the plate glass. I felt sorry for the poor stupid insect and wondered what its chances of survival would be, in the city towards which we were heading. Ideally, I would have liked to release it, but you can't go chasing around buses shoo-ing bumble-bees out of windows. So, looking brave and unconcerned when it was nowhere near us and looking very discomfited and self-conscious when it buzzed

173

up and down the windows only a few inches from our faces, we passengers let it suffer. Whenever it flew near the boys they panicked and tried to swat it with a crumpled comic; one had succeeded and I could see the creature under a seat dazedly stumbling about in the litter of cigarette ash, withered apple cores and toffee papers, the boy trying to find it to squash it with his foot. All eyes were on the bee and one could feel the emotional pressure of twenty or thirty consciences doing battle with their old enemies conventional conduct and fear of being laughed at. Suddenly I noticed the lad "Slug", his face white, he was biting his lips and clenching his fists. The bumble-bee stopped buzzing and began a temporary toilet, cleaning the cigarette ash off its furry body.

The lad with the comic, egged on by his two comrades, took aim, and to his utter surprise found himself flung back in his seat, his brilliantined head hard against the side of the bus, Slug's right fist, knuckles shining like chicken bones, exactly one inch from his nose. "You got the matches?" growled Slug. "Y-yes," the victim said, looking at his captor as if he had taken leave of his senses. He fumbled in his pocket, brought out the box and on Slug's orders shook out all the matches. Fascinated, the boys watched their leader bore two or three holes in the box with a pencil point, then with the drawer part of the box half open, deftly trap and catch the bumble-bee and shut it in the box.

The boy then turned to me and asked me the name of the village "where the bee got on". I told him and noticed him laboriously printing the name on the box. As he was doing this the conductor came up to see what the rumpus was all about. Slug looked at him. "Ow much to send a small parcel back out to Pensford?" he asked. The conductor told him and fragments of his conversation with the lads drifted back to us as we strained our ears, pretending not to listen. ". . . now make sure you let 'im go just by that 'ouse by the school with all the flowers round the door, won't you, Mister?" And after the chinking of passing coins: ". . . g'wan, I can always scrounge some fags off the old chap when I gets 'ome. . . ."

As we entered the Terminus the conductor walked back between the seats holding the grubby little matchbox, officially labelled, ticketed and stamped; from within it came a familiar yet hollow-sounding buzzing. Slug, his freckled and none too clean nose high in the air, followed holding his receipt, his gang, reflected glory shining on their faces, tagged on in procession behind.

We all averted our eyes and avoided each other as we made our departures.

BRIAN WALKER

❧ THE TROUT

He is probably the most famous character in the district and certainly the most sought after. He lives in the pool below the willow past the bridge and here he gives his audience. Never a crowd, for one of the unwritten laws among fishermen transforms what in these circumstances would be a common queue, into a series of tactful visits—one at a time.

Sometimes one can see a figure on the bank pretending to fish twenty yards downstream waiting for his turn. If one is extra observant, watch for the look of relief on his face when his "opponent" finally moves on—his patience tried and his bag unfilled.

I wait to visit him on days when his admirers can only sit at their desks and dream about him. There was a time when I went down there with only one intention—to bear him home to a jealous spouse. But my choicest baits were refused—the furriest, the sparkliest, the most entrancing objects were offered to him gracefully and humbly as one would present gifts at the feet of Buddha himself. He came up to look at each one, only to turn away in disgust, bubbling bluntly, "What do you take me for?"

"A fat old worm would get that 'un." said the voice of the smallest fisherman in the village as he crept up like the devil himself beside me in the long grass. "Johnny," I said, "if this chap's going to get a worm he's not getting it on the end of this hook or on one of your granny's pins—it would be a gross impertinence and you know it."

There's nothing so restful as watching fish and so I found myself constantly being drawn to that willow past the bridge. More often than not I left my rod behind and took with me instead some of my problems, and as I watched the sleek manoeuvring of the fish below me, his swift decisive action or just his quiet toeing-the-line in mid-stream, my mind would clear itself of a number of things.

He even cured me of his own slightly hypnotic effect on me; for one evening as I sat in my usual spot on the bank, my mind filled with a variety of ifs and buts, I unconsciously found myself watching for symbols. If he darts left it means this . . . if

He is probably the most famous character in the district and certainly
the most sought after.

Pied Beauty

he darts right it means that . . . if he dashes downstream . . . it must be this . . . , and so on.

Suddenly, as my concentration intensified, a piece of thistledown floated out of the dusk on to the water just in front of his nose, he leapt. The huge flash left an ever-widening circle of ripples on the surface. And when they cleared I saw the thistledown floating past him downstream.

"All that fuss over a bit of fluff," I said out loud in his direction and for the first time for many days I giggled.

BARBARA HARGREAVES

 Pied Beauty

*Glory be to God for
    dappled things—
For skies of couple-colour as a
    brinded cow,
For rose-moles all in stipple
    upon trout that swim,
Fresh-firecoal, chestnut-falls,
    finches' wings,
Landscape plotted and pierced
    —fold, fallow, and plough,
And all trades, their gear and
    tackle and trim.*

*All things counter, original,
    spare, strange,
Whatever is fickle, freckled
    (who knows how?)
With swift, slow, sweet, sour,
    adazzle, dim,
He fathers-forth who beauty
    is past change:
Praise him.*

GERARD MANLEY HOPKINS

❧ BUYING A SECOND-HAND GUN?

You meet a chap in a pub who offers to sell you a gun for only £20. It looks fine. The stock is nicely marked, it "comes up" well when you put it to your shoulder, and it even carries a well-known maker's name on the barrels. He declares it to be a "hard-hitting" gun that has killed its share of birds at sixty yards. You need a gun and this seems to be just the job. But is it?

I suspect this of being a fairly common situation in which quite a few people have handed over the £20. Some may have been lucky, while others may have been risking life or at least limb. The point is: How do you go about buying a gun when you know next to nothing about its finer points?

You could do worse than start with the proof marks, about which I wrote in *The Farmers Weekly* (November 6, 1959). I'm not going to describe the marks in detail again, but they can give you a fair indication of age.

Don't touch a gun that has black powder marks only, signified by the letters BP. Be very suspicious of a gun that simply carries the mark NP, standing for nitro proof, for this weapon was proved at least fifty years ago. NP with the addition of the recommended shot charge in ounces shows that the gun is between twenty and thirty years of age, while NP together with the length of cartridge case to be used places the last proof within fifteen years.

It's quite true that age itself is no positive indication of condition but at least it's a warning.

What really counts is the state of the barrels. Hold them up to the light and examine them internally. When the Proof-master does this he looks for the shadow thrown down the bores by a bright light. You can get the same effect by pointing the tubes at a window or electric light and moving them slightly so that your eye is off-centre. If the shadow you see is at all distorted, it is crossing a hump or valley.

Internal humps are not so serious; most shotguns get dents during their working lives and these can be "raised" quite easily by a gunmaker. It is the bulges that prove disastrous. Nothing can be done to put a badly bulged barrel back into shape, and series of bulges in a wave pattern are the death knell. Known as rivelling, these often show that the metal is thoroughly fatigued. To enable a shot charge to pass down the barrel the metal expands and should return to normal immediately. Rivelling shows that the barrel has expanded but failed to contract. Once this stage has been reached, there's only one thing to do—throw the tubes away and start again.

Bad pitting in the bore should be enough to make you turn down the gun straight away, and severe pitting in the chamber is even worse. Slight pitting does not necessarily mean the gun is a write-off, but before buying it I'd certainly demand a gunmaker's inspection, and if he recommends it, have the gun reproofed.

When you're satisfied about the barrels internally, hang them from your trigger finger by the lump at the breech end and give them a slight tap with something metallic. If they ring true, they're O.K.; but if they don't, the rib—the strip of metal joining the two tubes—is loose and needs resoldering. This is a very slight job, but in bargaining power it may save you a fiver on the cost of the gun.

There is another useful tip concerning proof marks. Thirty or more years ago barrels tended to be anything from 30 to 32 in. long—a hangover from the black powder days when tubes were made long to give the full charge time to burn. A gun with very old proof marks but only 29 or 20 in. in the barrel indicates someone has probably been at work with a hacksaw, and this makes the gun valueless and out of proof. Apart from any safety consideration it won't have much choke left in it.

Don't be misled by faulty or pitted extractors or ejectors. These should enable you to knock a pound or two off the price, but, if the rest of the gun is sound, they can be replaced easily and quite cheaply.

Good barrels are more than half your battle, and, indeed, account for half the price of the gun. (A new pair costs about £40.) It's very strange, then, that most people when buying a gun pay far more attention to the action and stock.

With the action the most important things to check are the

action faces—the flats surrounding the striker holes; they must be free from pits. A face can be rebushed, but if the gun has smallpox badly in this department it's probably safer to tell its present owner to hang it on his wall.

The action may be loose, but this doesn't make the gun a bad proposition if it is serviceable everywhere else. A loose action can be rejointed for about £5—another bargaining point for the buyer.

There is a simple test to check the tightness of the action. Take the fore-end off the gun and hold it parallel to the ground so that the triggers are uppermost, then push the top lever across and shake the gun gently from side to side. If the barrels wobble, it needs rejointing.

The other check worth trying at the same time is for looseness of stock. For this you put the fore-end back and lay the gun, triggers uppermost again, on a table with the butt overhanging the edge. Put your hand under the heel of the butt and lift. If it yields, then your stock is loose; but this, too, is relatively easily fixed by a gunmaker.

Far too many buyers are impressed by glossy woodwork, totally ignoring the mechanical parts except for a quick look down the barrels. In fact, almost any damage to a stock can be made good.

Dents, scratches and bulges are quickly got out by a gunmaker. You can have a stock shortened or lengthened to suit your physique for between £2 and £4. To re-checker and oil-polish the whole affair until it looks like new costs only £5. You can even have a complete new stock built for between £15 and £20, so don't be put off a good gun that is sound in action and barrels by a few surface blemishes.

These hints can keep you out of big trouble if you're buying a gun privately, but by far the safest course is to ask the chap who wants to sell it whether he minds you having it looked at by a gunmaker. If he's got nothing to hide he won't object. If he closes up like a clam you can draw your own conclusions.

Good gunsmiths are like bankers; they can't afford to take risks when they recommend you to invest in something. Some local gun dealers may not be quite so careful. A dealer's capacity to judge a gun can be assessed by asking him to gauge the bores for you. If he hasn't got barrel gauges, you might be well advised to think twice about buying one of his second-hand guns.

The gauges are simply steel plugs, which screw on to the end of a rod. They increase progressively in ten thousandths of an inch and correspond to the sizes at which guns are proved and marked, the measurement being a mean barrel diameter taken 9 in. from the breech.

If you look on the flats of your 12-bore barrels you will find among the proof marks either a mean bore size in inches, thus:

·709 in.   ·719 in.   ·729 in.   ·740 in.

or one of the figures:

13    $\frac{13}{1}$ 12 $\frac{12}{1}$

Reading from left to right, the two kinds of markings correspond, so that ·709 in. is the same as 13.

If your gun is marked 13 it should certainly not take a gauge marked $\frac{13}{1}$ for this would mean that its barrel has worn ten thou. since it was last proved. This is extremely unlikely to have been caused by firing alone. It has probably had a dent or two raised, or it may be rivelled. Either way, it is out of proof since a jump from one marking to another cancels out proof and makes the gun an illegal sale.

You should, of course, expect to pay more for an ejector than a gun fitted with extractors only. Sidelocks are sweeter than box locks when it comes to such fine points as even quality of trigger pull. You can tell a sidelock by the fact that the works, covered by a sideplate, are behind the action face. Occasionally, box locks are made to look like their betters by the addition of a false sideplate, so screw it off if you're in doubt.

But these are minor considerations when you meet that man in a pub with a real snip of a gun. Second-hand shot-guns shoot well enough if you hold them straight. The most vital consideration is: Are they safe?

COLIN WILLOCK

 *Thanksgiving*

For apples, yellow, green and red,
Among the leaves above my head;
For luscious plums, a-drip with juice
Awaiting jam for winter use;
For lettuce green and full of heart
Playing salad's better part;
For peas, with pods a-popping fast,
With lamb and mint sauce—good repast;
For beans a-hanging in their grove,
Bunched high and low, or interwove;
For potatoes in surprising store—
Spade signalling to dig up more!
For beetroot purple, swollen round,
Beneath expansive foliage found;
For onions on the surface sitting,
Spikes o'ertipped—in sockets fitting;
For carrots, turnips, swedes in rows,
To taste the stew when raw wind blows;
For cauliflower in splendid state—
A produce posy of some weight;
For Brassica of every kind—
Savoy and Brussels—Kale behind;
For all things come to their full fruit
From highest tree to lowest root.

T. E.

❧ JOURNEY THROUGH ENGLAND

I have just returned from a week's holiday in Scotland, having motored up and back. The attraction of using my own car was that I should be able to farm both sides of the road all the way. In case any reader should infer from this that I was obviously a road menace I hasten to state that I was not driving. Indeed, my only contribution to that department was to request my companion to realise the value of his cargo and keep to a speed that did not harass my nerves unduly.

Frankly, I enjoyed the journey. In the beginning it was good to get away from my own farm, with the knowledge that harvest was finished, and the combine harvester sold to another farmer who was still wrestling with the weather. Hampshire and Berkshire showed me hardly any grain still uncut; Oxfordshire rather more than I expected, but then, ripening is always later in the Cotswolds; while Northamptonshire seemed to have got a move on to some purpose.

It was Leicestershire that disappointed me everyhow. As I expected, in such a famous grazing county there was a much smaller acreage of grain per square mile, but a much greater proportion of this still standing, especially wheat. Why? Why was the harvest here so noticeably behind Nottinghamshire, Yorkshire, and even three hundred miles farther north? I thought we had reached saturation point in combine-harvesters everywhere.

Another thing that made me ask, "what is the matter with Leicestershire?" was the apparent paucity of livestock, especially of beef cattle. Where were the beasts that should be fattening on those wonderful pastures? Conspicuous by their absence.

I had always understood that as long as one can see Langton Church one is standing on some of the best grassland in the whole world. That is probably still true, but there seemed to be very few beef cattle on it, and not very many dairy cows either. During the last ten years or so beef cattle in the chalk country have appreciably increased, but my guess regarding the Market Harborough district is that their numbers have sadly dwindled. It may be that I am maligning Leicestershire, but my impression both coming and going, was that its farming —arable and grass—was not exactly happy.

In contrast the farming of Nottinghamshire and Yorkshire was obviously in capable hands. A much smaller proportion of the grain crop still to harvest, good crops of potatoes and sugar beet, and very definitely more and better quality livestock than farther south. We stopped the night at Boroughbridge, and next morning set off for Scotland.

The second day's motoring showed me nothing unexpected. Between the mines and factories Durham farmed well, and in a much prettier countryside than most people imagine. Northumberland showed me sheep and forestry in due proportion, and when we reached Carter Bar, Scotland was spread out below in brilliant sunshine—a very pleasant prospect.

Thereafter the proportion of oats appreciably increased, and so did the quality of livestock. So too, of course, did the steepness of the hills, and subsequently of the mountains. But nowhere, from Roxburghshire to Perthshire, did the grain harvest appear to be so lamentably behind as it did in Leicestershire. I shall probably be horsewhipped by some irate hunting squire for that, but am relying on my Scottish friends to defend me.

It was between Crieff and Aberfeldy that I got my first sight of the Central Highlands, saw grouse by the side of the road, and wondered how my stiffening joints would deal with these birds next day. What I should have wondered was how the Scots would deal with me, for I am long past striding lightly over or through the heather. Now I can speak from experience.

The procedure from my angle was as follows: by car to a house in the valley, thence by Land-Rover, corkscrewing upward ever upward until the limit of this type of vehicle was reached. At this point the fit and agile members of the party— mainly Scots—walked off on a short cut over the moor. I and other infirm southerners travelled by tractor.

In case anyone doesn't know this, I can vouch that two stoutish old men can sit side by side on a bag of hay in the transport box of a tractor. As a result my right buttock was soon stamped with the imprint of the coupling key on one side of the three-point linkage. In this fashion a tractor will and did take its load up impossible slopes, through manifold bogs and eventually come to a halt near to the butts.

On a fine day with the sun shining, at approximately fifteen hundred feet this is a truly gorgeous experience, even if one does find the Scottish grouse rather more sudden than the Wiltshire partridge. On a wet day when the moor is wreathed in swirling mist it can produce some frightening moments and even fears that one has reached the point of no return.

I really don't know how to sum up that week correctly. Without wishing to be either unkind or ungrateful to my many hosts I suggest that the whole business was rather daft—me for thinking I was fit enough to take part in it; my new Scottish friends for bothering so charmingly with such an obvious nuisance as myself; and my host, a Wiltshire neighbour who has not only adopted the Highlands but also been adopted by them. (I expect soon to see him in a kilt—he has the right sort of knees for it.)

However, I have returned to Wiltshire all in one piece, having missed many grouse and hit only a few. I now know the why and wherefore of Whisky, umpteen brands of it; only Whisky can enable human beings to walk across the heather, climb the slopes of a grouse moor, and put up with soft southerners such as myself. To repeat, that week in Perthshire was the daftest holiday of my life, but I enjoyed every moment of it, and would not have missed it for anything.

A. G. STREET

TURNING YOUR HEART OVER

I walked about twenty yards behind a woman down the road the other day. She was a stranger to me but I knew she was unhappy. Not because of the way she walked, or the set of her head. She was going a fair pace and looking ahead. It

was something about the outline of her shoulders or the way, perhaps, she held her shopping bags.

My curiosity as to whether I was right made me hurry and catch her up. I passed and then looked back. Her face was the face of the women at the Cross. Terrible in its tragedy.

I stood around a while, not wanting to leave her. But what could I do? She didn't appear to be the sort of person whose privacy you could impose on. She had locked her troubles inside. It would have been easier if she had stumbled a little or tears had fallen. Then I might have approached her with the conventional "Is there anything I can do?"

It took me a long time to forget her. But strangely enough it was not her tragic face that I kept remembering but her back view as I walked down the road behind her.

Back views tell a multitude of things. You know by looking at the back of a boy doing his prep whether he is concentrating, idling or worrying over his work. And is there anything so obviously contented-looking as the back of a baby's neck when he's sitting on the floor playing with his toys? That little inch of neck where the downy hair joins the nape; the sight of it has never failed to turn my heart over.

Strange, isn't it, the different things that turn one's heart over or make one catch one's breath? Not only the sad or the beautiful but that something which nearly every woman understands, but very few men. For though he may be impressed by beautiful objects he remains untouched by the backwaters and odd little side creeks of sights and events that crowd a woman's life. Perhaps it's something to do with his not being concerned with the detail of day to day living—perhaps it's just our woman's capacity for compassion which is responsible for the special sort of heart jerks we experience.

These emotional acrobatics are a disadvantage at times. They tend to blur one's view of the real issue and so they are often the means to an unprofitable end. For when one's heart turns over one's mind and commonsense tend to cut out—and what happens? You're just a woman surrounded by too many dogs, cats and lambs you couldn't bring yourself to part with, and one's entire spare time is spent pottering and looking and fiddling around after them.

But who would swap that luxury for anything?

"Have you any ambition?" somebody asked me the other evening when we were sitting idly gossiping round the supper table. "Just as much of it as I need," I replied, "to keep me in pottering time, which is less than most people I know want."

Perhaps that's one of the reasons why I thank Heaven every day of my life that I was born a woman. Just because I occasionally cut a tree down, have a go at trying to pot a rook and mend the electric fuses doesn't mean one would prefer to be male rather than female. Not on your life! For one thing, I can try my hand at all these so-called men's jobs, and being a female, I can afford to make a fool of myself over them. And for another thing, if I was the breadwinner my conscience just wouldn't allow me to muck about doing unnecessary jobs I like.

When you go and call the boy into lunch, for instance and find him out there fishing, you can afford, if you're his mother, to stand there a few seconds and watch him. Give yourself the luxury of such silly thoughts as, "Heavens, just look at those long legs . . . he'll be out of that jersey in a month or two . . . that silly great thatch of hair . . . where did he get it from? . . . what a boy . . . however did he happen to belong to me? . . ." And your heart turns over.

There you are, you see. A normal boy sitting fishing in an ordinary sort of way, with his ordinary Mum just standing there spending time that no ambitious woman or hard-working man could afford. . . .

BARBARA HARGREAVES

🌹 ORMERING

The old crack about living to eat and not eating to live comes to life when you see Fatty in action. (Everybody, for obvious reasons and with his approval, calls him Fatty.) A highly successful grower of Jersey early potatoes and tomatoes—spuds and toms—he is round like a ball with a beaming rosy face. And his passion where special dishes are concerned—like most Jersey farming folk—is ormers.

This is one of the Island's most famous farmhouse dishes and most have their own refinements of recipe. From time to time, on business of spuds or toms, I have been invited to share a farm dinner of these most edible sea-snails. And I can testify they are delicious.

But first, as Mrs. Beeton didn't say, catch your ormer. This means an ormering tide when the waters are low, the winds soft, the pubs, clubs and farm kitchens agog with prospects and the beaches, jetties and slipways dotted with cars, lorries, bikes and traps. The hunt is on.

Ormers lurk just below low water mark, so it means scrambling across slippery, kelp-covered rocks, cold wading in the sea, long-arm probing of crevices, up-turning of stones in ormering pools. And don't forget to put the stones back or good ormer "pastures" are destroyed.

Unalerted, ormers are picked off easily, forewarned they cling like clams unless levered off. So you creep, where you can.

Ormers measure about three to four inches by two across and if you get a dozen before the tide drives you in, you have a haul. For four ormers à la jersais are a feast for you and me, though not for Fatty.

A famous farmhouse recipe recommends to winkle them from shells, scrub white, beat tender, fry brown, simmer soft for four hours with a mess of vegetables and lemon juice and serve with a thick brown sauce of wine. The taste reminds one variously of chicken, veal, breast of turkey—never of anything fishy, possibly because ormers are vegetarians.

Ormer shells though encrusted on the outside are lovely nacre inside, and by the thousand they shimmer and tinkle in the island gardens and fields to scare off robbing birds. Californian ormer shells are used for mother-of-pearl buttons, inlaid toilet sets, etc.

Like oysters, ormers follow the gastronomes, months of "R's" and cold "Brrs". No self-respecting Jersey farmer's dinner menu would be without them at that period. But Britain has no native ormers and Jersey produces the nearest. The French know them as Oreilles de Mer, the Italians as the Ear of Venus (that must be tasty) and at the other end of the world the Maoris cook them on hot stones as Mutton Fish.

The female ormer lays her eggs in lovely green cloud-puffs, ten thousand at a shot, so there should be plenty. But Jersey ormers are diminishing and the island of Guernsey already restricts fishing them to the new and full moons and the three days and nights following. Jersey may have to follow suit.

Fatty, however, has his own cushion against scarcity. When the tides are lush with ormers, he sends out his minions to rifle the rocks, winkles a good harvest of succulent ormers from the nacre and puts the whole lot into his deep freeze.

J. L. JONES

✿ O LOVELY PUSSY,
O PUSSY MY LOVE!

In our Dale they go in for cats in a big way. The most we have
ever had is thirteen, and I dare say we can be outdone by this,
numerically speaking, especially if they are confined to barns
and outhouses.

There certainly have been processions of cats—green-eyed
monsters and yellow-eyed beauties, fluffy and smooth cats,
sleek and skinny ones. Yet, in the beginning there was an
Adam and Eve of all these cats, who were the offspring of
Earth and Sky, which is most appropriate for a creation story.

Sky, so named because of his cerulean blue eyes, was the
Siamese at the school across the valley, and Earth was his
black-and-white spouse. One whole spring they slept affectionately intertwined on the school kitchen window-sill and in
May were born black-and-white kittens of Siamese form and
intelligence.

Poor Earth went hunting one day and never returned, so
her kittens were left motherless when only one week old. A
little girl reared them tenderly with a fountain-pen filler and
two of them were presented to us.

Apart from a mother fixation (they used to suck buttons),
they seemed none the worse for their unconventional upbringing, but Papa Puss became a juvenile delinquent, no doubt as a
result of severe deprivation in infancy and insecure background.

Possessed of satanic ingenuity, he was rather like Macavity,
the Monster of Depravity (if you remember your Eliot), ex-
cepting only for his imperturbable amiability. Kick him down
the steps in a fury and he came up smiling every time.

He could enter the kitchen at his convenience by hurling
himself at the door and at the same time pressing down the
catch with one paw.

He also prised the lid off the cake tin and ate all the marzi-
pan off my husband's birthday cake, in the days when ground
almonds and dried fruits were almost unobtainable.

For this crime he was spanked, hurled unceremoniously out

of the door, but he "popped on his drawers" (as Mr. Spooner would say) and re-entered purring loudly at the honour bestowed upon him. Obviously he was a born expert in the technique of Gandhian non-violent resistance.

Nothing makes a cat more affectionate than to be brought up with small children. Ours used to become extraordinarily amiable. They were tied almost into knots without a squeak of complaint, dressed up in dolly clothes to be wheeled in the pram, and they submitted patiently to gross indignities without turning a whisker. When things became really too much you could sometimes see the odd sight of a cat in a bonnet streaking for home and shedding various garments in the undergrowth en route.

When the children were small, and I used to take them for a short outing each day, the cats always used to come too. Passers-by in cars appeared to be much entertained by mother with three children and six pussies all walking out together. Three-year-old Martin always tucked his Georgy under one arm, with plumy tail sticking straight up behind; they were inseparable.

One day in January we took friends up the hill through the snow to see the frozen waterfall, which looked like elaborate icing on a wedding cake. The intrepid little kittens came, too, but it proved too much for them and they presently burst out into a sorrowful chorus, of which the theme appeared to be "My Tiny Paw is Frozen". They had to be zipped up in wind-cheaters, with only their heads peeping out, or fastened up shivering inside warm overcoats.

We are reformed characters now and more ruthless with our kittens. Our four remaining cats are several years old. One of these is Marco Polo, the great explorer, who wears full evening dress, though his suit looks in need of a refresher at the cleaners, owing to long nights of dissipation.

Marco can never forget the day when his dream came true. One Christmas Eve he wandered upstairs into a bedroom and found . . . what do you think? An absolutely outsize turkey on a huge platter, reposing (for safety, I had thought) on top of the chest of drawers. When I discovered him he was sitting beside it, too utterly flabbergasted and dumbfounded to think of tucking in.

He has never forgotten. Somewhere in his feline brain lurks this memory of Paradise—a Transcendental Turkey, with a golden aureole.

He saunters casually (much too casually) through the dining-room but the minute he turns the corner those great jack-rabbit legs of his sprout wings and before you can say "Christmas", he is up the stairs. He can be found sitting on that chest of drawers, dreaming of the Vision Splendid.

And there, for now, we will leave him.

ELIZABETH LARGE

🌹 Can You Cap It?

We're a family of four
But you'd think we must be more
If you saw the hats we have in our collections;
In the hall, in every drawer,
Even kicked round on the floor!
They're a weird and wonderful, varied selection.

There are rain hats, plain hats,
Cleaning-out-the-drain hats,
A deer-stalker, handed down with pride.
There are cloth caps, cord caps,
Buckle-on-my sword caps,
Some worn straight and some tipped on the side.

There are bobble hats, fuzzy caps,
Furry-as-a-pussy caps,
Like the Russian cossacks used to wear,
There are school caps, ski caps,
Purchased-by-the-sea caps
Stop the meal from getting in your hair.

Alice-bands, yankee hats,
Made-from-knotted-hanky hats,
French berets to keep the memories warm;
But every time it rains
We can look and search in vain
'Cause the blessed things will all be up the farm!

MRS. JANE LEGGE

❧ A SELFISH SUMMER ARTICLE

Have you ever eaten Easter Ledger Pudding? Late to talk about Easter when it is summer, and flowers are out everywhere. And anyhow "Easter Ledger" will be Double Dutch if your farm is in Cornwall or the Midlands.

But not in the Lakes. Just now "Easter Ledger" will be out in the late hay meadows, pink and exquisite (though I doubt if it improves the hay).

There are odd things about flower names when you look deep enough. Why Easter Ledger? Because at Easter in the Lakes the leaves go into a pudding with dandelion, nettle, barley, and hard-boiled egg? Yes and No. Some people up north call the plant Easter Magiant—a magic-sounding name which really means "Easter Food " (from manger in French). But what is a "ledger"?

Here is the explanation. This wild plant (which the books, I should have mentioned, called Bistort) was once named Aristolochia or Aristologia, which mixed itself up into Easter Ledger. And in Greek—a long way from Ancient Greece to a Northumberland hayfield or a Cumberland orchard—Aristolochia meant "best birth", and once upon a time farmers' wives knew that they ate Easter Ledger Pudding with their bacon or veal in hope that the leaves would help them to have good strong babies safely and easily.

Names of our plants vary from county to county. Bistort, Easter Ledger Magiant—this beauty of the meadows doesn't grow everywhere. But it is also called Patience Dock or Passion Dock (Easter again, the dock of Passion time), and Meeks, and gentle Dock, and Red Legs, and Adderwort.

Turn from hay to corn. Odd names grow among the wheat (real summer this time). Or they used to in the old days before cleaner seed and our pick-and-choose weed-killers. Poppies, Cornflowers (real sea-blue cornflowers, not rather dreary Scabious), Dyer's Rocket, White Campion—believe it or not, farmers once rather liked such weeds, and did not fancy the corn without them. They thought Poppies and Campion,

195

for instance, protected the corn, and so were not to be picked.

That is why in some counties they still call both the Poppy and the White Campion by names such as Thunderbolt and Thunderflower, and why Poppies are called Blind Eyes and Head-aches. It was dangerous to pick them, would cause a thunder storm, flatten the crop, give you a head-ache, make you blind.

Corn-cockles farmers did not like, because they gave a bad taste to the flour. And I have not found many names for the Cornflower or Blue Bottle, which used to turn English fields into lakes of summer blue. Across the Channel how wonderful it is (if you are not a french farmer) to see acres of bluest Cornflower through the wheat, perhaps next to a field of that scarlet Napoleon Clover we used to grow.

Talking of France and flowers and summer, on the edges of great chalky French cornfields there grows a ravishing weed which the French call Fox's Tail—Queue de renard—brilliant as a cassata ice, green, yellow, purple, pink, all on one stem. Luckily, I suppose, this Field Cow-Wheat (that's our English book name) is very rare with us. I happen to know one of the few English wheat fields where it flowers (it is an annual) summer after summer, in a chalky French situation on the Wiltshire downs, beside the road into the farm.

I am not sure if the farmer knows about it. But every summer brings its pilgrims to the grassy bank along the edge of his wheat—myself included—anxious to see this brilliant weed once more, anxious that it may have disappeared. If the farmer doesn't know, he must be getting puzzled to find cars in July and August drawing up just at that one point.

Back to the front door or back door, or to what we call the linhay in my native Cornwall. Do you have Welcome-Home-Husband-Though-Never-So-Drunk on your lean-to roof, over the door—in other words, the cheerful yellow of stonecrop? Or do you grow House Leek? Or does Feverfew, a little weedy, persistent, daisyish thing with white and yellow flowers and pungent leaves, appear whether you like it or not on your walls or your paths?

These are my last three. I suppose that first very long name for a very cheerful little flower explains itself. As for number three, Feverfew, it is because it used to be grown as a febrifuge, something which put fevers to flight and brought temperatures down—in pre-aspirin days the aspirin of the farmer's wife.

As for House Leek, there's my prize exhibit and my constant reminder that times don't change as much as we think.

If picking a Poppy caused lightning, House Leek kept lightning away. We have forgotten that, but we go on growing the fat comfortable clumps and still remember another fire-repelling quality of House Leek—that it makes a good soothing ointment.

Still, more than 2,300 years ago a Greek tells us it was grown on roof tiles. It was a kind of insurance sign against lightning. What firm issued the policy? The firm of Zeus, the Father of the Gods and Men, who wielded the lightning, but kept it away if you grew his sacred rosettes. House Leek today is as much a domesticated creature as any around the farm. Perhaps more so, because a wild form of it isn't known anywhere in the world.

What House Leek names do you know? Or use? Singreen, which means "evergreen"? Bullock's Eye? Foose, which is North Country? Luibh an toitean, which is Irish, and means "fire plant"? anyhow, just think of the antique you are preserving on your wall.

GEOFFREY GRIGSON

🌹 DORSET

The county of my dreams, you ask? Why, Dorset, of course. No one will ever convince me that any one of the other 38 counties in England is a patch on Dorset. However far away from it I may roam in my life, a corner of my heart will always be here, in this beautiful county, where I was born.

What is so wonderful about it? Well, for a start the view from the hills on a clear summer's day. The wooded and peaceful Blackmore Vale from Bulbarrow; Portland, the Chesil Bank and West Bay from Portesham; the rolling downs from Trendle Hill over Cerne Abbas. All three are sights worth seeing. Each is a complete contrast to the other two. For that is what Dorset really is—a county of contrasts . . .

MISS S. HOLE, *Sturminster Newton*

🌹 THE MAGIC OF AN ISLAND

At teatime on Sunday afternoon I found myself on an island with the sun shining overhead and bright flowing water all round me. A swan arched his neck at me as he glided by, a swallow swooped down to scoop up a fly and a few yards off a water vole was cleaning his whiskers. Romantic enough surroundings, but hardly romantic circumstances, for I was drinking tea out of a chipped mug, scooping hot potato out of its blackened skin with my penknife and listening to a flow of piratical language that would have done justice to the fiercest member of Captain Hook's crew.

But an island is an island to me even if perhaps I had, in my younger days, dreamed of a little more guitar music and a palm tree or two. And this potato-clamp-sized piece of terra firma stuck in the middle of a brook within spitting distance of my own house was my present heaven. My watch I had left on the dressing-table and my captors were not only obviously preferring their own camp fire cookery to anything a mainland stove could turn out, but had firmly thrown my Wellington boots across the river in order that I shouldn't escape.

Sitting on this little tuffet of land with the water flowing past me and the sky and sun shining down I gave myself up to discovering the bliss of timelessness and the joys of imprisonment.

The trouble about so many of us women is that we haven't the ability to relax. Perhaps it is because we live so much on top of our work. We can't shut up the shop and go home. Cleaning the paint shows up the dirty door knob, which draws your eye to the floor which reminds you that it's a few weeks overdue for a polish, and so on. I often think it would do us a lot of good if sometimes we could let the house go hang, put our heads out of the window and look at the sky. For doing the housework is rather like shopping in the sort of store that has everything on display; there's always something you must buy because you can't do without it. It's the same in the house, there's always something you think needs doing and so you never stop doing things.

In fact, it occurred to me sitting there under the sky, that I was far more often a prisoner in my own house than I was on this island and entirely through lack of my own efforts to leave a few things undone. I don't mean leaving them for other people to do—this new-fangled notion of getting the family to help with the washing up, etc., is all nonsense—it's far quicker to do it oneself than run round after somebody else and do it all over again. No, I mean just simply leaving God's good dust to settle a little longer on the shelves or one of His spiders to weave another web between the pelmet and the lamp bracket and some of His good earth to linger a little in the hall!

Which is all rather a long way from what must have been the thoughts of the man who wrote that song "The Isle of Capri".

Islands—what is it that's so fascinating about them? Somewhere down in most of our souls they ring a little bell. Perhaps it is this sense of being cut off from the mainland. Of being cut loose from over-substantial ties. Of the need to escape from everyday life that lies deep somewhere in our sub-consciousness.

But whatever the reason for the fascination of islands, be it to explore them or to escape to them, a little fantasy does you good and, if you're like me, you will get rowed over to any island which is in easy reach of any seaside place you visit.

Along the rocky coast of South Wales lie several rocky promontories which at high tide become separated from the mainland and turn into tiny islands and on the flatter parts of many of these you will see little cairns of stones, doubtless built by young and not-so-young explorers who, as they built, watched in an agony of pleasure the tide coming in to cut them off and as they fixed the last stone dash back to safety, having made their mark on new territory. Each one in his tiny way a descendant, in spirit, of Drake and Columbus.

As dusk fell on my river island I found myself dreaming of gondolas gliding up to fetch me to the opera and of schooners with their holds stuffed with gold and a handsome captain at the helm when suddenly someone yelled, "Hey, has anybody got a puncture outfit, there's a big slit in the rubber dinghy!" And I came back to earth.

How did that song end? . . . "but she wore a plain golden ring on her finger, so 'twas goodbye to the Isle of Capri".

But it's as well to wake up from a dream for the magic would soon die if one slept on and perhaps islands would lose their enchantment if one never came back to the mainland.

BARBARA HARGREAVES

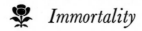 *Immortality*

These fields, which now lie smiling in the sun
Were tamed and schooled to harvest long ago
By men whose nameless lives we cannot know,
Who went in silence when their work was done,
Their furrows slowly traced, their crops hard won
Have vanished like some ancient winter's snow.
Their heat's dispersed in dust have ceased to glow
Mere random bones declare their race is run.
And yet within the fields there lie in wait
Strange virtues which to them not us belong.
And as we plod behind the plough which bores
The gracious earth they wooed, we know the strong
Compulsion laid by them, on all their heirs
And cannot chose but drive our furrows straight.

MRS. NEVA MACDONALD

🌹 THE GUEST WHO DIDN'T COME

It was Christmas Eve afternoon and all the time I was doing the last minute preparations I expected the strange knock on the kitchen door, he'll be here between three and five o'clock I thought—I do hope he comes. Five o'clock came, it was dark by now, and I feared that he now wouldn't arrive as he always comes before dark. Later on, when all was ready, I was feeling rather sad. The family came back. "Hasn't he come?" they all said. "No," I replied. "I wonder what has happened to him."

For, for nine years we've had our Christmas visitor. Sometimes he stays for a few days, sometimes a few weeks and sometimes till the weather improves in the spring. We know very little about him—where he comes from or where he goes to when he leaves us—but while he is with us he is a perfect guest. He doesn't require a bed or bedding or even a room in the house. An outhouse or shed is what he is used to and a bale of straw to lie on is a luxury. In payment for the food we give him he will do all sorts of jobs very well but rather slowly— he has plenty of time, that is all he has—you see, he has no address.

We would like to know what has happened to our "Knight of the Road". Has this wet autumn been too much for him?

Christmas was not quite the same without him.

MRS. JEAN HARPER

🌹 THE LAST OF THE GREAT TRUFFLE HUNTERS

Truffles grow without leaf or root under dark cool earth of forests and woodlands. They are food for gourmets and gods and were once "hunted" with dogs through the beech forests of the Home Counties. Today, they are hunted only by gypsies and perhaps a few amateurs but, before the war, truffle hunting was a curious and fascinating rural trade closely associated with the Collins family at Winterslow, Wiltshire.

I went recently to Winterslow to pick up the dimming scent of the English truffle. My visit was to Mr. Alfred Collins, the son of the old truffle hunter, another Alfred, who was the last to follow this rural pursuit.

Mr. Collins told me that his father hunted truffles with dogs for sixty years. The principal hunting grounds were the big country estates and, as the truffle season follows roughly the season of game, he was a welcome guest at many of the shoots where he found the truffles for the stuffing. He received a pound a day with all expenses paid and often had a car put at his disposal.

In between country house invitations he hunted within a twenty mile radius of Winterslow in the Wiltshire-Hampshire border country. He would set off on his bicycle, a canvas bag on the handlebars, and two dogs in the huge pockets of his coat.

The dogs were usually curly-coated terrier types with a dash of poodle and as single-minded as bloodhounds when on the truffle trail.

Major, the last well-remembered dog, was a spaniel poodle cross and served for fourteen years. The method of training was to rub the dog's nose with truffle, which was hidden under a tree. The dog then dug for the scent and for tit-bit rewards that came later. They were extremely fond of truffles and would eat them as fast as they found them, if allowed.

Truffles near the surface were soon scratched out by the dogs but for the deeper ones the truffler carried a truffle spike with which he dug them out. The tool weighed nine-and-a-half pounds, with a spike at one end and a two-pronged fork at the other.

The richest finds came from under the beech trees on the soils of the south-west counties, and a big fall of beech mast in the autumn was regarded as a favourable augury for the truffle season.

They were supposed to be most plentiful in wet seasons—a dry coat and an empty bag went together, said Mr. Collins.

His son remembers that where the scent of a fully ripened truffle was strong his father was able to smell it out himself. Leaning over the gate into some woodland he would sniff the air with a wrinkling nose and say, "Truffles there to-morrow, boy." He always hunted in plimsolls so that he could feel the truffles near the surface with his feet.

Truffle size varied from a "pea to a Jaffa orange". The average was a few ounces, though Mr. Collins once dug one up over 1½ lb. in weight. The price was 2s. 6d., later 5s. or more a pound. Throughout the season, truffles were sent to all parts of Britain by post.

Even today, the postmistress of Winterslow has an inclination to wrinkle her nose when she harks back to the days of Truffle Post. The truffles were brought in by Mr. Collins, done up in 2-lb. shoe boxes, and there were often far too many for the little office to handle even with an extra postman.

They went out three times a week and the surplus had to wait until the next day, but no longer, for their penetrating, earthy smell, with a hint of ripe gorgonzola added, made the whole office reek and saturated the mail bags. Even eggs assimilated their all-pervading odour. But Mrs. Pearce, the postmistress, who received truffles as gentle thanks, says, "Truffles are nice with bread and butter, but in rabbit stew they are perfection." Now there are neither rabbits nor truffles.

Apart from flavourings and truffle stuffings, the English truffle is said to be at its best well boiled and served piping hot with plenty of butter. The black, warty outer skin is scraped off to get at the grey-pink flesh underneath. They were served in napkins so that they could be more easily dealt with. There is nothing with which to compare the flavour of the truffle. The nearest description seems to have been "nutty". Alfred Collins, who remembers being given the "small ones" after numberless hunts, says that people used to eat them raw with bread and butter.

Meanwhile, virtually nothing remains of the old truffler's equipment. The spike has disappeared, but Mr. Collins still has a few truffles preserved in an old tin box. They are a quarter of a century old and certainly the oldest and probably the last truffles to be found by a professional in England. In between truffle hunting seasons, the old man followed the trade of a hurdlemaker, which is now carried on by his son.

Truffles today are imported from south-western France, Italy or Sardinia. The French train sows to sniff them out—the training starts at about two years of age. In Sardinia they use goats and Italy has a famous school where truffle hounds are trained for the job.

One method of spotting a ripe truffle, described by the experts, is to lie on the ground and look into the light for swarms of little yellow flies. Attracted by the smell, they hover near the site of the truffle.

J. L. JONES

LIME BLOSSOM WINE

"Air-swept lindens yield
Their scent and rustle down their perfumed showers
Of bloom on the bent grass.
And woodbines give their sweets and limes their shade."

Someone planted a lime tree in the hamlet where I live and it gives us pleasure the whole year round, especially on a hot summer's day when the bees make a continual hum in its branches.

There is a delightful legend about lime trees that tells of a very old shepherd and his wife who gave hospitality unknowingly to the gods Jupiter and Mercury. For this their humble cottage was turned into a temple and the old couple into two beautiful limes. In consequence the lime became the symbol of married love.

The flowers are creamy yellow and deliciously scented, and can be dried to make lime-tree tea. They make this drink in France and call it Tilleul. It is good for one's complexion and for debility and sleeplessness. A decoction made from the flowers is valuable in muscular weakness of the eyes, and I am also told that anyone suffering from high blood pressure would find this herb beneficial. That seems to me as good a reason as any for making lime-blossom wine.

LIME BLOSSOM WINE

2 pints of lime flowers
1 gallon of water
1 lemon
3½ lb. sugar
½ lb. raisins
¾ oz. baker's yeast or a wine yeast tablet.

Put the flowers into a large pan with the water and thinly-peeled rind of the lemon and simmer for 15 minutes. Pour this over the sugar and raisins and stir well. Allow to cool to lukewarm, then add the yeast and the juice of the lemon. If baker's yeast, mix with a little lukewarm liquid and add. If a wine yeast, activate it three days before you need it; the directions will have come with the wine yeast tablets and are easy to follow. Cover the bowl closely and keep in a warm place for three days, stirring daily. Now strain through two layers of butter muslin and poor liquid into a fermentation jar. This can be a gallon glass jar or a stone jar. Insert an airlock or cover the neck of the jar with a piece of polythene held in place with a rubber band. If you use an airlock, see that the U-bend is filled with a little cold boiled water. Leave the jar in a warm place until signs of fermentation have ceased. This may take six weeks or six months. Taste the wine before bottling, and if it isn't sweet enough siphon it off into a storage jar (a jar similar in shape and capacity to the fermentation jar) and add sugar to taste. Re-insert airlock or cover, and remove to a cool place for a month. It should then be ready to bottle.

It is important that the fermentation jar should be absolutely clean and sterile before you put the wine into it.

DOROTHY WISE

❧ THIS HAY JOB

In a way, this year is rather like our prairie hay crop in Western Canada for there in a dry season we made lashings more hay than in a wet one. In spring the snow water ran off the frozen land into depressions in the landscape called sloughs. We ploughed and cropped with grain as near the water as we could. Later we cut the dried-out circumferences of these sloughs for hay, obviously cutting many more acres in a dry summer than in a wet one.

There was another curious thing about our haymaking there. For some unknown reason this natural grass never heated. One cut it today, raked it up and coiled it tomorrow, and stacked it next day. And was it heavy to pitch! Indeed, before starting to do that one had to sharpen the tines of one's pitchfork on the grindstone—otherwise one could not get them into coils or pooks. In fact, haymaking was hard work, the hardest I have ever done, for memory tells me that the grain harvest, which at that date meant pitching sheaves, was child's play by comparison.

A. G. STREET

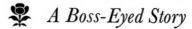

A Boss-Eyed Story

There was a boss-eyed farmer,
Who owned a boss-eyed pig.
He had a wall-eyed pony
Who used to pull this gig.

One day the poor old farmer
Went to buy some hay,
And with the boss-eyed pig,
Said he would gladly pay.

The boss-eyed pig did hear of this
And was most annoyed.
The farmer being boss-eyed, too
Was easy to avoid.

But driving through the wood one day,
The poor old farmer saw
His boss-eyed pig that disappeared
And after him he tore.

This tale comes to a sudden end,
Because the shafts got broken.
The gig has been here ever since
Abandoned and forgotten.

DAPHNE OSBORNE

FROM MRS. HONEY'S DIARY—"SORRY MUM"

Jim spotted a pigeon in the orchard the other day, and having read an article on pigeon shooting he dashed in for the gun to try out his theory. Bo taking advantage of the open door escaped pronto; Jim came racing in a few minutes later with his gun in one hand and Bo, suspended by his trouser straps, in the other. He said shakily, "Sorry Mum, I didn't mean to do it." For one awful minute my heart stopped beating, but Bo soon gave the game away by saying loudly, "Jimmy, Jimmy, down!" Tibby and I gasped before we started laughing! He may be a blinking nuisance sometimes—all children are—but we should be desolate without our Yogi Bear.

BABS HONEY

RELAX ON WHEELS

Given the A.B.C.'s not out of date, the porter doesn't put me on the wrong platform, that I've only got a nightie and a toothbrush to carry, that I don't have to change and that the journey's long enough to merit all the fiddle and finding out, I rather like travelling by train.

It's such a rest. Nobody can dash into your compartment and tell you you're wanted on the 'phone or the boss wants to see you in his office right away. You just bowl through the countryside oblivious of any crisis.

If you're tired you'll be dead out before you've passed the tenth field of Friesians. If time begins to drag you can play a marvellous guessing game with your fellow travellers.

Has that glum-faced man opposite you, for instance, quarrelled with his wife, or is he about to face a tricky directors' meeting? What's a young man in beatnik trousers doing reading *The Times* in a train on a Wednesday afternoon? Can't be a holiday. Is he going to a Ban the Bomb meeting? Couldn't he be Adam Faith?

You wonder how far that woman in that crazy hat will last sitting bolt upright. She certainly couldn't possibly lean back or it would fall straight over her nose. Perhaps she's got her hair in curlers.

I'm probably what the Americans call a "stuffed shirt" on train journeys. I prefer to sit and watch people than get into conversation with them. A baby or dog, of course, alters the whole situation. If it's you with one or someone else with one you're bound to start talking even if it's only: "Gosh, I'm sorry, he doesn't usually do this sort of thing."

I'll never forget my first journey to Weston-super-Mare when Simon was very young. My mother had very sweetly offered to pay for a first-class ticket. I was already expecting another baby and hadn't got over the seedy stage. "You go first class, dear, it'll be much more peaceful."

I don't know about peaceful. It was certainly quiet. Nobody spoke a word the entire journey. A bishop sitting right opposite —complete with purple leggings, and bib, kept looking across at Simon, obviously wondering whether he was going to do something terribly non-U. He did.

For the first half of the journey the child slept or watched entranced out of the window. After that, the journey began to pall and I gave him a biscuit to keep him quiet.

He munched this contentedly for a while until suddenly out of the window he saw something he recognised—what's more, something contained in his limited vocabulary. "Puffer," he shouted with his mouth full of biscuit and the Bishop's purple waistcoat was forthwith covered in spit and crumbs.

He just managed to squeeze out of his cassocked frame the wateriest of smiles while he dusted off the crumbs with an im-maculately laundered handkerchief.

Train journeys can be the most exciting or depressing affairs according to whether you're looking forward to where you're going or unhappy about leaving it.

Railway stations for the same reason look either like grim fortresses or exciting castles according to the mood in which you're departing from them. "Journeys end in lovers meeting" goes the sonnet but they also begin with lovers parting. And I've seen many red-eyed girls on platforms as I've seen shining-eyed ones frantically searching a train as it slows into a station.

I remember one evening coming down from the North. A girl was sitting opposite me in the carriage. We hadn't been travelling more than a quarter of the journey when she took out her powder, lipstick and comb from her bag and carefully made up her face and fiddled with her hair. Having done that she opened her book and settled down—I thought—to read.

The second page was never begun because she jumped up and pulled her suitcase down off the rack and from it extracted a pair of white gloves. After which she took out a bottle and dabbed scent behind her ears and on her wrists just as the magazines had told her.

I was right, of course, her young man did meet her the other end. But what amused me was the careless way she stepped off the train. Her whole attitude suggested that she'd been absorbed in her book the entire length of the journey and had just managed to put a quick comb through her hair and grab her suitcase as the train slowed to a stop.

The poor young man didn't look all that self-assured and I longed to tell him she hadn't thought about anything else but him since the train left the platform four and a half hours back. . . .

If like me you have to put up a fight against your own energy. That is, giving far too many yes'es and far too few no's to taking on something extra, then I advise you to put any holiday money you have into a return ticket to the furthest away town on your nearest main line.

Take a good novel, some writing paper, a sketching block if you're artistically inclined, comfortable shoes, an old skirt and a loose coat—nearest respectable thing to a dressing gown and slippers, in fact. Reserve a corner seat in the first-class carriage for silence and an antimacassar, or second class if you want to eat fish and chips or chew toffee. Either way the telephone won't ring for six or more glorious hours.

BARBARA HARGREAVES

❧ HOW TO BUY A CAR—
AND WIN

For many a farmer, a car is like a wife—something he must have but can't really afford.

I have yet to meet the sharp-pencilled economist who is prepared to say definitely whether it is better to buy a new car and flog it to death; buy a new car and replace it regularly; or take on a veteran and run it into the ground. I suppose there are too many factors—as in choosing a wife—for anyone but a fool to risk advising his friends on so personal a topic. Taking a wife has, at least, the merit of finality.

To those who find a car a problem I give the solution at the end of this article. First, let's explore the possibilities.

Beginning at the lowest, the enthusiast buys something for under £200—a van, truck, or car. He kids himself he knows enough to keep it on the road.

"If it last four years," he says, "It has cost me under £50 a year—and then there's the scrap value."

These vehicles have two great advantages. Any nut and bolt in the assembly, and many other parts, can be replaced by baler twine on the road and later repaired properly with wire. This is not possible on newer cars. Just try tying up a 1962 model with wire—it looks frightful, but in ten years' time it will be all right. Secondly, it is possible to walk upright, or almost, when you take the grease gun round underneath, whereas with a modern car you need to be a mole if regular visits to the garage are to be avoided.

These old vehicles are fine until you teach the wife to drive. She, poor dear, will never master your cunning Mark III choke—a cotton reel suspended under the dash with a wire to the carburettor.

Either because she now drives or because you think you deserve something better you will change long before the four years are up. The temptation now is to go for comfort. Big, expensive cars drop their prices quickly and look like bargains as five-year-olds. They will impress the neighbours too. New wives and new cars head the rating for local gossip value and provided they are not too outrageous they send your status up considerably.

The salesman, justifying his giant quality car which converts your old one into a dissipated wreck by comparison, will say: "The engine, gearbox and transmission are the same as on their 3-tonner, sir. Last you a lifetime."

As you sink into the smooth leather seats you are already committed. "You could always leave £200 on H.P.—she'll still be in first-class shape when you pay the last instalment in eighteen months' time, sir," he confides. You leave £250 on and drive away, comforted by the thought that it will haul a trailer or caravan if need be.

The first repair job comes up when the starter packs in. You can manipulate the 4-ft. long crank needed to nose a path through the superstructure of bumpers and grilles—but not the wife. You go to the garage.

"But it's only the starter motor," you exclaim when a price is quoted for the job.

"Oh yes, sir, but this is a heavy-duty motor, not a run of the mill job. Besides," he adds gloomily, "on these cars you have to take off the oil filter, petrol pump and clutch housing and loosen the steering box before . . ."

You swear gently gently at man's incredible inhumanity to man. The intelligence, or lack of it, by which designers make cars, tractors and implements in such a fashion is beyond you. As an engineer once told me, "You have to be crossed with a monkey to replace that part." One can only surmise that the designer was that much nearer his antecedents.

Of course, with both the cars so far mentioned you'll have to face the M. of T. test. My own experience with our 13-year-old, Jo, should enlighten you.

The inspector placed a heavy instrument on the floor which was to register Jo's reaction to pressure on her foot brake. She rated 85 per cent. Too low to pass, but high enough to catapult the battery from its mounting on to the cylinder head. I reshod the brakes and a fortnight later we tried again. This time she rated 98 per cent, and shot us into close association with a lamp post.

I still don't know if I could claim for the battery acid and tyre rubber or the repairs if we'd hit the lamp post.

Anyway, in the end the garage had to adjust the brakes themselves. They also discovered the steering box had parted company with the chassis and this had to be welded. I was too slow in clouting the off-side lamp when they switched on so that had to be repaired too.

Don't kid yourself, the test is no walk over. So it seems in the end that a new car is the only answer. It loses £100 a year in value but costs nothing in repairs. Apart from the fact that a further new model appears within weeks of you buying the "sparkling, tried and tested Familiman de luxe," you're on a safe wicket.

Many plump for the station wagon, estate car or cross-country vehicle. "So useful for taking pigs to market," you say, justifying your purchase before the neighbours. Then you recall that only last month you were asking: "How can Dick afford a new car? Friesians must be the answer after all." And you added more tartly: "He'll need a few more churns on the stand to pay for that one."

Work it out how you will, she—I mean the car—will cost you money. So now to the solution.

Buy yourself a pick-up or van out of the farm's money. Tell everyone that without it you'd need another tractor and link box for running around. Use the vehicle for everything, everywhere, including cross country. Keep it well stocked with cattle marking sticks, nails, staples, rags, oil, petrol cans and barbed wire. All costs associated with it are then charged against the farm.

For your wife, who understandably will not be seen in the truck, you buy a decent, quiet, middle-priced second-hand car. In your generosity you tell her it is for her alone—you've got your own. She will then find all the money to run it out of the housekeeping allowance. When it needs mending you say airily: "Better get it done properly at the garage, dear." And she pays.

Each husband will know how to manage this exercise with more finesse than I have described but the principle is, I'm sure, sound.

HENRY LAURENCE

❧ HOW GREEN AREN'T MY FINGERS

"A garden is a lovesome thing . . ." "What rot," I would add to lines which could only have been written by somebody who employed a full-time gardener.

Can't you see the writer of that poem strolling along the crazy paving (no grass springing up between the cracks) on to the lawn (mowed every day to putting-green smoothness), gazing at the herbaceous border (no gaps, no weeds, no dead-heads). Turning to admire the rose bed (all blooming, no drooping). Stepping off the lawn (edges cut dead straight) to peer at the honeysuckle and clematis (tied neatly with raffia against the wind).

Sitting on a freshly-painted garden seat consciously ignorant of where spade and fork are kept, I suppose a garden could look very lovesome. On one's knees with midges buzzing round one's ears, endeavouring to uproot an unending row of deeply entrenched elder before the light fails, it looks to me as lovesome as a toddler in a tantrum.

Those other famous lines about blood, sweat and tears are far more appropriate.

Garden hats, garden chairs, garden umbrellas—the magazines and shops are full of them. Bought, I suppose, by a whole new generation of "lovesome thingers" with gardeners, husbands or bob-a-jobbers to create the background to all this paraphernalia.

I've only got to sit for a couple of minutes on one of our rickety old deck chairs to feel I must up and attack yet another monster with roots as powerful as a boxer's arms.

There are moments in life—I'm sure you know what I mean —when one suddenly feels the whole world is against one. Problems of one sort or another seem to pile up and propagate more petty problems until you're about ready to break.

This is the moment of crisis. One can either fling oneself on to the bed and have a good cry, or get angry and have an all-out attack on the situation. Either choice will do the trick equally well. I usually choose the latter because it's quicker.

At this time of the year every square inch of our half-acre garden is against me. I sometimes feel that if I stood still the stuff would grow up and close in on me like the way things happen in Disney films. So I put on my hideous jeans and more hideous headscarf and armed with an old kitchen knife (better than any garden tool) I go into the attack.

Weed's don't even grow in the conventional places in my garden. Do your dandelions grow straight up in the middle of your michaelmas daisies, for instance? Do your buttercups take up abode bang among the lillies, so that by kicking out the lodger it's almost impossible not to kick out the landlord along with him?

The flowers of chickweed, willow herb, and bindweed are in fact charming. If only one could break people of this snobbish attitude to plants, think how much easier gardening would be. I've only to glance at a dahlia or a rose for it to sicken and die, whereas if I could establish the rarity of a certain little blue-flowered plant which finds our garden just the place to indulge its natural creeping habits, and which has developed such a fondness for the place it returns each spring, bringing more of its family and friends, I would never need to put hand to trowel again.

I could stroll about the place in one of those shady straws, with a trug basket, gathering armfuls of Blissful Blue for my own special shove-'m-all-in-at-once flower arrangements and win dozens of prizes all round the country.

Chaff me as they may about green fingers—"my wife's got the darkest brown fingers in Berkshire"—if it wasn't for me there wouldn't be any garden. Neither would it revert naturally to half an acre of fairish grazing. It would become one vast compost heap composed of lawn mowings, hedge trimmings, rose and fruit tree prunings, and broad bean thinnings. Is it man's prerogative never to clear away such things? If so, it does seem a bit hard that we are left with the boring part of a not unfascinating task.

If I had my way, I tell the family, after an unlovesome struggle with a crop of nettles in the rose bed, I would just have one of those Spanish kind of gardens. Just a big court-yard with tubs and big stone urns full of flowers.

Reply: "Perhaps you're right but I personally would have

thought it much easier to put the plants straight into the ground rather than have to fill those pots and things full of earth."

Lovesome thing!

BARBARA HARGREAVES

Growing Pains

I've planted stocks,
I've planted phlox
Sometimes they grow,
Sometimes they don't
I've planted lots
Of young shallots,
Sometimes they will,
Sometimes they won't
Upon my knees
I've planted peas,
Some of them thrive,
But not the rest.
One thing stands out
Beyond all doubt—
The wretched weeds
Still grow the best.

E. T. S.

🌹 OUT FOR A DUCK

Every pond will not make a good flight pond for wild duck, but every pond is potentially a flight pond and the chances are that wild duck can be encouraged to come to it regularly.

Of all forms of shooting this is the most rewarding in proportion to outlay and labour. The size of the pond is not vital but much depends on the district; in some parts of the country duck seem to prefer what could only be described as glorified water holes. In general, however, a fair stretch of water or bog is necessary, say about a quarter of an acre. Much over two acres usually becomes awkward to shoot and requires too many guns around it to ensure that the duck come within shot.

Ideally, the pond should be in a quiet area yet within easy reach so that regular feeding can be carried out. If close to the farm or other habitation a screen of trees or shrubs is a good idea. Shallow water is best; ten to twelve inches is plenty for a reasonable area around the edges, so that the duck can reach their food on the bottom.

Fluctuations in water level according to the season are inevitable but avoid, if you can, a pond which habitually dries up in summer and autumn. The water table is usually at its lowest in October and November and this is when water is vital.

Duck, as any farmer knows, are greedy creatures and food of the right sort put down regularly is the key to the whole situation. They will usually find it within twenty-four hours even on apparently unfrequented ponds and from the time of first finding, food must be provided every day without fail. Hopper feeding is not satisfactory. Food should be scattered in shallow water to prevent other birds from taking it. Moorhens and coots must be controlled; one method of doing this is to put a cage trap with a funnel entrance at ground level on the edge of the pond and bait it with food.

The favourite food of wild duck is barley, with wheat, maize, split peas, beans and potatoes as alternatives. Potatoes must be well rotted or parboiled before being put into the water.

Feeding should start in July when the bachelor drakes are roaming the ponds in search of food. Having found it, they soon bring their wives and families. Once started, the feeding must continue daily until March and during this time the number of birds coming should increase so that food, which at first consisted of only a few handfuls, will have to be increased.

Once a regular flight has been established it will probably grow in size year by year. One pond of my acquaintance builds up each year to a flight of about two thousand duck every evening in mid-winter. This pond is about an acre in area and requires some two hundredweight of barley daily.

If the pond freezes over, scatter some cavings or chaff on top so that food does not get frozen into the ice.

Duck flights are normally of two types; the evening flight when duck come in at dusk and stay all night to feed before going off in the morning, and a morning flight when they come in at first light and remain all day.

From a shooting point of view, it is obviously more convenient to have an evening flight, otherwise it means an early start to be at the pond before the duck. However, once a flight is established it seems impossible to alter it from one routine to the other.

No satisfactory plant food seems to have been evolved in this country which can be grown in the pond. Duck, like any other birds, like to be able to sink into hiding at the advent of danger. Rushes, if controlled, make excellent cover. They are also essential if there is a resident stock on the pond which breed and can give seclusion to the young ducklings.

Shooting should be infrequent—not more than about six times in the season, probably not at all the first season. The guns hide in good cover for a wild duck has eyes just as keen as a pigeon's. No smoking, dark clothing and a hat or a cap are essential for flighting.

Do not shoot when the moon is full for duck will then come to the pond any time during the night. The ideal night is moonless, cloudy and windy, when the duck will usually flight straight in without previous reconnaissance.

Having encouraged the flight, perhaps the farmer will replace those shot by rearing a few duck the following year. They are extremely easy to rear and make a useful addition to the wild visitors.

C. H. MINCHIN

SNOWDROP WINE

SNOWDROP WINE

Sufficient snowdrop petals to loosely pack 2½ pint pots.

1 gallon water	3 lb. sugar	½ lb. raisins.
1 lb. rice	1 oz. yeast.	

Boil the snowdrop petals and water together for 15 minutes. Add the rice and boil for a further 10 minutes, then strain, throwing away the petals and rice. Pour this liquid over the raisins and sugar, stir well until all the sugar is completely dissolved. Cream the yeast with a little of the liquid and pour this into the jar. Leave to ferment for 12 days, then strain and bottle. If possible, bottle this in a gallon jar until any surplus sediment has settled on the bottom and then syphon the clear liquid off into dry bottles. Cork firmly and keep until after August Bank Holiday.

J. M. HACKETT

AN EGG IS AN ADVENTURE

"An egg is always an adventure: it may be different." These words of Oscar Wilde's provoke us into looking again at our breakfast egg and may set up a train of thought leading far from the British Lion or even chocolate eggs for Easter.

Eggs have been part of the basic diet of the people in this country for so long that they have even grown into superstitions they still acknowledge. A true Cornishman, for instance, will never leave the shell of a boiled egg unsmashed after he has eaten the egg. Pixies were supposed to sail out to sea in eggshells and get drowned, but as these creatures are thought to be lucky, their lives must be preserved at all costs and they must not be allowed to go to sea! West country gypsies even believe that colds can be cured by burying an egg at midnight at the nearest crossroads. Further north in Lincolnshire, one is not allowed to throw eggshells on the fire, for it is believed here that the hen that laid the egg will never lay another. Some folk even go so far as to believe that the presence of eggs on board ship will cause contrary winds.

Many strange "egg" customs are still practised. In the parish of Coleshill in Warwickshire, the vicar is allowed to hold his glebe only on condition that he receives a hare before ten o'clock on Easter Monday. In exchange for this he has to give to the man who caught and brought it, a calf's head, one hundred eggs and a groat (fourpence). In Preston, Lancashire, hard-boiled eggs are dyed every conceivable colour and rolled down the slopes of Avenham Park as a form of competition. Games and even miniature battles with these eggs form part of the Easter entertainment.

The manner in which eggs are served and eaten has changed over the centuries. At the close of the thirteenth century, before forks came into common use, precious vellum was given up for teaching these things. "A fried egg does not need instruction, but dig not at it with your thumb turned down— move it about with the point of your knife." The rules concerning softly poached eggs were somewhat different. It was written that, "One egg must never be served between guests, there should be one each, and after stripping off the white with the fingers, you may mop up the yolk with a piece of bread."

Mediaeval manners at once bring to mind mediaeval recipes, and this recipe, said to be the forerunner of modern custard powders, is believed to have come to this country with the Normans. Perhaps it formed part of the menu served to William the Conqueror after his victory at Hastings, who knows? "Nym eyeren and sweeney well together. Chaufe ale and do thereto. Lye it with amydon. Do thereto a porcion of suger and a perty of honey and a perti of saffrom. boillehit and gif it forth."

Egg nogs were apparently as popular in the days before the first Queen Elizabeth as they are today, and this is no surprise if all recipes were as good as this one. "Take the yolks of two eggs and a tablespoon of sugar and beat to foam with a glass of brandy. Boil a pint of milk and pour over the egg mixture, stirring at low heat until a custard forms. Add shred almonds, nutmeg and a very little finely-cut candied lemon peel. Allow to cool. Next day beat the whites of eggs with castor sugar and a flavouring of brandy, mix with an almost equal quantity of stiffly-whipped and flavoured cream and pile upon the custard before serving."

Eggs have been included in feeding the mind as well as the body, apparently, for literature has many varied allusions to this food. The very first one is the origin of the word "egg" itself, which has its roots in the Norse language and means "awe". Our Saxon rulers, whose names are usually the cause of mirth in the history lesson, should therefore be treated with great respect: Egbert, for example means "formidably bright".

William Shakespeare in *The Winter's Tale* writes: "Will you take eggs for your money?" For eggs in those days were so very plentiful that to offer eggs instead of money was considered an imposition. Mark Twain made use of the egg to give an unusual twist to an old proverb: "put all thine eggs in one basket and—watch that basket!" But it took Samuel Butler to sum up a world of philosophical contention with "A hen is only an egg's way of making another egg."

Robert Lynd, in a passage which surely the Egg Marketing Board ought to have seized on, states quite firmly, "If I were given my choice between an egg and ambrosia for breakfast, I should choose an egg." Even if, "it may be different"?

RITA ALLEN

 *Our Cat*

Her tail, an abbreviated stump, not Manx,
Nor yet a long and swinging branch,
But small and curled as with the hot iron made,
When girls at night their twisted hair crimp up.

Biscuit her colour and her name,
Slumbering in deceitful quiet . . .
Now, backs are turned, and with a sudden speed
Swiftly a piece of cake out from the tin she scoops.

With upright slits in yellow eyes, she curves,
Claws on the carpet sharpens,
For midnight forays when the house is dark,
And down thro' the silent farmyard slips in shadow.

Suddenly a dash, a scratch, on the wooden floor
Tiger by instinct, untamed, wild as the flitting clouds,

Yet now beside the fire's warmth
Her pads alone she shows, and she is soft
A child's pet . . . our cat.

MRS. JUDITH MANBY

🌹 THE GOOD FARMERS OF "PARADISE"

"We are farmers, we are fishermen, we are builders, we are jacks of all trades—but first we are farmers."

Last October the speaker, together with the rest of his tiny community, left his island home of Tristan da Cunha and was brought to England. There was little choice because the island volcano was threatening violence.

Soon they will know if they can go back. To what? What is their farming like? And after a year in England what do they think of our farming?

A Tristan talking about his island never fails to excite the listener. "Grass grows by itself, winters are often as good as summers and the water is as clear as gin. We do everything by hand," he will proudly tell you, "even spading the ground for potatoes."

After a comment like that it is easy to suggest that someone ought to teach them how to farm, sell them tractors, seeds, better cattle and all the paraphernalia of modern agriculture. But do they want help?

They keep cattle, sheep, donkeys, hens, and they grow potatoes. The stock all run together and each animal is distinguished by his owner's mark. They lie out all the year and live off grass.

"We do not make hay because we do not need it. If the grass gets a bit thin we part the donkeys out and take them to another part of the island which is fenced off."

The Tristan farmers can't say how many cattle and sheep they have got—except that they have got enough. When a farmer wants meat he kills it, when he wants wool he shears it and when he wants money—which isn't often—he works for a fishing company that comes to the island.

"We only need a little money for some groceries and drink from the supply ship."

Because the Tristans need so little money they don't have to worry unduly about high production. There is always enough stock to provide wool and meat for themselves. One reason for this is that they have few disease troubles and they have enough land to keep the stock numbers well above the minimum.

The island is divided into three "fields". Two are in grass and in the third the islanders have their potato patches. Each farmer can grow as much as he likes. "We grow so many potatoes that sometimes we have to throw half of them away. Of course if one man's crop fails, his neighbours give him some of theirs. We never go hungry."

This is their secret. They help each other in every way they can from building houses to digging potatoes.

The Tristans are a proud, happy and friendly people. Their way of life and their farming is very different from our high-pressure society. Our farms impress them but they could not and would not try to farm over here. But to think of them as bad farmers would be a mistake because on Tristan da Cunha—like a paradise—there is no such thing as a bad farmer.

RANDAL CHARLTON

🌹 FRAGRANT LAWN

Those who have rested on a bank of Pennyroyal, occasionally found on the banks of a stream, have been amazed at its recuperative powers when one is tired after a long tramp— the countryman has long known of its value. The same relaxing qualities may be enjoyed by making a small fragrant lawn at home, preferably in a dry, sunny position, and it must be on well-drained ground.

Besides Pennyroyal there are a number of other plants with a carpeting habit and which are deliciously aromatic when walked upon. Camomile is one, the fragrance of which, Parkinson, gardener to Charles I, likened to that of Feverfew.

Plant with the Camomile a few plants of the Mountain Vetch, *Anthyllis montana*, which also forms a mat and bears crimson clover-like blooms with the sweet perfume of pea flowers, the leaves being attractively covered with down, though the plants will not stand walking on in the same way as will Camomile or the thymes.

It is the thymes that make a fragrant lawn so interesting with the rich colouring of their tiny blooms and the various aromatic perfumes of their foliage, but only choose those species with a prostrate habit.

Of the "wild thyme" of Shakespeare's lines, a native of our chalk downlands and so attractive to bees, *T. coccineus* with its bottle-green foliage and crimson flowers, and its pale pink companion, Annie Hall, are delightful representatives of the creeping thymes which grow no taller than one inch.

Two others of charm are Pink Chintz, which covers itself in deep salmon-pink flowers, and the pure white Alba. Besides the native wild thyme there are others of similar creeping habit. *T. doeffleri* forms dense grey mats and bears richly scented rose-pink flowers, whilst *T. micans* makes a bright green mat studded with mauve, and is strongly pine scented.

Two whose foliage bear a distinct and rich fragrance when trodden upon are *T. herbarona*, smelling strongly of carroway-seed, and the strongly citron-scented Lemon Curd. Those who like the refreshing lemon fragrance should also include *Citriodorus aureus*, which is strongly lemon-scented and has the additional charm of golden variegated foliage.

A rare thyme is Membranaceus, a native of Spain, which bears attractive white tubular flowers and has strongly pungent foliage. Another with creeping habit is *T. caespititus* which covers itself with rosy-purple flowers.

Yet another delightful carpeting plant which is strongly aromatic is a rare, but inexpensive, form of the lad's-love, *Artemesia lanata pedemontana*, which makes a tiny shrub of almost protrate form, the interesting silvery leaves being highly fragrant when trodden upon.

The lawn should be made by setting the plants six inch apart —and here and there plant Pennyroyal and Menthapulegium, which will quickly spread amongst the other plants, adding its refreshing fragrance to the pungency of the others.

The best time to plant is in spring, any time up to the end of May, so that the plants grow away rapidly; by mid-summer they will completely carpet the ground to make a lawn which the more it is walked upon the more dense and fragrant it will become.

The lawn will require no attention apart from occasionally removing any shoots which tend to grow taller than the usual habit of the plants. This may be done with a pair of shears.

Weeding should not be necessary if planting is done in clean soil for the plants will quickly form a dense mat and will smother all annual weeds, but before planting be sure that the ground is quite free from all perennial weeds, such as nettles and buttercups, which would, in their turn, choke out the carpeting plants before they had become established.

The plants will grow in any ordinary garden soil, though they enjoy best a sandy soil, well drained so that water is not unduly retained to prevent walking over the plants during showery weather.

If the soil is of a heavy nature, incorporate plenty of grit before levelling the bed; this may be by way of boiler ashes, coarse sand or sea-shore grit, or even crushed stone or brick. Manure is not required in any way. The drier and more well drained the soil, the more aromatic will be the plants, and always choose a position where the plants will receive some sunshine, full sun suiting them best of all.

A small quantity of peat worked into the soil at planting time will retain sufficient moisture during the driest weather.

ROY GENDERS

🌹 A PLEA FOR BETTER SCARECROWS

The ideal scarecrow should look as much like a human being as a few sticks and a bundle of old clothes can make him. If we don't set about constructing one with this object in mind we might as well save our time and energy.

And this human being should be alive, doing something recognisably human. Standing up straight in the middle of a field with both arms stretched sideways is not a recognised human activity. For more than five minutes it is hardly a recognised human possibility. Try it.

So what should we do? Comb the junk-dealers for discarded dress-shop dummies? Their appearance in his fields would possibly gladden the farmer's eye when he passed that way. But his wife and the parson might have different views.

As for their effect on the birds—well, the attitudes of these dummies can scarcely be called vigorous, and no doubt the birds would soon be treating them with the contempt they already show for the traditional arm-stretching nonentities.

No; without departing from the use of sticks and old clothes, I think we can still bring a scarecrow to life. We can, of course, make it look as if it is levelling a gun by adding a long straight stick. Or we can put one of its arms in the air and make it look as if it is waving.

A good test for a scarecrow of the latter type is to hide behind a hedge and wait for a passer-by to show up. When he does, shout a cheerful greeting, still taking care not to be seen. If he waves back at the scarecrow you've made a good job of it. If he asks it to come for a drink, emerge from your hiding-place. To buy your silence he'll stand you more than one.

The artistic individual will not be content with a waving scarecrow, however, once he gets the knack of life-like arrangement. If, for instance, he used two bent pieces for the arms dozens of fresh fascinating combinations are made possible.

Some of these possibilities are, quite frankly, vulgar, and the farmer of taste will quickly, if a trifle wistfully, reject them. But others will suggest themselves, perhaps resulting in peering scarecrows—with one arm bent to head and one to hip—or even angry fist-shaking scarecrows.

Indeed, scarecrows, properly constructed, can serve the secondary purpose of expressing the personalities of their creators. The happy farmers can make dancing scarecrows, the ill-tempered can augment the shaking fist with a stamping or kicking foot.

Once we get out of the rut of thinking in terms of standing scarecrows, yet another field of possibilities will be opened. Then we may see crouching scarecrows, kneeling scarecrows. stalking scarecrows. More, if we can equip a croucher with a couple of lemonade bottles strapped together to represent binoculars, we shall have created what is surely the greatest bird-scarer of the lot—the Amateur Birdwatcher.

But like his fellow-artists in the normal spheres of activity the inspired scarecrow-constructor must fully exploit the potentialities of his simple materials without having to fall back on expensive trappings. He must do the best he can with old cast-off clothing and must never be tempted into using complete suits of fancy-dress. Such Smart Alec practices should be left to his dilettante ex-theatrical neighbours.

Talking about neighbours, however, reminds me of one possible excuse for elaboration of dress. If the farmer does happen to have a neighbour he strongly dislikes, or a Ministry Inspector he particularly loathes, he may find deep satisfaction in dressing his scarecrows as near like these people as possible. Such visual insults, if well prepared and cunningly placed, can be far more telling than the verbal.

Finally, an extra word of caution. Scarecrow-building can soon develop from a chore into a hobby, from a hobby into a real obsession.

Take the case of Mr. Henry Sedge. He started modestly enough on solitary kneelers and crouchers. Then he began to go in for groups, one of the earliest being the notorious Boys Playing Marbles. This was the group that attracted the attention of Dr. Herbert Grunt, the eminent art critic, who came to examine, to praise—and alas, to corrupt.

Soon the Sedge fields were filled with scarecrows of every conceivable kind, in groups and ranks and rings. Their fame spread far and wide.

Coach companies of all the principal Midlands towns began to run regular sight-seeing tours of the Scarecrow Meadows. The tulip farmers of Lincolnshire sent in strong protests to Bedford Square. In Coronation year, Sedge attracted hundreds of thousands of trippers to see Drake Playing Bowls and the Soldiers of the Queen, all done in scarecrows. But Sedge had been neglecting the normal duties of the farmer. He had to sell his livestock. Weeds grew. Fences fell into disrepair. And this, as the Chairman of the County Executive Committee put it, this was "hardly in the best traditions of good husbandry".

So Sedge had his land taken from him, and, since his first abortive season at Blackpool (where the sand proved to be too loose to support his creations), nothing more has been heard of him.

E. W. HILDICK

Summer Storm

Angry and ruffled, the sky blushes darkly
With luminous gloom behind stark outlined trees
Deep in the silence is born sudden movement
Ominous chill heralds threatening breeze.

Back to the cottage! The drops falling heavily
Penny-size, scattered, but gathering fast
Unite in a downpour as lightning cracks blindly
Roar follows roar as the thunder rolls past.

Shut all the windows! the water beats madly
Leaping white flash with each deafening peal
Vast panorama of war-gods in combats!
What will the climax be? Can it be real?

Suddenly lessens the spattering rainfall
Quiet the thunder, and fainter the flash
Heavy dark storm-clouds are rended asunder
By watery sun lighting rain's final splash.

Gathering strength shines the sun in its heaven
Timidly, birds start to sing once again
Everything green seems to sigh, and reach upwards
Grateful, refreshed by the cool summer rain.

MRS. J. LEGGE

GETTING TO KNOW YOU

I have long been conscious that the countryman, while the soul of kindness, and possessed of a deep in-bred sense of courtesy, is slightly scornful and even suspicious of a townsman, and even more so of a townswoman. Well, fair enough, the same view is held, vice versa, by the "townie", but perhaps not quite so politely disguised. After all, who has not heard the expression "country bumpkin"?

Now, although not actually farm bred myself, my forbears were good old farming stock, and I must be a throw-back, because life on the land means everything to me. However, after years of living in towns, my speech and dress have somewhat camouflaged the fact that I am a daughter of the soil!

It is not surprising, therefore, to be treated with a certain amount of reserve by the local people when we first settle in on a new job on a farm. "Going calling" is practically a thing of the past, a Head Herdsman's wife is not likely to have Lady Dingwithers calling on her, and for that matter I haven't noticed any desperate keenness on the part of the Vicar's wife these days!

We have arrived after a long tiring move and found a fire blazing in the grate of the empty cottage. To go and say thank you is a "must" but even this can be a stilted, forced affair if both parties are a bit shy. No, the only thing to do is potter about the farm on a fine day, lend a hand if possible, try and make an intelligent remark or two about whatever is going on at the moment, and take a large jug of hot tea down to the cowshed on a bad day.

And finally, carefully refrain from looking disgusted if you happen to step in something, or fall flat on your back in the mud! This course will wear the men down in the end, and they will finally agree that "She'm not a bad little'n," and go home and tell their wives so. . . . Having got this far, life becomes considerably easier, a sack of logs, or a drum of paraffin will be dropped off at the back door by the tractor men, to save my husband the business of humping it himself.

It was a little thing that gained me a firm friend one day. The oldest tractor driver was a thin, hard, leathery man, with penetrating crinkly blue eyes. I had never felt that I really measured up in his estimation somehow, they said he was a bit anti-social. I passed him early one lovely spring morning, with my husband's gun tucked under my arm, on my way up to a little valley on the downs, where I had seen a few rabbits the previous day.

He peered up at me from his beloved engine, and nodded. I heard an indistinct greeting, and I was pretty sure that I also heard a disapproving snort, and I had the feeling that he was looking round to see that there were no young heifers within range! It didn't take me long to reach the place that I had earmarked for my morning's hunting.

Now, I am not a female sharpshooter, I have never brought down a pigeon in my life. I have a horrible tendency to shut the wrong eye, and I am still overcome with breathlessness at the crucial moment. I seem to be gulping for air and shaking like a jelly at the same time, but it is fun and once I have got to the point of squeezing the trigger I usually get what I aim at. On the ground that is!

On this particular morning my luck was in, I got a nice running shot, and brought down a big buck rabbit, and then a few minutes later I crept round a little hillock, and there in the middle distance was another one sitting (yes, I am sorry, sitting) nibbling in the sun, a perfect target. A very, very brief wrestle with my sporting conscience ensued, after all cartridges were an awful price these days, a deep breath, and bang! The deed was done. Some deed! When I went to pick him up, I found that I had got two for the price of one, Mr. Bun's sister must have been sitting right beside him. . . .

Within ten minutes I was walking back through the yard again, I hadn't been gone a half an hour, and Bill was getting ready to leave for the fields. The clear morning air must have relayed my two shots as loudly as if I had fired them in the yard. He looked at me, and he looked at the three rabbits hanging (just a little bit obviously?) from a stick, and he touched his cap as I passed.

The next morning, fired by my success, I sallied forth again. This time there was a difference. When I reached Bill's shed he came straight out to me, fumbling in his pocket. His bright blue eyes were twinkling as he said, "Marn'in, Missis, ef'n you

don't moind me arst'n, cud yew be brungin' one down fer oi?
Oi dun'nt git much toime for such loike," and he put two cartridges in my hand. No greater accolade could I have had. I
did bring him back his bunny, and more in the days to follow,
when he became my friend, adviser and champion. It's the
little things that matter in the country.

PAMELA ROBINSON

🌹 BLACKBERRIES

You won't find the blackberry (botanical name: *Rubus fructi-
cosus*) in the book *British Herbs*, but our old friend Culpeper
mentions it and writes that it is "under the dominion of Venus"
and "if anyone asks the reason why Venus is so prickly, tell
them it is because she is in the house of Mars."

Culpeper knew a thing or two more about blackberries. He
wrote, "the buds leaves and branches while they are green are
of a good use in the ulcers and putrid sores of the mouth and
throat and of the quinsey and likewise to heal other fresh
wounds and sores . . . the berries of the flower are a powerful
remedy against the poison of the most venomous serpents."

I remember many years ago setting off on my bicycle with a
little round wicker basket to gather blackberries. I hoped at
least to half fill it but I stumbled across a bank of the best blackberries I have ever seen in my life and I filled my basket to
overflowing and returned home purple-mouthed. All this was
a long time ago and in my native Anglesey, but the delicious
warm smell of those berries is with me yet. They were destined
for the preserving pan and some for blackberry syrup which is
an excellent and pleasant way to cure a sore throat, especially
with the addition of lemon juice and honey.

An infusion of blackberry leaves and unripe berries is a good
remedy for diarrhoea, as Culpeper somewhat indelicately puts
it, "They do much bind the belly." But as far as I am concerned the best use for blackberries is to make wine out of them
and here is a recipe for a sweet blackberry wine guaranteed to
chase away the blues.

SWEET BLACKBERRY WINE

6 lb. blackberries	3½ lb. sugar
1 lemon	1 gallon water

¾ oz. baker's yeast or 1 level table-
spoonful dried yeast or one tablet
of all-purpose wine yeast.

METHOD

Put the fruit into a large bowl with the thinly-peeled rind of
the lemon and pour over one gallon of boiling water. Stir and
crush the fruit, cover and allow to stand for two days, stirring
daily. Strain through butter muslin on to the sugar and stir
well. It is as well to heat it for a minute or two to enable the sugar
to dissolve. Add the juice of the lemon and the yeast when lukewarm. Cover and leave in a warm place for twenty-four hours.
Now pour the liquid into a fermentation jar. This can be of
glass or stone but should have a small neck. Insert an airlock
or cover the neck with a piece of polythene or cellophane held
in place with a rubber band which will serve as an airlock.
Keep in a warm place until all signs of fermentation have
ceased. Syphon off into a storage jar and add more sugar to
taste if necessary. Keep in a cool place lightly corked or again
with an airlock in place for six months. You can now bottle off
and, if you wish to, sample the wine. But remember all wines
taste better after a year in store.

DOROTHY WISE

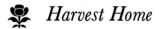 Harvest Home

Last year I had a record crop
Of oats and barley, wheat and rye.
This year a stranger crop than this
Meets the Farmer's weather-eye.

Who sows the dragon's teeth for seed
Reaps harvest dread of war and pain.
What seeds are these then I have sown?
What rue, what hemlcock or what bane?

With care I tended every field.
Small wonder this my ire arouses—
This year there is a record yield
Of several hundred council houses!

MRS. N. M. T., *Herts*

PATIENCE ON A WATERFALL

"Dogs and children are all right in their place," a crochety old aunt of mine used to say, and that's what I feel about water. I like it in lakes and rivers, in taps, pipes, and bath tubs. I like it hurtling down a hill or rushing through a sluice—anywhere where it is picturesque or useful. I do not like it gushing down the side of the house and beating a loud tattoo on the stone path below. Not only do I not like it—it worries me.

When I lie awake at night and listen to it pouring down during a rainstorm, I can quite understand the effectiveness of the old Oriental torture of dripping water on to a man's head to make him talk.

Of the multitude of things we have had done ourselves to the house in the past few years one thing has always hung fire—the guttering. It has always been the next-timer on the job list. And I suppose it's just bad luck that for me it happened to be the most important job of all—definitely more vital, say, than putting a new door on the shed or a hinge on the gate. Good strong wire and a prop will fix both these things with only the slightest inconvenience to man or beast, but what can one do when on rainy days and nights, the whole house becomes a jumping-off ground for hundreds of gallons of water.

On the face of things I agree that water ricocheting off a roof and back into the good earth from whence it came doesn't sound very alarming or destructive, but if you could see the moss which was already settling at the bottom end of our house as a result of the super nourishment it was receiving from above; if you could have seen the little hole which was slowly widening as a result of an extra gush through a particularly rusty bit of guttering, and if you'd taken a look at our water wagtails enjoying a deeper bath every day as a result of a natural pond which was forming at the end of the house where the drainpipe should have been but wasn't, perhaps you'd have understood my uneasiness as the winter drew nearer and my eagerness to prevent the possibility of the garden turning into a skating rink when the icy weather comes upon us.

To plough is to pray—to plant is to prophesy, and the harvest answers
and fulfils.

R. G. Ingersoll

Who can wrestle against sleep?—Yet is that giant very gentleness.

Martin Farquhar Tupper, of Beauty.

Already our house is situated more or less in the middle of a bog. The river runs round the edge of our garden and the house is on a level with it, and if you want to drive a fencing stake or a gatepost into the ground you have to bale out a foot of water as you dig. Therefore when the rain was coming down and splashing round the house, damp dogs and children to-ing and fro-ing and one could hear the river running over the stones under the bridge, I began to wonder whether we lived in an aquarium instead of a house.

Hence my anxiety—I'm told it's neurosis—about the state of the guttering and pipes round the house which, if mended would at least provide some exit for the extra gallon or two of Nature's ale. Hence, also, the reason for my pressing the point —I'm told it's nagging—before the really bad weather began.

For three years my powers of persuasion have failed and all "the more important" jobs have got done instead. In fact if I'd mentioned a mink coat and guttering in one breath, I honestly believe I would have got the mink!

No wonder then that after this summer's deluge I almost admitted to having a neurosis about water running down the wall.

Imagine my surprise, therefore, when last weekend I saw the trailer turn the corner of our lane with an enormous ladder in it.

"What are you going to do with that?" I asked, hope and fear alight in my breast.

"I'm going to make a start on the guttering," was the reply; "'bout time it was done."

The unutterable smugness of this remark to someone who had been quietly going balmy for three years was almost too much to bear. However, I kept my mouth shut for fear of sabotaging any plans for getting up that ladder. At that point I would have gladly allowed myself to be cut up into short lengths to mend those gutters.

I went to do my shopping—indifference had to be kept up at all cost, for any suggestion that by doing the guttering I was also being done a good turn had to be scotched immediately or there would have been a grand display of absenteeism. The pleading eye, for some reason or other, is apparently irritating to even the most humane of men.

There was a certain amount of discomfort—even hazards—during the repair stages, but oh, in what a good cause! It was quite usual, for instance, to walk out into the garden and find yourself suddenly drenched with a shower of water from the roof. "Just testing for leaks," shouted a voice from the top of a ladder in lieu of an apology.

Twice walking round the house I got anointed with blobs of black sticky stuff they were using to glue the gutters together with. To say nothing of being nearly annihilated by a falling drainpipe. But oh what a glorious martyrdom, I murmured to myself as I ducked to avoid a starlings' nest full of muck and old feathers.

When the job was done I could hardly wait to see whether it worked but wait I had to because, for the first time since the spring, there was a long succession of dry days. I kept looking up at the sky hoping for a cloud—just like when you're a child and have just been given a new mackintosh.

Then one glorious evening, as I was cooking the supper, the rain fell. I dropped everything and went for the torch, jamming on my old straw hat as I ran out of the back door. It's odd that more people don't use this sort of headgear in the rain. It acts like the thatch on a roof—all the water drips off the edge, and since mine is nearly the size of an umbrella my shoulders kept dry as well. Chinese coolies learnt this fact decades ago.

I trained the torch on to the guttering. Glory be! Not a sound or a sight of water. I examined the first downpipe and there, oh best beloved, was water actually coming out of the bottom of it. After a tour of the house I returned ecstatically to the kitchen. Unable to wait to announce my discovery I walked through into the sitting-room with a dripping hat on my head and the torch still alight.

It didn't occur to me that I had said anything funny or that I looked at all peculiar when I stood in the doorway and shouted, "It's coming down the pipe," so that the shrieks of laughter were quite unexpected and I was almost offended when one of the family said, "Now go and look at yourself in a mirror and see whether we're right when we say you're neurotic."

BARBARA HARGREAVES

❧ BORAGE BRINGS COURAGE

Borage and bees have been associated in my mind since child-hood days. Last year I had my first hive of bees: this year I planted borage.

At the end of March I sowed the seeds and eleven weeks later the plants were blossoming. It was not long before my bees discovered them and now there is scarcely an hour of sunshine that does not see them busy in the blossoms.

Borage is seldom cultivated in gardens now. Robinson, whose *English Flower Garden* had so strong an influence at the end of last century, spoke of it with disdain saying it was "not worth a place in the garden proper, being coarse and taking up much space." One sometimes sees it naturalised in places where it was once grown, for it seeds itself freely. It is not a showy flower, but was held in great repute up to the present century. "A good pot herb, good for bees, and most comfort-able to the heart and stomach," says the 17th-century *Countrie Housewife's Garden*.

The modern housewife would no doubt hesitate to use borage for this last purpose, or "to make a tarte of borage flowers" as recommended in *The Proper New Booke of Cookerie* in the time of the first Elizabeth. She might, however, try a cool tankard. The ingredients are wine, water, lemon juice, sugar, a sprig of borage flowers on top.

The cooling effect of the herb is well known. It contains potassium nitrate, which dissolves out in liquids and imparts a coolness to them. I have tried it in lemonade and fruit juice drinks, and it certainly gives not only coolness, but a faint pleasant cucumber flavour. This flavour comes out if you use the young leaves in salads. The blossoms are edible and give a piquant touch of colour to the salad.

The old herbalists made extravagant claims for this plant. Evelyn quotes the centuries-old adage: "I borage, always bring courage", and he claims that the sprigs in wine "are of known virtue to revive the hypochondriac and cheer the hard student". Bacon asserts that the leaf "hath an exellent spirit to repress the fuliginous vapours of melancholy and so cure madness".

It seems there is something in borage to give one a feeling of exhilaration: or was it in the wine in which the borage was soaked?

Another herbalist recommended boiling the ashes of the plant in mead or honeyed water and using it as a gargle against inflammations of the throat. When the "virtue" of a plant was established, the herbalists were apt to outdo each other in prescribing it for every complaint!

Before the days of embroidery transfers, ladies went to their gardens to find inspiration for their designs. If there is any flower that simply asks to be "enterposed among the flowers of women's needlework" it is this purest blue, clean-cut, star-shaped blossom, with its white eye, and prominent black anthers. It appears in the lovely petit-point panel ambroidered in 1625 showing the wedding of King Charles I and Henrietta Maria, starring among the Tudor roses, Scottish thistles, honey-suckle, and grape.

One can recapture the summer blue of borage even in the winter, by candying the flowers and using them for cake decoration.

CANDYING

Candying apparatus is simply made from an old baking tin, at least $1\frac{1}{2}$ in. deep. Cut a hole in one corner and fit with a cork. A fine-meshed baking tray on short legs fits into this tin, and the flowers to be crystallized are arranged on it.

Prepare the syrup by boiling 2 lb. loaf sugar with 1 pint of water till a temperature of 220 degrees F. is reached. Allow the syrup to cool to blood heat (98·4 degrees F.). (N.B. Use less water in hot weather.) Pour the syrup carefully over the flowers and place the tin in a cool, dark place for several hours.

A hard crust forming on the top is a sign that crystallization has taken place. Pull out the cork, allowing the uncrystallized sugar to drain off. Leave the flowers on the tray till quite dry and store them separately on layers of paper in a tin and keep in a cool dry place.

ALISON FYNCH

🌹 SOMERSET

... When I think of Somerset it is mainly of the farmhouses—solid, mellow, gracious, and when we journey into other counties we miss them. They are usually of ham stone, golden and Cotswoldish, with mullioned windows and drip stones and graceful two-storeyed porches, quaint gables and twisted chimneys, or else cool, solid blue-lias, usually accompanied by vast stone tithe barns and orchards, at one time of year glowing with cider apples—in the spring a pink bower of blossom.

Yes, I can say, with all honesty, happy are they who call Somerset their county!

MRS. M. BABER, *Yeovil*

🌹 ONE AFTERNOON LAST SUMMER

Have you ever felt like a man trying to run a four-minute mile in lead boots? That's how I felt one afternoon last summer when I went to milk . . . but perhaps I had better begin at the beginning.

I run a small relief milking service on my own for local farmers. As any relief milker will tell you, this means all sorts of jobs. On this particular afternoon I had to milk Mr. Brown's forty Ayrshires—a job I do once a fortnight more or less without incident.

The layout is an abreast type in-churn parlour of four machines and eight raised standings—quite enough for one at the best of times, although no doubt there's some clever johnny who uses five, six or seven and still has time for a nap.

First job was to get the cows into the collecting yard, put the first eight into the parlour, switch on the engine, and wash the first cow.

245

I got under way, and everything went swimmingly for a time, then the gremlins got to work. It was one of those warm days in early summer when flies abound. Each cow was accompanied by a fresh cloud. I hunted around—no spray to be found. Eventually it happened—the first machine hit the floor in several pieces.

Anyone who has worked with Ayrshires knows what happens when they hear an unusual sound or movement. It was a case of up tails and away we go! The beast who threw her machine away stood firmly on parts of it; she defied all my efforts to release it, and took several swipes at my person into the bargain.

As I said, it was early summer—flush of grass and all that— so by now the place looked as if a muck-spreader had passed through. These things happen, however, and it's a poor man who can't overcome a few small difficulties like these. The machine was eventually freed and washed.

The other cows were by now somewhat overmilked and had to be dealt with quickly. I brushed the muck off the standings, but didn't stop to put it in the wheelbarrow. The next lot of cows were ushered in, and things settled down a bit. I took the uddercloth to wash the first cow; she lashed out and caught me off balance on the side of the leg, and I collapsed on to the far-from-spotless floor. Nobody told me there was a kicker.

I staggered up and managed to get near enough to see she had a cut teat. I grabbed a pair of bulldog clips, limped round to her head and tied her up. The sight of me round in front was so unusual that fear and panic seized them all. Another stream of digested grass took the floor. A machine on a three-quartered cow started to suck air; I approached with all possible speed—but too late. I picked it up and wiped it with a hand which I hadn't had time to wash. Another machine collapsed in the same state through loss of vacuum.

It was at this moment—when two machines were in pieces on the floor, one cow strung up to break her neck, the whole floor and myself filthy—that a vision appeared in the doorway. I say vision because she had a white coat, but after one glance her face matched her coat. There were several moments of pregnant silence, then a voice shaking with emotion announced: "I've come to take a milk-sample."

ANON.

 LAUNCH

The wind had been rising all evening, and although I was snug enough, watching television, in the back of my mind I was worrying about it. A north-easter here is rare, but when it does get up, sweeping for hundreds of miles unobstructed down the North Sea into the bottleneck of the Straits of Dover, even the Goodwin Sands do not hold back the sea which

247

smashes with terrible force out there and south-west into the Channel. So when the first maroon went, I was out of my chair and into my coat, and the second maroon fired as I reversed out of the garage. A bike was flung on to the pavement, and into the car shot one of the lifeboat crew (who is also my milkman). He knew I'd get him there quicker than his bike. When we got there the lifeboat was ready to go.

She sits on a high ramp with a slip below to the top of a steep shingle bank; it was dead low water and they had laid out the big greased woods to the water's edge sixty yards down the sloping bank. Someone knocks out a shackle which holds her and away she goes. Slowly at first, the yellow oilskins of the crew shining in the searchlight; her own lights burning and her engine already running. She accelerates fast down the slip, and over the steep edge and on to the bank with a crash that throws sparks from her keel and breaks three of the woods.

She goes over on to one bilge keel and tears straight down to the sea, smack into an enormous wave, disappearing in a great burst of spray. Her momentum and her engine carry her clear of the surf and soon it is only her masthead light we can see swinging in great arcs as she rolls and pitches, for she is only a little boat, and the seas are steep.

I can see, out there beyond the sands, the swinging beam of a lightship where none should be. A quick check, and I know it must be the *East Goodwin*, miles off station with the sands right under her lee. It was exactly seven years ago that her sister the *South Goodwin* went with all her crew but one in exactly the same way. The crew of the *South Goodwin* must now be watching as we are, and wondering just how it is going to end this time.

You know how it ended, it's all been on television; but I saw the lifeboat come home this morning. She'd had to put into Dover harbour once and when her coxswain, Fred Upton, brought her in today, three days later, it took them a couple of hours to get her up the beach and back on to the ramp which had been badly undercut by the seas. Then she was tidied up, and we could all go home. But Fred Upton, still in his oilskins, his face white and very tired, for he is not a young man, turned, and looked out to where the lightship is anchored now, with her Trinity House tender beside her. I don't know what

Upton was thinking, but I know that I think those lifeboatmen are a bunch of ruddy heroes.

SUZANNE BEEDELL

🌹 GOING CUCKOO

I sometimes think it would be better if I did all my shopping from the top of a bus. I always seem to see the very thing I'm looking for from there. Yet if I go out a'purpose to buy something I invariably come home with the opposite or nothing at all.

My ground level efforts yesterday afternoon couldn't have been more of a failure if I had stood in the middle of the road with my eyes shut and pointed at the first thing I saw. Had I been in that girlish sort of mood where one believes what people want you to believe, I should have returned from that shopping jaunt with my annual contributions to the local jumble sale.

"But Madam's got just the face for the new 'sailor'—and Madam's feet can take these pointed toes . . . and Madam's legs would flatter the shorter length . . ." and on they "babble of green fields" while I think how lovely it would be to believe what they say, and look in the mirror with horrified astonishment at the truth.

I laugh about it now, but at the time I felt more like harnessing on a sandwich board and marching up and down Piccadilly claiming Better Clothes for Nicer Women. Like the king who only wanted a bit of butter with his bread, I was only after a pair of shoes, skirt and hat, but in my efforts to achieve them you'd think I was trying to buy a wedding dress for Siamese twins.

There are certain phrases in a shop assistant's language which, after a while, cease to be merely irritating or monotonous and become a threat to one's sanity. "But Madam, it's a very popular style this year," or "They're wearing them belted now . . ." Selling phrases I've no doubt, or customers like me would have forced them to change their tune or shut the shop long ago.

My shopping expedition which started in a cheery mood of hope, changed gradually to a haughty I-don't-care-two-hoots-what "they're"-wearing, to finally, one of quiet desperation.

As the pile of discarded shoes grew bigger and more hats were tossed aside I began to wonder whether it was me. Perhaps I was already heading for lavender and lace and didn't know it. I was out of date, dowdy, in my dotage and as I slumped along Oxford Street I was already preparing to give birth to a load of grandchildren.

Then suddenly in the next shoe shop as I stood up to gaze down on the umpteenth pair of navy blue gondolas, I went cuckoo.

I can only describe it as a state of abandon which takes over at the point of desperation and fills one's whole being with a couldn't-care-less sort of rapture. It has often come to my rescue over the years when the only alternative is to burst into tears. One might call it a form of hysteria, I don't know. I don't care. It's as good as owning Aladdin's lamp.

When the children were small they would watch this cuckoo mood come over me in food queues. "Have you heard this one," I would ask the rather startled woman in front of me and then I would recite a long dull poem learnt at school, sing a song or read a long political column out of the newspaper. The odd thing was that nobody ever told me to shut up. They obviously thought I was dotty and the children gazed at me wonderingly as if I was a solo Punch and Judy show. "Only Mummy gone cuckoo," I would whisper to them and the word stuck.

And so last week I beamed down at those incredible shoes pointing half-way across the floor. I beamed at the girl and the girl beamed back at me. "You know," I said, "I don't think I need buy any shoes, after all. I've just remembered there's a pair just like this in our dressing-up chest. Nicer actually, they've bells on the toes."

In the hat shop the girl was rather alarmed, as she carefully tilted over my nose the tenth little straw sailor, when I broke into *Yo Ho Ho* and a bottle of rum, and decided to choose a beret for my daughter.

On my way back to the office I almost caught up with the girl walking along in front of me with her skirt above her knees. "You shouldn't, dear," I was going to whisper in her ear, "your legs are very bandy." But I didn't—the cuckoos by that time had flown.

BARBARA HARGREAVES

🌹 GARDENING UNDER FOUR QUEENS

Gardening is one of the gentle arts and can only flourish where there is peace, so it was natural that the earliest gardens should have been those which were protected from the trouble and strife of the world within the sheltering monastery walls.

When the first Queen Elizabeth began her reign the constant fighting of mediaeval days were already over; there was no longer any need for the noble families of the land to protect themselves from danger behind moats and impregnable castle walls, and gardening in England had become a secular instead of a monastic pleasure.

The growing of vegetables, herbs and fruits was still considered of much greater importance than the growing of flowers. Apples, pears and peaches, grapes, cherries, damsons and "apricocks" were grown in all the big gardens. Gooseberries and raspberries were just beginning to come into favour and wild strawberries were brought from the woods and planted in the garden.

Vegetables did not, as yet, play a very important part, except in the diet of poor people who mostly gathered wild plants for food, but they were liked for flavouring and garnishing. Globe artichokes and lettuces, cucumbers and melons, runcival peas, leeks and cabbages were all known and grown.

It is often said that Sir Walter Raleigh brought the potato to England but there is no proof of this, although it certainly arrived here, via Spain, some time between 1580 and 1590. At first it was regarded simply as a curiosity and it took a great many years before it became a popular vegetable and replaced the skirret, which we have now almost forgotten.

You could not, in those days, slip round the corner and buy a packet of seed as you do now, so Tusser gave this advice:

> Good husvifes in sommer will saue their own seedes
> Against the next yeere as occasion needes.
> One seed for another to make an exchange
> With fellowlie neighbourhood seemeth not strange.

And among keen gardeners the exchange system has lasted to this day.

Knot Gardens

When we think of a Tudor flower garden we immediately visualise the intricate design of "knots" which were such a very characteristic feature. These "knotted beds", usually placed close to the house, were often railed in or surrounded by bricks or tiles, and then planted in an intricate pattern with box, thyme, rosemary or similar low shrubby plants. The spaces between were filled with flowers or sometimes simply with coloured sands and the more complicated the geometrical design, the better it pleased.

The choice of flowers was very limited compared with the present day. Gillyflowers or pinks were great favourites in knots and borders and so were violets and roses, cowslips, daffodils, daisies, marigolds, wallflowers, periwinkle, lilies of the valley, cornflowers and poppies, nearly all of them native flowers which could be transplanted from the wild. A few "outlandish" flowers had also begun to make their appearance by this time, among them "jacinth, tulipas, flowedeluces (irises), crown imperials, larkspur, evening primrose, sweet sultan, balsam and lobelia.

Arbours and "alleys" were also very typical of Tudor gardens, but unlike the "knots" which can still be found, none of them have survived to the present day. They were the forerunners of the modern summer-houses and pergolas and usually made of wood trellis covered with climbing plants such as roses, honeysuckle, jasmine and traveller's joy.

Sometimes alleys were formed by living trees with their branches pleached and twined together to form a covered walk, and they usually led from the house to the arbour. This was often built on a raised mound so that you could get a good view of the outside world, for the idea that a garden must of necessity be sheltered within high walls or thick hedges was still so deep-rooted that every Elizabethan garden was, in fact, an enclosed garden, completely shut off from the surrounding countryside.

Genuinely Elizabethan

Topiary work was popular and Tudor gardens were full of cut bushes. Of these, quite a few yews have survived and, for example, at Heslington, near York, the topiary is genuinely Elizabethan in origin.

The first fountains in England also appeared at this time. The Queen herself had a beautiful fountain installed at Hampton Court. It was described by an eye-witness in the following words: "A splendid high and massy fountain with an ingenious water work, by which you can, if you like, make the water play upon the ladies and others who are standing by, and give them a thorough wetting."

The Elizabethans loved flowers, not only in their gardens but in their houses as well. Flowers and sweet-smelling herbs were strewn on the floors. Anne Blizard held the post of "herbes strewer to her Majesty the Queen" and a certain Robert Jones was paid £10 a year to supply boughs and flowers for her Council Chamber. Flowers were put in vases all over the house and worn as personal ornaments in posies, garlands and buttonholes.

Window boxes and pot plants indoors were already popular and a Dutch traveller, Levimus Leminius, who visited England in 1560, wrote this charming description of English homes. "Their chambers and parlours strawed over with sweet herbes refreshed mee; Their nosegays finely intermingled with sundry sorts of fragrant floures, in their bed chambers and privi rooms with comfortable smell cheered me up and entirely delighted all my senses."

When Queen Anne came to the throne, gardens were no

longer the comparatively small enclosed spaces of Elizabethan days. The grand ideas of the French designer, Le Notre, had spread to England and William and Mary had introduced many features of Dutch gardening. Every house of note now had to have a terrace in front of the principal rooms, to give a good view over the grounds.

The knot garden was replaced by the parterre, a similar idea, but carried out rather differently. The intricate patterns were now cut in clipped grass and planted with very low flowers or simply filled with different coloured sands, and the geometrical designs had changed to scroll work.

The gardener's aim was to imitate fine embroidery "like we have on our cloaths". Topiary was still fashionable and had in fact become almost too popular. Some writers of those days complained that not a single tree or shrub was left to grow in a natural manner. Bowling greens, well screened by high hedges or rows of trees clipped to a certain height, and then allowed to feather naturally at the top, were a feature, and so were wide grassy walks radiating out from the house.

Fountains, formal pools and canals, cascades and statues were considered essential in any garden worthy of the name. Many fine-wrought iron gates date back to Queen Anne and wonderful avenues, sometimes stretching for several miles, were planted to link the garden with the country beyond. All the great gardens of this period were strictly formal in design; everything had to be symmetrical, the parterres and terraces, the walks and avenues were laid out with mathematical precision.

Many plants from abroad had been introduced by this time and greenhouses, usually called orangeries, were a feature in most big gardens. Orange and lemon trees, planted in tubs, were moved out on the terrace in summer and protected from the cold under glass in wintertime. Fruit and vegetable gardening made great strides and many new varieties were introduced.

Gardeners were beginning to try their hands at forcing vegetables out of season, a trick they had learnt from Holland and France. Vineyards were still being planted and nursery gardens which raised plants for sale had become quite common, especially round London.

Landscape Gardening

The years between Queen Anne and Queen Victoria saw tremendous changes. The old formal gardens became hopelessly out of date and landscape gardening was all the rage. Gardens were no longer set apart from the surrounding country, but instead designers tried to bring a tamed version of wild nature right up to the very doors of the house. The beauty of clumps of trees, lakes and streams, the sweep of hillsides became all-important and flowers were neglected or pushed into the kitchen garden. Stately avenues were felled, hedges uprooted, walls pulled down and terraces destroyed because "Nature abhors a straight line".

Men like Capability Brown and Humphrey Repton laboured to try and make the landscape conform to their own ideas of romantic beauty. It was a grand style for those who could afford the tremendous cost, but there was also something rather forbidding about it. As Jane Austen so aptly said, "Everything in the garden must now be horrid."

To the majority of people untamed nature has little appeal and another factor which worked against true landscape gardening was the tremendous flow of new plants which now came into this country from every part of the world.

Flower Beds

When Victoria ascended the throne formality had been welcomed back and flowers came into their own, particularly the many colourful and spectacular half-hardy plants which gave occasion for the Victorian bedding system which still survives in a moderated form.

The sweeping green lawns were now cut up into flowerbeds of every shape and size and for a few months of the year they were filled with dazzling geraniums and calceolarias, snapdragons and begonias, making a perfect blaze of colour. When that was over most gardens reverted into rather dull and dismal places and you had to look for flowers in the conservatory instead.

The pinetum and the shrubbery were other Victorian innovations, a new way of showing off the many foreign conifers and flowering shrubs which the eager plant hunters sent

255

(Continued on page 258)

🌷 Corn Dolly

But when we finished the harvest, arms brown and our hair
Ribboned with light, then we brought laughing in
The big last sheaf we call the barley queen.
With brawling horseplay came and hung it here
In the raftered barn to light the spring next year.
—Now in these frozen fields the sun unmanacled
Persuades no root to grope. The Iron land
Deadlocks generation, iron air
Harrows the breath. But see, shining there,
Our summer straw queen. Though to stoic touch
The plowshare steel be cold at death, yet such
Largesse of light lives in this yellow sheaf
As proves the resurrection of the leaf,
Attests the bud, confirms the sober rain.
Next year is quick in last year's hung-up again.

R. S. LEHMAN
from "Sonata"

Corn Dolly

The mellow autumn came, and with it came
The promised party, to enjoy its sweets.

 *From Don Juan*

The mellow autumn came, and with it came
  The promised party, to enjoy its sweets.
The corn is cut, the manor full of game;
  The pointer ranges, and the sportsman beats
In russet jacket;—lynx-like is his aim;
  Full grows his bag, and wonderful his feats.
Ah, nut-brown partridges! Ah, brilliant pheasant!
And ah, ye poachers!—'Tis no sport for peasants.

BYRON. Don Juan

home from America and Asia. So many new roses had been produced that a rosery became necessary if you wanted to display only a few of them and in warm districts sub-tropical gardens were planted.

Towards the end of the Victorian era there came a reaction against the crude and very brief glories of the formal summer bedding system. William Robinson and Gertrude Jekyll showed the way towards a more natural style of gardening and suggested the possibilities of naturalising fine garden plants in a wild background.

Dense shrubberies were opened up into glades, rock-gardens were constructed to make natural homes for the many new alpine plants, and herbaceous borders were planted for long seasons of bloom. And so, gradually, the gardens we know today emerged—a blend of formal and informal, which so far as we are able to judge, makes the best of both systems.

Universal Hobby

From the time of the first Queen Elizabeth until the beginning of the twentieth-century, gardening had been a rather exclusive pleasure. Now, in this second Elizabethan era it has become an almost universal hobby. The days of the enormous private gardens are over and their place has been taken by the municipal parks, but instead it is true to say that almost every house which stands on its own small plot of land now stands in a garden which is tended with care and pride and filled with flowers far more beautiful than any our ancestors ever knew and cherished.

We now heat our garden frames with electricity instead of manure, we are familiar with chemical sprays, artificial fertilisers and root promoting hormones but in essentials, gardening is still the same effort to make things grow as we wish.

In an age when so many of us are further removed from nature than ever before, more and more people find peace and solace in handling the soil and tending the plants which spring from the good earth.

MOIRA SAVONIUS

🌺 PIGS AND KIPPERS

I wasn't hungry when I boarded the bus. Certainly the talk behind me, on the cost of bread, did nothing to set the saliva flowing. But as the bus rolled on. . . . It was an elderly gentleman who was making the conversational pace.

"She allus baked her own loaves," he said. 'And she'd pop some thin-cake in the oven with 'em. . . . I like a bit o' thincake. . . ." The lady he was talking to said, "Oh yes?"

"Aye! Nice with fish and chips. And I'll tell you what else it goes lovely with . . . a pair o' kippers! Nicest fish there is." The lady said well—yes—she liked a kipper herself. "Only you want to have 'em on a cold frosty day," said the man. "It seems to bring out the flavour."

I thought of kippers and thickly buttered thin-cake on a frosty day. I was beginning to warm to the topic. But then he said something that froze the gastronomic juices in my veins— or wherever it is they do flow.

"A kipper," he said, "will cure a sick horse." I didn't catch the woman's reply to this. "Either a poorly horse or a poorly cow, I'm not sure which. . . . But if you can get it to eat a kipper it'll be right in no time." There was a short silence. "Like a pig and a bad apple," he said.

The lady had been distracted by a friend who was just getting on the bus. With a hint of annoyance in his voice the man repeated his statement. Then he continued:

"If a pig is poorly and you can get it to eat a bad apple it'll put it on its feet better nor owt I know. . . ."

"Perhaps that's why apple-sauce goes so well with pork," said the lady. This remark was ignored.

"If it's off its food—and a pig has to be poorly to be off its food—you give it a rotten apple and you'll see the difference."

I thought of a sty full of sickly pigs and a farmer frantically pacing up and down his kitchen, pausing every now and then to snarl at his womenfolk and ask if those so-and-so apples were rotten yet. . . . The woman said she liked a bit of pork; the man said aye, and so did he. The woman said "loin?" and the man said "Aye, but I like belly pork best."

The reason he liked belly pork was because there was always

some nice fat left in the tin afterwards and he did like a bit of bread and fat to his supper now and then.

"And I do like a bit o' fat with me beef, too," he added.

"Yes, I do," said the woman, suddenly vehement. "That's just what I do like! They make me sick these days when they go in and ask for a bit of lean beef."

"Brisket," said the man. "A bit of fatty brisket." "I like rump myself—only it's so dear nowadays," she added wistfully.

"Brisket makes good gravy. Good rich brown gravy. . . ."

I gulped, glanced at my watch and saw with dismay that there was still another couple of hours to go before the next meal.

"A bit of horse-radish," the man was saying as I hurried past him, "just sets it off nice."

E. W. HILDICK

Life Begins At 53

Life begins at fifty-three,
At least it's going to for me.
Youthful ardours long since over,
I prefer maturer lover.

If your eyes to others stray
I shall not beseech and pray.
You'll come back and still be mine.
Have some steak and pass the wine!

We shall prove the poets wrong
Making youth their endless song.
We have turned a further page,
Sing the praise of middle-age!

MRS. AINSLIE

🌹 YORKSHIRE

. . . Yorkshire is never half-hearted. It seems to me to be bold and vigorous in its beauties, whether they're Abbeys (and where is the rival of Whitby Abbey's setting?)—beaches—Redcar really has miles of first-class sands—dales, wolds or moors. There's nothing wishy-washy, pretty-pretty or "fiddling and small" about Yorkshire. . . .

MRS. H. TRENHOLME, *Ripon, Yorks*

🌹 I LOST MY HEART TO SCOTLAND

It draws me still, with a call both gay and sad, like the slow march on the pipes; draws me north and west to the Highlands and the Isles, to my Land-of-Might-Have-Been. . . .

Ben Slioch, cloud-capped, mysterious, beckoning. Wooded islands set one longing for a boat. From Shieldaig, on Loch Torridon, the sun is setting over the Western Isles and it is so lovely that it almost hurts—"the ache that lies at the heart of beauty."

But I should not go quite so far north on my sentimental journey. Port Askaig, Isle of Islay, in the Inner Hebrides, would be my goal. I'd pitch my tent again on the slopes below Heather House, looking across to the Paps of Jura beyond the sound. And if it so happened to be in the month of October, the distant roaring of stags would come drifting across the water from the Jura shore.

Could reality measure up to the dream? I honestly think it could.

MRS. H. B. SALTER

✿ A GOOD CRY

As a nation we British strongly disapprove of weeping. We are embarrassed by any public display of emotion and, if we were truly honest with each other, we would also admit to being slightly embarrassed by it in private.

However much we are capable of sharing someone else's sorrow, however willingly we lend a shoulder for someone else's tears, secretly we hope that the weeping part will be over quickly. "Yes, that's right, my dear, you just have a good cry," we say to a friend or relation with a burden of trouble, knowing it to be the remedy for pent-up emotions. But we prescribe tears rather in the same way a doctor prescribes aspirin for a high temperature, hoping that when the fever has passed we can get down to helping them work out a practical way of easing the trouble.

Perhaps we are conscious as we grow older that our tears mature with us, and that as our sorrows cannot ultimately be solved by anyone but ourselves we are not so much impatient with tears but realise that only when we have done with them can we begin to do anything about what caused them.

Poem after poem has been written about tears—many more than have been written about laughter. Perhaps because there is always a story to tell where there are tears. The end of a chapter—the end of a dream—the breaking of a word, of a tie or a belief.

Laughter has no story—it is the background music in the lives of people who enjoy the particles of life. The music in our ears that makes light of tough work. Makes maddening things funny and turns crises into funny tales to tell our menfolk when they come home.

Laughter is not just a noise coming out of a grin but a whole warm attitude to life and maybe even the master key to good living. There is no story to tell simply because laughter speaks for itself.

Tears are the punctuation which form the sentences of life and as we get older we make fewer dots, dashes and exclamation marks. Sorrow may touch us more deeply as we mature, but our expression of it is more secret. So that even at a moment when our thoughts may "lie too deep for tears" we can afford to smile at those great big crocodile tears of our extreme youth.

My son, I reckon, must have put in more than his fair share of crying hours on account of a theory current at his babyhood which was to "stick to routine at all costs". He had to be fed, bathed and put to bed and cuddled at the same hour each day and on no account was this time-table to be altered. Baby might suffer to begin with but he would be all the better for it in the end. So they kept saying.

This theory I stuck to like a fanatic. I married very young, more or less straight out of school, and was used to taking orders. The result was not a terribly happy relationship between mother and baby. How could it be, really, when she would stand over him with eyes glued to her wrist watch until it should reach precisely the minute for his feed while he lay in the cot and bawled his baby head off?

A baby's continual crying is torture—third degree torture. It is, without doubt, the most maddening, infuriating, terrible noise—in every sense of the word "terrible"—that anyone could possibly devise, and once I saw the light—as it were—I knew that heaven intended that it should be so in order to have it stopped immediately.

Suddenly half-way through one night as I lay listening to the crying from the cot next door I rebelled. There and then I rebelled. "To hell with the silly idea," I said, in a loud voice, and jumped straight out of bed and picked the baby out of his cot.

Oh, those awful shuddering little gasps that come for so long after a bout of baby sobbing. That fearful little red tear-stained face. I looked at it lying in my arms and wondered how I could have ever gone on letting this sort of thing happen for so long. In aid of what? Of producing in the end, I suppose, a polished, perfectly schooled little gentleman. "Pooh, Pooh, Pooh," I said, aloud, as I did all the old-fashioned things like rocking him in my arms, crooning to him and giving him a good meal.

That was the best night we'd ever spent. For not a murmur came out of him for the rest of the night. We both slept soundly and peacefully. If he could have spoken his thoughts I suppose he would have said, "Well, thank goodness, we're over with

all that silly nonsense. Heaven only knows why we babies have
to put up with such ignorant, biased, short-sighted, so-called
adults."

The Victorians may have put a great deal too much flannel
on their babies, but they had the right idea about nice cosy
things like rocking chairs, cradles, large laps and big bosoms.
I don't know much about today's babies, but I'm told the
theorists are "going back" to all these things again. Going
back to mothering—interesting, isn't it?

Toddlers' tears are different. It's then they have to begin to
learn the one big lesson of life, which is that you can't have
something you want by crying for it. Remember the old negro
song:

> Do you want the moon to play with?
> Or the stars to run away with?
> They'll come if you don't cry.

And you battle on, gently persuading, firmly stating that
crying doesn't pay in the great big tough world you're about to
enter. And wise mothers don't get too many years, for there
are so many fascinating things to find out when you're two or
three or four, and if they'll let you look for them, well, there
isn't much time for tears, except when nobody quite knows
why, least of all you. . . .

The tears of our teens are perhaps the most extravagant of all. Oh, the times we flung ourselves down on our beds in paroxysms of weeping, certain that life had no further meaning for us, until one morning the sun rose miraculously once again in our hearts, and before we even had time to question our former anguish the process had started all over again.

And we with daughters are watching, or will watch it all over again. We say nothing, however much we know, for they won't want words of advice. "Don't be a goose," my mother used to say at such moments as she left me to work out my own salvation with a cup of hot milk.

BARBARA HARGREAVES

🌼 GETTING TO KNOW ABOUT GUNS

I was brought up with guns; good old hammer-guns which were once in the corner of every farmhouse kitchen; guns elaborately engraved, tucked away in baize-covered cases, guns hung together with string and wire and fired with a prayer which yet brought home the bacon. It is strange, though, how familiarity can foster sweet feminine ignorance. In those days I had always considered that given a barrel, a stock and a trigger to pull, a gun was just a gun and that good marksmanship was just a combination of a steady hand and good eyesight.

Since marriage I am getting to know about guns.

In the front hall, sacrosanct and inviolable, stands the holy of holies. Once or twice a day, my husband draws back the glass front with a triumphant slam and dawdles to dandle and fondle the five guns standing at the ready on the green baize. One day, greatly daring, I pause to peer over his shoulder. He picks up one of the twelve-bores and raises it to his shoulder in a snap action. The barrel veers dangerously in my direction.

"Looks a good gun," I venture timidly, backing away.

"Cheap, Belgium-made," he says contemptuously; "no

damn good, no balance, heavy as lead, handles like a hedge-stake. Might be all right for a duck a long way off—if they were flying very slow."

"BSA target air-gun," he announces, withdrawing the next weapon in line.

He has no need to describe this gun. I know it all too well. This firearm, the joy of the local air-rifle league, the delight of urban nephews and the bane of all animal, bird and plant life, is the weapon to which his hand automatically goes when the boar, after many previous "warnings off", is seen to be yet again in the fodder-beet. A boar, like an elephant, has a long memory—especially for air-gun pellets in ticklish places.

We gloss lightly over the ·410 converted from a rifle, whose only discernible use is to sit primed up and shone up for 364 days in the year, waiting for the 365th when one of our high-flying guinea fowl is on the menu, and pass on to the No. 3 Garden gun, whose uses are summed up tersely as "Just right for putting the fear of God into rats, cats and stray dogs".

"And rabbits," I add under my breath, rather hurt that he should not have remembered the day, long since past, when I went out with this gun and shot my one and only rabbit. Renewing acquaintance with this weapon of very miniature bore, I realise that this feat must either have shown remarkable luck, or remarkable marksmanship.

He extracts the rearguard, a rather solid-looking twelve-bore, wipes an imaginary speck of rust from its barrels with an oily rag, and makes a scowling pass at an illusionary pheasant soaring near the lamp bracket.

"Gun I got off old Thomas in exchange for those broody hens," he announces gloomily.

"What's the matter with it?" I inquire, rather relieved that the mystery of the disappearing broodies should, at last, have solved itself.

"Heavy," he growls, shaking his head. "Heavy as a ruddy crowbar; it'll kill at close range, but it wouldn't bust a bar-rage balloon at sixty yards."

Although his shoes are nearly always well clasped with the good clay and his coat invariably sags like a sack, his guns must always be groomed like show ponies. Aristocratic guns, it seems, should have blue barrels and grained stocks, which gleam with a rich patina. Until he found the perfect preparation for "bluing" barrels in the chemist's shop in the neighbouring town, he was wont to bemoan the unmellowed steel of his own armoury.

He tried everything, including an infallible recipe for colouring gun-barrels prescribed by a keeper in 1819. It was most unfortunate that the fashionable colour for gun-barrels in 1819 was a rich rusty red which took considerably longer to remove than to apply. Now he thinks he has found the perfect brew for french-polishing gun stocks and sits shining away, hopeful that they will come to gleam like coffin lids or grand pianos.

As the surface mellows, so does his mood. I am treated once again to his reflections on guns, past, present and to-be. I hear of his very first air-gun, with which he and his gang of budding poachers pot-shot the keeper's latter portion. Of the series of antique muzzle-loaders which alarmed the neighbourhood, and of the punt-gun, of great age and doubtful safety, which they tied to a gate post and then detonated, by yanking the lanyard, from behind an improvised air-raid shelter.

I hear of guns carelessly fouled by mother earth, whose barrels split like a half-peeled banana; and of the rifle with the telescopic sight, which he trained on a distant rabbit, only to find, just at the very moment he was about to squeeze the trigger, that it was also trained on the vicar's wife, picking primroses in direct line astern.

I cast a doubtful glance at the figure polishing with such concentration—who says that juvenile delinquency is just a modern problem?

The chronicle of the halt and the lame, picked up at auctions for a song, continues. I hear of guns that would fire, guns that wouldn't fire, and guns that would, but unexpectedly. I hear of guns sold for profit, guns chucked on the scrap heap, guns which came to a tragic end, such as the one whose stock was shattered in finishing off the rabbit the barrels had failed to kill.

His eyes assume a wistful expression. "That was the gun," he rhapsodises: "Light-balanced—handled like a Rolls. Worth a hundred quid at least. Kill anything, anywhere, anytime. Had it from old thingamme's sale; silly old fool had fired too heavy a load in it and bust the lock. I never dared to use it —too risky!"

"Why on earth didn't you solder or weld it?" I inquire, mindful of his slap-happy repair of other farm implements.

His look of pained deprecation makes it very plain that it is not customary to solder or weld guns.

In his philosophy no activity on earth is more important than a day's shooting. Whistling more loudly than the incessant downpour, he will set off blithely for a day's hard labour, through oceans of waist-high kale, shoals of sodden beet and turbulent seas of foaming bracken, with only an extra pair of trousers and a small supply of very dry sandwiches between him and slow death by drowning.

And when he returns at night, soaked, famished and wearied, does he remove his saturated garments, yell for his supper, or inquire after the sow that produced the sixteen during his absence—with me as sole midwife? No—self-negligent as a prudent horseman, he will fetch me his pull-through and bottle of cleaning oil and will give that faithful firing-piece a thorough grooming.

And as he grooms, his eyes will have that grim and calculating glint, which forebodes an act of major surgery— perhaps he'll load the butt with lead, or maybe he'll just take a saw and shorten it by two or three inches. Its deficiencies must be remedied, no weapon can ever . . . shall ever . . . be allowed to come between a good marksman and his target.

KAY TARRANT

The Farmer

My Father is a farmer,
He's proud of it too,
As 'e works through the day,
'E'll sing to you.

O, blest be a farmer,
O, blest be 'is day,
O, blest be a farmer,
For ever and ai.

'E works in the cornfield,
'E works in the ploughed,
'E brings us the bread,
And of that we are proud.

'E brings us the milk,
Both even and morn
'E'll work to 'is death
From the day 'e was born.

O, blest be a farmer,
O, blest be his day,
O, blest be a farmer
For ever and ai.

'E works in the rain,
And 'e works in the sun,
'E sows and 'e reaps,
'Til the day be done.

'E's tanned with the wind,
'E's 'ardened and brown,
'is face is as old
As Willoby Down.

O, but my father's a farmer,
'E's worked for 'is due,
Oi'm proud of my father,
Well, wouldn't you be too?

SUSAN TRERISE (*age 15*)

🌺 DORCHESTER

"Bye," we called. "Goodbye. Let us know if we can do anything." And Margaret was borne away from us on the London train. She was off to Secretarial College, having spent two nights with us on the way.

And that, we thought, as we turned back to the Land-Rover, is the last we shall see of her. A pity, because she was pretty and very glamorous. For that reason the bright lights were obviously for her—not the mud of our farm.

As if to show how wrong we were, a telegram arrived a week later—"Piglet arriving by 7.15 please meet stop Margaret."

I read it through three times and told the waiting boy, "No reply." Then I took it out to my husband in the rick yard. We decided that either Margaret—it must be that Margaret for the message came from South Kensington—or ourselves, were mad. I would have to find out. Anyway we could not have the pig because there'd been an outbreak of swine fever near by. Although we have no pigs it still affected us.

Indoors I spent half an hour finding Margaret's telephone number. Her landlady answered and I waited while Margaret must have come down from the highest garret.

Yes, it was Margaret's wire all right and she was terribly sorry, but could we do something? We were the only people she knew in the country. I said we were sorry and explained why not and how had she come by it? She'd won it.

"Won it, how?"

"Oh, in a tombola, at the Dorchester actually."

She asked to speak to Robert. She was sure she could persuade him. It was really the sweetest little pig. But a bit difficult in London, that was all.

I thrust the receiver at Robert, but he remained firm. No pig until restrictions were lifted. In the end Margaret said she would write all her problems in a letter and Robert promised he would answer them.

The letter which arrived next morning would have made "Nurse Grey's Postbag" look silly. It began with Dorchester's weight (as a guide to age), worked through his present diet and an attempted walk in Green Park to his wonderfully clean

"habits", and ended with the thought, "What if the landlady discovers him?" Then there was a postscript saying that Margaret's boy friends were all most kind about Dorchester, but none of them could help as we could.

Robert had me send "Teach Yourself Pig Keeping" and "The Artificial Rearing of Pigs" by express post. He also put in a note to the effect that Dorchester's presence in Margaret's bed sit. could well be explained away—He was young Lord Dorchester who had unfortunately been turned into a pig by an ill-wishing fairy. As in all the best stories he only needed to be loved to be cured. . . . On second thoughts I took the note out.

The following Sunday a suave green sports car came down the drive and a young man in suede shoes got out, shutting the door hastily behind him. He introduced himself as David Willoughby-Drake. With him was Dorchester.

We were so sorry for the poor boy (the pig had got loose in his car) that Dorchester had to stay. With David's help we prepared a loose box, my husband grumbling all the while. He hates pigs.

According to David it was really all his fault, he bought the tombola ticket. Well, then we got Dorchester out of the car. He was a Tamworth—ginger and obviously a runt. He took life very seriously for a pig, but cheered up when put into the box and dived headlong into the straw. David went back to his car and proceeded to muck it out.

When Margaret comes down next week-end she will see Dorchester's litter—ten more tiny Dorchesters. She is with us quite frequently now. The reason being, I think, that none of her London boy friends have the remotest idea about farming and she must find a suitor with a farm, or at least an estate—for Dorchester.

I hope she is successful soon.

DAPHNE LIDDELL

THE SMELL OF THE PAST

. . . It was my own little home—and . . . I smelt it suddenly—on the road, when I called and you wouldn't listen, Rat—and everything came back to me with a rush—and I wanted it! O dear, O dear—and when you wouldn't turn back, Ratty—and I had to leave it, though I was smelling it all the time—I thought my heart would break—We might have just gone and had one look at it, Ratty—only one look— it was close by—but you wouldn't turn back, Ratty, you wouldn't turn back! O dear, O dear!*

Driving back with my mother this summer from an agricultural show we passed the lane that leads down to the house where my sister and I spent every holiday from the time we were five to when we left school. It was my grandmother's house and my second home.

"Do let's pop down and see what it looks like," I said to my mother on an impulse. My grandmother had been dead many years now, we'd never been back since and had no idea who now owned it.

We parked the car at the top of the lane and walked down between the avenue of fir trees which somehow looked far smaller than when I was last there.

One of the fascinating things about returning to a place one has known intimately after a gap of years is the way familiar objects immediately recall happenings which until that moment had completely disappeared from one's mind and memory. And one of the nicest things about my mother is that she has the most satisfactory reactions to a mumbo-jumbo of thoughts being spoken out loud. For from the moment I had passed the third fir tree I began to remember things and to anyone but her the "oh my goodnesses" and "well I'm bothereds" and "who would have thought-its" would have been both incoherent and tedius.

My dear Mama, however, responded to all of it in just the

* *From* "The Wind in the Willows" *by Kenneth Grahame. Reprinted by courtesy of the Secretary to the Curators of the University Press, Oxford.*

right way to make this little excursion enjoyable for both of us. Particularly since I recalled little happenings of my childhood of which until that moment she had been ignorant. I was even providing her with the odd little shock which in those days would have given her cause for anxiety but which now merely served to amuse her.

"You don't mean to say you came up here after dark," she said, as one particularly menacing old fir tree reminded me of the fright my sister and I both had on one of our moonlit flits up here with a loaf of bread and a lump of cheese we'd pinched from the larder. . . . I could see old Willy's face now, staring at us from behind that tree. We didn't dare scream for fear of being caught out there in the middle of the night, but we flew—heavens how we flew, and I could remember how we collapsed on our beds panting with fright and relief that we'd reached home safely. Poor old Willy, I expect he enjoyed the abandoned bread and cheese. He was only the harmless half-dotty son of the old cowman, but to us children he was the ogre in the fairy tale and, as surely, one of the chief characters in our fantasy world. It certainly wouldn't have occurred to us to wish him out of it for all our dread.

We turned the corner of the lane and there was the house. Absolutely unchanged and looking just as it always did years ago when we turned the corner at the end of our afternoon walk as toddlers or swung round it on our bikes or ponies in later years.

There was the big bedroom window on the first floor at which my grandmother always sat and did her knitting and watched for our return. And where we had once seen her, having crept out early on a mushrooming expedition, doing her exercises. Arms forward—arms up—arms sideways . . . and "with only her petticoat on" we whispered to our unbelieving cousins when we got back to the nursery. There were whisperings amongst us for days after this for Granny in her neat buttoned-up-to-the-neck clothes was a fixed thing in our lives like the flower borders, the trees and the colour of the curtains. It would no more have occurred to us that Granny could be seen in a petticoat than the flowerbed in front of the dining-room window would have asters in it instead of antirrhinums.

We walked right up to the front door. There seemed to be nobody about so we went round to the back. And there, bent over double weeding the garden path, as I had seen him day after day, was old Alf Price. His back was towards us but I knew it was he. There's nothing so reliable as a shape that has carved itself into the back of a child's mind over a number of years.

He didn't recognise us at first. But when he did he kept shaking our hands till I thought he'd never stop. He bombarded my mother with questions about the family. My father—what was he doing now—my sister? On he went, waiting only the merest second for the answers.

"I'm still weeding the old path you see, Mum—don't suppose I've left off since I saw you last." And with that he slapped his leg and roared with laughter till I thought he'd burst.

"And don't you remember, Miss," he said, turning to me, "the day your grandma was so cross when you trotted down this 'ere path on your pony." And he slapped his leg again and burst out laughing. "Oh, I'll never forget that day," he said. "Never—thought she'd blow up, your grandma, I did. Never seen her that cross in all my life." And he laughed till the tears rolled down his weatherbeaten old face.

After he had mopped his face with his red spotted handkerchief again and again, he asked us if we'd like to see round the garden. "The folks are away this afternoon but they won't mind you looking round."

"Do you still put nails in those to keep them blue?" I asked Price as we walked past the big hydrangea bed. "Not nails any more, Miss," said Price gloomily, "but something out of a packet the Guv'nor says is just as good, but I still tells 'im they're nothing like as blue as they was in your grandma's time."

Then we came to the pond. The muddy old pond which was really the centrepiece, the main artery, the pivot—call it what you will—of our whole playtime existence in that place. And as I stood there and looked down at it the smell and even the silence spoke volumes. Covered with bright green duckweed in the summer, ice in the winter and splodgy with rain all the year round, it was an ocean to us. The means by which we travelled to all parts of the world in the space of an hour or an afternoon. We fought battles on it with matchbox boats. We played Nelson and Vasco da Gama from an old rowing boat which my father had used in his boyhood on this same pond. My grandmother's rockery was cliffs to be scaled.

"But where is the rockery?" I said, turning to Price. "I knew you'd be asking me that, Miss. It's there right enough under all that muck. I keeps meaning to get down to it but some'ow, what with them paths wantin' weedin', there never seems to be time." He shook his head sadly. "Your grandma would turn in 'er grave if she could see it now, that she would."

She certainly would, I thought to myself, for that rockery was her pride and joy. In fact, she spent most of her time tending it herself. And we children had to keep a sharp look-out for her when we were playing games which involved storming the heights, for if she ever found one of us within inches of her precious rock plants, "the rocket went up", as Price put it.

"And what's happened to Isabella?" I asked Price. "Don't tell me she's buried under all those weeds somewhere."

"'Fraid the Guv'nor sold the young lady to a gentleman who buys antiques," said Price sadly. "Oh, I did miss 'er when she went; in fact," he said, "if the truth be told I'm only just getting over it now and that were five year ago she went."

Isabella was a wooden ship's figurehead that my grandmother brought back from somewhere and stuck in the rockery at the turn of one of the little paths. She was an exceedingly decorative young woman and we were all devoted to her. Every spring Isabella received her annual make-up at the hands of Price. It was a very serious business and we always sat on the nearest rock and watched the whole process from start to finish. First he would paint her dress all white. Then her bodice blue, her hair black and her eyes pale blue. But the moment we waited for was when he painted her mouth cherry red. When he had finished, I don't mind telling you, Isabella looked anything but a respectable young woman, which was rather odd, since Price was one of the most proper of men. His wife and daughters were, to say the least of it, plainly turned out and he was always scorning the goings on of the modern miss. Yet there he was every spring putting paint on Isabella's lips as thick and bright as any Hollywood star's.

Perhaps Price's imagination ran as much riot in that rockery as ours did—who can tell?

BARBARA HARGREAVES

DEFINITION

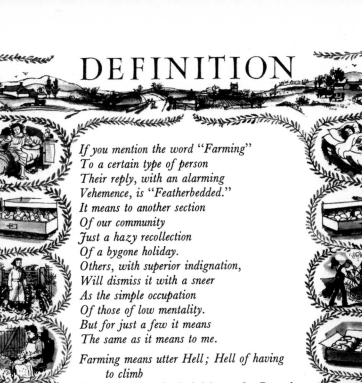

If you mention the word "Farming"
To a certain type of person
Their reply, with an alarming
Vehemence, is "Featherbedded."
It means to another section
Of our community
Just a hazy recollection
Of a bygone holiday.
Others, with superior indignation,
Will dismiss it with a sneer
As the simple occupation
Of those of low mentality.
But for just a few it means
The same as it means to me.

Farming means utter Hell; Hell of having
    to climb
Out of bed into the dark iciness of a December
    dawn
And it means sheer Heaven; Heaven at
    night-time
Of regaining bed's delicious warm embrace
    again.

Farming means Mobility; the undeniable,
    living mobility
Of an Incubator full of newly-hatched chicks
And it means Sterility; the futile, dead
    sterility
Of trays of eggs that failed to hatch.

Farming means Mud; Mud deep, sucky, black,
Or slippery Mud, making all movement a
    slithery skate.
And it means Sun; Sun beating on your back
Like a blessing when you're making hay.

DEFINITION

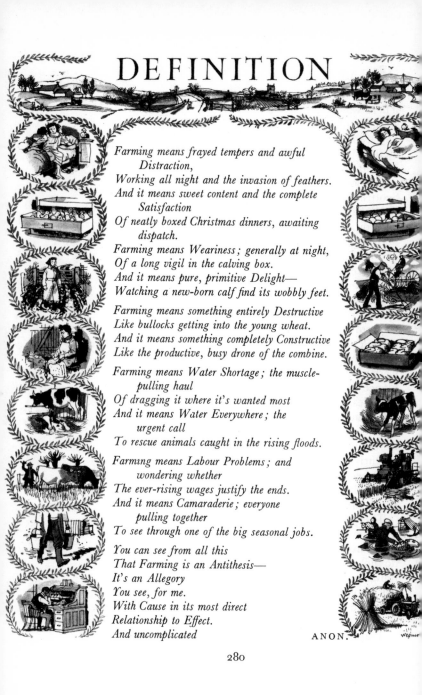

Farming means frayed tempers and awful
    Distraction,
Working all night and the invasion of feathers.
And it means sweet content and the complete
    Satisfaction
Of neatly boxed Christmas dinners, awaiting
    dispatch.
Farming means Weariness; generally at night,
Of a long vigil in the calving box.
And it means pure, primitive Delight—
Watching a new-born calf find its wobbly feet.

Farming means something entirely Destructive
Like bullocks getting into the young wheat.
And it means something completely Constructive
Like the productive, busy drone of the combine.

Farming means Water Shortage; the muscle-
    pulling haul
Of dragging it where it's wanted most
And it means Water Everywhere; the
    urgent call
To rescue animals caught in the rising floods.

Farming means Labour Problems; and
    wondering whether
The ever-rising wages justify the ends.
And it means Camaraderie; everyone
    pulling together
To see through one of the big seasonal jobs.

You can see from all this
That Farming is an Antithesis—
It's an Allegory
You see, for me.
With Cause in its most direct
Relationship to Effect.
And uncomplicated

ANON.

280

❦ MAKERS OF MOLEHILLS

There was a time when a moleskin cloak was a considerable status symbol for a woman. Today, however, there is scarcely any trade in moleskins at all. The fur breeder and the manufacturer of synthetic furs have put paid to the commercial exploitation of the skins of moles.

Our local mole-catcher at Catcleugh, near Carter Bar on the Scottish border, has told me of the days when moles were well worth taking for their skins' sake.

"You could only trap them at certain times of year," he said "because when they were breeding the pelts smelt awful and nothing in the curing could get rid of the stink."

I once knew a labourer in our village who had a waistcoat made of moleskins. It certainly smelt terrible, but whether the moles which went to make up this garment had been caught in season, or the pelts had not been properly cured, I never learned.

Moleskin trousers for men were very popular towards the end of the last century, and the beginning of this one, but they were made of a velveteen cloth which had a superficial resemblance to moleskin.

Moles, like hyenas, were once believed to be hermaphrodites and this is understandable when it is realised that the female mole scarcely shows her sex at all until she is in a state to receive the male.

During the rutting period, the reproductive organs of both sexes become greatly enlarged and presumably it is during this season that moles become so odoriferous that their skins are not worth preserving.

There are still a number of professional mole-catchers about, but their main function today is to control the numbers of moles in a particular farming area. Actually moles themselves do not do much harm to agriculture—though they are a nuisance in a seed bed or a hay field.

On permanent pasture, moles may be a positive benefit provided the heaps are spread once they appear, but grassland studded with innumerable piles of earth is not a pretty sight.

Trapping moles is not a difficult job once you know the ways

of the animal, but the entire elimination of the moles of any
one area is well-nigh impossible as pairs always seem to survive.
Perhaps mole-catchers are like the old-time rabbit-trappers,
who always saw that a remnant of rabbits were left to ensure
their future income!

Moles are insectivores, and like their distant relatives, the
hedgehog and the shrews, they have colossal appetites for
their size. A mole will eat its own weight in worms every day.

Although he is a greedy feeder, the mole sometimes puts a
store of food aside, presumably for a lean period. This he does
by immobilising worms with a bite in their progressive end.
After this operation worms continue to live but they cannot
travel so that the mole has a hoard of fresh food against a
hungry day.

In the past, many naturalists believed that several of our
British wild animals were in the habit of hibernating throughout the winter months. This belief has now been mostly dis-
proved and only the dormouse in Britain is now regarded as a
true hibernator.

Moles, in company with hedgehogs and bats, were once
considered to be winter-sleepers. It is hard to say how this
belief persisted as mole heaps are always particularly noticeable
during snow or frost and their appearance during such periods,
in the depth of winter, is a very common indication that they
are active.

Moles are amongst the animal world's greatest excavators.
With their powerful shoulders and spade-like hands, armed
with tough nails, they can travel underground at a great rate.
In many ways, much of our modern earth-shifting machinery
has a lot in common with them.

HENRY TEGNER

🌷 A TURKISH BATH

If you really want to know the nearest thing to Hell you should
try a Turkish bath. I know, because I was there last week.
I had never been to one before and had certainly never con-

sidered the idea of ever going, but it all happened as a result of a perfectly innocent lunch with a friend of mine who had come up to London for the day.

I had thought that I was going to escort her round a few shops to give a helpful second opinion on her choice of a spring suit, but halfway through lunch she suddenly announced that she was going to a Turkish bath ". . . and hang the spring suit! What's more," she said, "you are coming with me . . . make you twice the girl . . . do you all the good in the world . . ." and so on.

Well, I went. It all sounded a lot of hard work to me, but I consoled myself with visions of myself emerging from the place like a dewy milkmaid. Besides, it would be a great deal more restful than tramping round after the right suit.

The building looming out of the London winter looked more like a prison than a place of indulgence. We paid our five shillings at the box office and entered. No Turkish carpets, no eastern scents, no yashmaks, but a linoleum-covered hall with cubicles all round and a fat, white, uniformed attendant reading *Woman's Own*.

I stood waiting for instructions when, to my amazement, across the lino came a creature of uneven dimensions draping a very small portion of her anatomy with a very small towel. She was scarlet and looked exhausted. I almost ran to help her when it suddenly dawned on me that the poor thing was at the end of an experience that I was about to begin.

My companion appeared not to notice her and ushered me into a cubicle next to hers. Now I am not a prude, but I must confess to being slightly diffident about removing all my clothes and emerging among strangers draped in a handkerchief. But of course I needn't have worried, as you will see.

"What I like about all this," said the voice next door, "is the moral boost it gives you looking at all the others—I always come away thinking I have a figure like Ava Gardner." Later, I understood the significance of this remark.

We descended to the lower floor—hissing hot air rose up to meet us. "We had better book our massage now or we'll never get one," I was told, and my friend disappeared into a tiny little office where three large women attendants, partially clothed, had wedged themselves in for a gossip. If these were the masseuses all I can say is they were poor advertisements for their trade, and very depressing for those who came here as often as once a week to take off weight, to see such stubborn poundage on women who spent every day in the place.

I booked somebody called Florrie for a massage in an hour's time.

That done I was introduced to the "vapour" room which looked exactly like my kitchen when I've left a boiling kettle on the stove—what it felt like was nobody's business.

Through the vapour I saw dim shapes sitting about. I supposed they were alive. I looked at the thermometer on the wall—it read 140°. I remembered reading how a 90° in-the-shade heat wave had killed off dozens of people in New York last year.

I was just managing to arrange my breathing in order to stay alive when the door opened and an old lady draped in a large bath towel came in. She sat down on the wooden seat as much at ease as if she had been in her own drawing-room. She said to me, "I wonder, my dear, if you would mind looking at the thermometer; I haven't got my spectacles with me," as calmly as if she had asked me to go out into the hall to look at the barometer.

"We'd better go down to the dry heat now," said my friend. Was it a dream or did Dante's *Inferno* describe Hell as being three stages of torture?

As I closed the vapour door behind me I saw a notice hanging on the handle which read NO FRUIT DOWNSTAIRS. This could only mean that the clientele of this establishment were the sort who left orange peel and grape pips about. I wondered whether I would have been wiser to have gone a bust at a less cheap bath up West.

The dry-heated room was more cheerfully lit and gave me a chance to have a look at some of my bath mates more closely. I have never been a great admirer of the human form, the beaches of England fail to convince one otherwise, and I have also often wondered whether the beautiful Greeks were more highly evolved beings or whether it was just that their sculptors were over-romantic. But if you ever doubted for a second that man was the higher animal then go to a Turkish bath to drive away your doubt, for there you will see such a variety of astonishing shapes—the like of which would make a hippopotamus green with envy.

Suddenly in the midst of all that torpidity, I felt strongly convinced that all of us would do far better to go for a long walk across a ploughed field on a frosty day in tweed up to our necks.

I tried the really hot room just to be devilish and only the devil could have stayed more than a minute, for the floor was so hot that I did a "cat on hot bricks" tiptoe round the room and fled.

I forgot to mention that up to now the silence (for there are notices everywhere saying SILENCE REQUESTED) was disturbed every so often by sounds like the distant beating of drums. Somehow it seemed rather appropriate in this sort of Malayan jungle atmosphere. I asked someone what it was and discovered that it was one of Florrie's team at work in the massage room, the drums being somebody's extra inches, the drumsticks Florrie's fists. But it was now 5.10 and time to listen to my own drums.

The massage room looked like a sort of butcher's back room—all marble slabs. Florrie told me to get up on one of these and no sooner was I flat on my back than she threw a bucket of water over me. She then proceeded to knock me about. After which she took what looked like an enormous whitewash brush which she swept across a cake of washing soap and lathered me all over. I couldn't make up my mind whether I was an old tug being tarred, or a side of bacon being cured. There was certainly no human element in it.

After the lathering Florrie beat me up again . . . "You aren't half coming up nicely," she informed me. I opened my eyes expecting to find myself covered in weals and bruises, but what she meant was that she was getting me a nice pink.

Florrie threw another bucket of water over me and I was done.

Hosing was to be the final stage, and Florrie led me to what did, indeed, look like the ideal place to clean your car. She stood me up against the wall, walked back a few paces, turned on a tap and literally fired at me with the hose. After a minute or two she turned off the tap and wrapped me in a decently large towel. I slipped her a shilling and walked upstairs to freedom.

As we walked towards the car, my friend and I, she said, "I'm absolutely walking on air ... it's really as good as a tonic ... I feel years younger ...." etc., etc., ad nauseam.

All I know is that I felt as if I were just recovering from a long illness. Never again.

BARBARA HARGREAVES

🌸 APPLES IN MY PINNY

It is a long time since I wore a pinny—or to give it its full name—a pinafore, in fact it was during the first World War. I was one of a large family and lived in a small country town in Derbyshire.

Going to school was my first big adventure and this did not mean hopping on a bus at the end of the road, drinking milk from a bottle with a straw or eating a subsidised dinner in company with three hundred others. I set off on a two-mile walk at the age of four and a half with an older brother and sister. There was no school uniform but my sister and I were always dressed alike in sprigged poplin blouses, dark serge tunics, stout black boots—and of course a clean starched pinny. On weekdays the pinny was fairly plain with two shoulder frills and what was called "needlework" yoke but on Sundays and special occasions the yoke had pale pink or blue ribbon threaded through it.

There were two ways of going to school—either by the road or over the meadows. In winter the road was preferable though sometimes even that was impassable, so deep were the snowdrifts. I am solemnly assured by my brother that on one occasion when he was taking me to school on a particularly bad day he looked down to see only my small gloved hand protruding—the rest of me was under the snowdrift!

After climbing the iron bridge over the little railway we went through a small wood thick with ferns, bluebells, harebells—and even a few grass-snakes! Once past the quarry the path led straight through two fields until it joined the road and then school was in sight.

The school was a grey stone one-storey building smelling of ink, chalk-dust and wet raincoats, but it had glass jars of wild flowers on the window-sills and hot-water pipes that we sat on in winter despite threats of mysterious illnesses resulting thereby. The cloakrooms were dark and damp and possessed no looking-glasses, so we improvised by one person standing on one side of a window and holding up a dark coat so that the person on the other side could see herself. Whenever I hear the expression "see through a glass darkly", I feel I know exactly what it means.

Playtime then wasn't really very different from playtime today except that there were one or two skipping games that I never seem to hear now. I can well remember "taking my end" and chanting with the rest:

> Queen, Queen Caroline,
> Washed her hair in turpentine,
> Turpentine made it shine,
> Queen, Queen Caroline.

Another jingle which I haven't heard since then ran something like this:

> I like cocoa, I like tea,
> I like sitting on a black man's knee,
> Down in the cellar, see my Auntie Bella,
> Sitting on a black man's knee.

One of our favourite games was "fivestones", but that wasn't our name for it—we called it "snobs", why I never knew. Our set of "snobs" consisted of four square coloured stones and one white pot ball called a "potty". My children dissolve into laughter when I tell them about this, but there was nothing funny about the name when we used it then.

Besides my sandwiches I was always given a penny to spend. The spending of this penny was a matter for weighty consideration. There were only two shops in the village—the post-office, which sold everything from stamps to sticking-plaster and butter to bootlaces, or the little "house-window" sweet shop. This was kept by an old lady suffering from a severe goitre or "Derbyshire neck" as we called it. I was acutely aware of this affliction and was thankful that the shop was so dark that I needn't see her very well.

In the autumn my penny was not spent on sweets. I crossed the street and went down the lane to one of the neighbouring farms and asked for a pennyworth of apples. Back came the farmer's wife with a deep crock of golden russets. "Hold out your pinny, love," she said, and I obligingly held up the two bottom corners. Down tumbled the luscious apples—two, four, six, eight, I never knew how many—it was just a pinny-ful.

And as I sauntered off to the fields with my bulging pinny I knew that I had at least another half-hour before the school-bell would ring. The sky was blue, the scent of the hay was rich and heady, and I felt that nature had indeed poured her riches into my lap.

AGNES KENNETT

DOWN A GARDEN PATH

When we first came to our cottage we found it a real problem to keep the main pathway presentable.

This path is of the type common to old country gardens—flat stones of varying shapes and sizes, with a wide border running alongside made up of pebbles and stone chippings.

It was this pebbly part of the pathway that created our problem, for every weed imaginable (and others besides!) came to settle there and raise their offspring.

I thought of laying concrete but I didn't really like the idea.

I hesitated to use weedkillers because here and there amongst the unwelcome guests I had unearthed scraps of aubretia and seedling primroses.

It was from these self-sown plants that I got the idea of

utilising the stones and turning the pebbly part of the pathway into a sort of moraine or scree.

I made a list of plants which it seemed might prove happy under such conditions, and as they were practically all available in pots I was able to buy a few at a time, and to spread out the plantings from early spring into the late autumn.

Generous deep holes were scooped out of the stones, the space filled with good sandy loam, and in the little plants went. I was careful to loosen the ball of roots first, so that they had an immediate chance to seek fresh nourishment, and except when the weather happened to be ideally showery all plants were watered in.

I was very lucky because not a single thing was lost, and now, some years later, the plants have spread and merged into a colourful fragrant carpet.

For the better part of the year it is a riot of bloom, beginning in the spring with clusters of snowdrops, purple, mauve and white violets, and aubretias ranging through all the shades from pink to crimson, and pale blue to purple. There are great sheets of golden alyssum, pink and crimson saxifrage, the white perennial candytuft, and primroses in a glorious range of colours. (These, incidentally, provide odd blooms all through the winter months, except when the cold is unusually severe.)

In the summer the thymes come into their own. *Thymus serpyllum* and the two varieties, *coccineus* and Annie Hall, the one producing flowers of rich crimson, the other pale pink. There is silver thyme and golden thyme, and one whose scent is suggestive of caraway seeds, and another which smells exactly like lemons. These thymes are in bloom from June to August, and how the bees love them!

About this time, too, the fragrant dianthus are in flower, and tiny violas and rock roses, whose bright blossoms are enhanced by the sober grey of the leaves. Dwarf phlox appear in all sorts of gay colours, and *veronica prostrata* flaunts flowers of gentian blue alongside a creeping scarlet verbena.

Houseleeks are included as much for their fleshy rosettes of leaves as for their flowers, for these remain attractive even in mid-winter. *Achilleas* and santolina are also valued for their foliage, which is a lovely silvery grey, as also is that rampant grower popularly known as Snow-in-Summer. There is a blue flowered ajuga too, with leaves the colour of copper beech, and these are as glossily beautiful in December as June.

In addition, effective use has been made of carpeting plants such as camomile, the creeping mint, *mentha requueni*, various *arenarias*, and *raouli australis*, appropriately nick-named silver fur.

LEE DENNY

🌹 PLAYING AT FAUST

Anybody looking through my kitchen window last Saturday might have imagined I was either playing at Faust or indulging in a spot of opium smoking. All I was doing, in fact, was bottling off my apple wine but it involved my sitting on the floor in order to be low enough down to get the wine started through the rubber tube.

I needn't have sat on the floor at all, of course. I realised that after I had done all my bottling. What I should have done was to have put the big jar of wine on a stool on top of the table and achieved the fall that way, but that just shows you how clottish an averagely intelligent person can be.

How I managed to get off the kitchen floor at all after the operation I can't imagine, for starting off the flow through the tube from jar to bottle gives you a fair swig of the stuff and as I'm only a beginner at the game of wine-making I swallowed a good deal more than I needed to each time. And it's very potent stuff!

A good deal nicer, however, than goldfish water, which I tried hard not to swallow once when I had to clean out their tank by the same process.

But I'm an amateur at it all right. I must have wasted a good half-bottle on the floor and what didn't go down my throat went down my neck.

I was as usual defeated by my total inability to do two things at once. For while I was concentrating on keeping one end out of the sediment at the bottom of the big jar, I'd forget I'd got the other end in my mouth and I would suddenly find my cheeks bulging like a trumpeter and the bottle out of reach. Then panic, with me trying to pinch the end of the tube to stop the flow and having to swallow what I'd got in my face all at one go. I couldn't get to the basin to spit it out because I daren't let go of the end of the tube. All that was necessary at that moment was for the Vicar to call. He would have to have passed me the bottle before I could say "Good afternoon" to him!

Eventually the wine was all safely gathered into six Hock bottles, which I stuck at the back of the larder with a sack over them to forget until Christmas.

BARBARA HARGREAVES

SCUFFLES AND SQUEAKS

Strange that a prettily formed little animal with fur like feather-down, puck-like ears and baby brown eyes should strike mute terror in the hearts of some of the toughest, most emancipated women of today.

Stranger still that the bedtime stories some of these women read to their little ones are so often about these charming little creatures dressed up in gingham dresses and Kate Greenaway pants . . . "Mummy Tittlemouse said to Daddy Tittlemouse, etc., etc. . . ."

As for the picture of the terrified woman standing on a kitchen stool with her skirts pulled up round her knees while a mouse scampers round the floor, I thought it had been painted by an artist with a special licence.

This is not to say that I myself have a deep affection for the little creatures, but they certainly don't give me any chills up my spine, and as long as I'm not kept awake at night I've no objection to their keeping house in my wainscots.

About a month ago, however, it did occur to me that their

numbers were increasing and that perhaps I ought to do something about it. And once or twice when I'd had to chuck a bedroom slipper at the wall to stop their squeaks I swore I'd obliterate the lot; but when I woke up next morning I forgot all about it.

And then shortly after this an old friend of mine telephoned me from the north of Scotland, where she lived, to say that she was making one of her rare visits to the south and could we put her up for a few days.

"Certainly," I said, "but you'll have to look after yourself for three days while I'm up at the office."

Oh that would be quite all right, she said. She'd look after the house for us—she wouldn't be bored—she was just going to enjoy breathing in the air of the south and having a change.

I made her welcome on the Sunday and on Monday morning departed for the office.

Rather guilty of having neglected my guest for three solid days, I arrived home on Thursday night full of plans for her weekend's entertainment.

A lovely smell of cooking meat met me as I opened the door and there was my visitor in the kitchen busy grilling chops. "Oh you angel," I said, "I'm starving."

I noticed then that her reactions were not of the ebullient kind which, being one of the warmest-hearted people I know, were usual to her. Though maybe that was because I was being too hearty for words. But then I noticed that as she turned the chop over on the griller her hand was shaking violently.

"Rosemary," I said, "whatever's wrong?"

She sat down on the kitchen chair and burst into tears.

This was so completely unlike her that I knew there must be something really the matter.

I made a pot of tea—that old brown magic—and took her and it into the sitting-room. All sorts of possibilities of what might be wrong galloped through my mind . . . she'd lost her money . . . her dog, her cat, her necklace. Perhaps she was ill. Could the doctor have told her something awful. . . .

"Now come on," I said as I poured her a cup of tea, "you've just got to tell me."

"I hardly dare," she murmured, "I feel such an absolute ass, such a complete fool . . . I'm such a coward . . . but the fact is I'm absolutely petrified of mice."

It was difficult not to burst out laughing with relief alone, but I could see she was really very, very upset.

When one is not in the least frightened by a particular thing such as this, it is essential, in order to understand even minutely another person's distress, to bring some parallel fear of one's own to mind. With me it was snakes. Once, to my shame, I had run all the way down the river bank away from a harmless grass-snake curled up on the path.

I told her this. Whereupon she seemed to relax somewhat and words began to pour forth.

"From the moment you left," she said, "they were running about the place like—er—like mice"; and here she actually raised a laugh. "I was sitting in the bath one night," she went on, "and one actually came and sat on the bath mat and cleaned its whiskers; I didn't dare move. I had to sit there till the water went cold before it moved off."

"And when I was doing a bit of dusting," she continued, "they seemed to run out from behind every piece of furniture. In the end I clapped my hands loudly before I entered a room; I sometimes even took one of the dogs and pushed it in front of me. But the worst part about the whole thing was feeling such a complete darn fool and not being able to do anything about it. I can understand now how a snake can paralyse a rabbit into immobility."

"Oh, please don't mention those things," I said purposely with my hand over my eyes. And that made her laugh again a little.

"Right," I said, taking the tea tray into the kitchen, "we'll deal with these little monsters right away tonight."

The tin of Anti-Mouse took some looking for. I knew it was somewhere for my mother had presented it to me during one of her visits. "It's the only stuff," she had told me, but I had only half listened; not only because I'm used to my mother's ravings about brand names, but because at that time I was untroubled by mice.

I found the tin eventually in the cupboard where I keep my spares—things like tinned fruit and jam for emergencies, extra flower vases—and to my horror it was standing alongside a tin of Benger's Food which I keep for rare invalids. I say "to my horror" for the two tins were exactly the same colour. What if . . .

But I needn't have worried for when I opened it the powder was of a deep blue colour and could not have been mistaken for Daz by even the most absent-minded of my family.

For three solid days I conducted my mouse campaign like a female Napoleon, placing my little saucers of blue powder in strategic positions, replacing the ammunition when used up and switching positions where fire was not drawn.

After three days there wasn't a sign of a scuffle or a squeak. And Rosemary was noticeably in a much more relaxed state of mind.

"Don't you remember that old nursery rhyme," I said as I helped her pack her bag one evening to go home, "you're a farmer's wife, aren't you, you should have chased round after those mice with a carving knife!"

"If you remember," she replied, "those particular mice were supposed to be blind—and the worst thing about a mouse is those little beady eyes." She gave a shudder. "Don't remind me of them."

When I put my weekly telephone call through to my Mama I told her how effective her Anti-Mouse had been. At that she did a whole lot more raving. ". . . and the most marvellous thing about the stuff is the way the mice disappear . . ." she exclaimed.

"Where do they go then?" I said.

"Oh, I don't know," she said crossly, "and I don't want to know, but they disappear."

Magic doesn't convince me and a couple of days ago I distinctly smelt something nasty in the spare bedroom. If it doesn't go away I suppose I shall have to have those floorboards up next weekend.

BARBARA HARGREAVES

🌹 THE BIRTH OF A TATTIE-BOGLE

As a bairn I often assisted at the birth of a tattie-bogle. It was usually the herd who supervised the accouchement, using what he called a "stuckin'-post" to serve as vital statistics or sometimes an old bussm shank which he set up in a strategic position in the midst of a field of adolescent turnips.

"Shouldn't it be called a 'neep-bogle'?" I once asked him in one of my rare brighter moments.

The herd had more to do than listen to my flights of fancy and seldom gave me any answer other than a grunt. But on this occasion he added a look and said gruffly, "Howts', ca' it what ye like, lassie, as lang's it keeps awa' the speugs an the hoodie craws. We'll need to cleid it. Awa' an' fetch some auld duds."

This was the part I liked best, for it was not until the bogle was "cleid" that it took on a personality. I hurried importantly to rummage in the old kist in the garret, and the results of my researches determined not only the characteristics but also the sex of the newly-born bogle.

Though it was more often a male who emerged, with a tattered tweed topcoat hiding his wooden body, there were times, depending on what I had unearthed in the garret, when a lady-bogle materialised with trailing skirt, hug-me-tight and hat bedecked with faded flowers. There was even one unfortunate occasion when we mixed the sexes and dressed the bogle in plus-fours, moth-eaten chiffon blouse, feather boa and bowler hat.

"Howts, what's the odds?" grunted the herd. "The craws'll no' ken the difference."

I was not so sure. The birds seemed to sense when a bogle meant business, and fled from the field when they saw one, fearsome and forbidding, flapping his empty sleeves in the breeze. But they soon fraternised with another who stood woodenly among the turnips, too fushionless to frighten them away.

Some of the bogles stick in my memory because of their

strong personalities—particularly The Man Who Broke The Bank At Monte Carlo. There he stood with an independent air and a straw-basher perched rakishly on his head, sporting a striped blazer and an old pair of patched pyjamas. He looked the picture of gaiety as the wind filled his flannelette legs.

Gentleman Joe was an entirely different character, so respectable with his lum hat, swallow-tailed coat and dark trousers that he might have been an elder at the kirk plate. Even the herd showed some respect for him and remarked, "Ay, man, ye look every inch a Christian"; and the birds, after circling enquiringly round him, flew off with their feathers fluffed out and kept their distance.

But I think I was fondest of the Highland gentleman, Roderick Dhu, with his tattered kilt and Balmoral bunnet. The herd made him a face of sorts and stuck an old pipe in it, and "Man," said he, regarding his handiwork with pardonable pride, "I've seen waur in the waxworks."

I used to worry about the bogles when it was raining and on one occasion, much to the herd's disgust, fixed up a tattered parasol over the head of Mary-Ann, one of our lady-bogles.

She was clad in bedraggled finery, with a sequined dolman over her shoulders and a long feather fluttering from her hat; and I was sure that if she had any blood in her veins it was bright blue. She stood so straight and looked so lady-like—until the sad day when a gale toppled her on to her side and her namesake, Mary-Ann the cow, got into the field and ate the feather off her hat.

On moonlight nights, if I keeked far enough out of my bedroom window, I could see the turnip-field with its silent watchman still keeping guard.

But surely he was moving; I could see him waving to me and pirouetting round in his kilt. And that was real smoke, wasn't it, puffing from his pipe?

Even though I had seen his beginnings from the "stuckin'-post" or bussm shank, I was never quite sure that he was inanimate. The herd might accuse me of having "a heid fou' o' daft notions", but who could be positive that a bogle was only a piece of wood and "auld duds"?

LAVINIA DERWENT

BILBERRIES AND BLUE TONGUES

"Like to come along? We're going 'wurtling'," said my hostess when I had arrived after toiling uphill on a warm August day at her house perched on the edge of the fells a mile from the station.

"Rather," said I, not being quite sure what "wurtling" was. But when she began to put on her heftiest shoes and armed the two children with baskets and crooked sticks, I groaned inwardly as I realised I was in for some sort of a hike. My ignorance about "wurtling" was quickly dispelled. Bilberries, of course. How could I have forgotten their local name! Whortleberries or "wurts", blueberries—blaeberries—to give them their botanical name, *Vaccinium myrtillus*—grow in high places on tops of hills, moors, fells, and, of course, we had to climb. Over rocks and boulders, dry stone walls, if there wasn't a convenient gate, among bracken and heather, across moorland streams with stepping stones by which the peaty brown water swirled, finally reaching the heights where the small blue-black berries were ripe. They grow on tiny shrubby plants, their green leaves having a reddish tint. First the berries are green, then a waxy red, then a deep indigo with a grape-like bloom. When cooked they are of incomparable richness.

Climbing in the fresh air on the moor, I forgot I had been treid when I started, the wind was exhilarating and blew my unscarfed hair in all directions. The soft springy grass was warm under my feet and with delight I gazed at the miles of moorland stretching to the horizon in a purple haze. Heather was in bloom, intermingled with splashes of out-of-season gorse, and it was quite hard to keep one's mind on the picking of bilberries—though it mattered little! My thoughts flew off at all kinds of tangents while I searched for the elusive little fruits.

The children, full of energy and excitement, followed the path up the hillside towards the pile of rocks at the top. Their interest in picking bilberries was somewhat superficial, though having eaten a few raw ones and screamed with laughter at their purple tongues, and spilled the few they had gathered, they appeared to be thoroughly enjoying the day out.

Up on the moor the bilberries grew in profusion, in patches and clumps, and the crop was a good one. My hostess and I managed to pick about four pounds of berries between us, no mean feat, when you find how intermittently they bear their fruit. She considered this a good harvest. "I shall make a tidy bit of jam with them," she declared.

Bilberry jam is especially rich and delicious, not so seedy as blackcurrant, but somewhat similar in colour and consistency. If a little apple is added, it makes the berries go farther and set well. They bottle very satisfactorily, too, and are most succulent in pies and tarts, or simply stewed with a little sugar or honey. My hostess served some for tea, stewed, with thin pastry fingers and large dollops of thick cream. Definitely they were worth the trouble we had taken to pick them, and the children's falls into the brook where the stepping stones were wobbly and all the other minor calamities that accompany children on a day out; and the blue tongues that were the order of the evening!

The bilberry, I believe, was originally a native of Scandinavia, but it has become acclimatised in this country on the high hills in Scotland, the Pennines, Dartmoor, the Yorkshire moors—and particularly on Ilkley moor where you always get a good blow if you go "baht 'at". But whether you tramp the heathery stretches around Leith Hill in Surrey or tackle the boggy sides of Ingleborough or Whernside, the fascinating fells, or any other moorland, be it in Dorset or Derbyshire, you will find bilberries only at the high levels.

In Canada blueberry pie is a great favourite, and this is the same kind of fruit, slightly larger and more prolific and, I believe, much more common. I wonder no one has troubled to cultivate this delectable berry, because it has a distinctive flavour of its own unlike any other fruit.

There are sometimes other berries growing in the near vicinity of bilberries, but don't let the children pick or eat them, unless you are sure of their identity. There are some which are quite good to eat that are frequently found in company with bilberries, growing on small bushy plants with spiky leaves, the berries are very like blackcurrants and grow up the sides of the stems, being quite shiny without the bloom of bilberries. These are called crowberries and can safely be mixed with bilberries, though they have not sufficient flavour to use by themselves, but they will add to the bulk of the basket and mixed in will take on the bilberry flavour and eke out the supply. I have myself eaten lots of them and suffered no ill effects, though it is well to be quite sure you identify them correctly.

P. MITCHELL

🌹 STAFFORDSHIRE

. . . Then, of course, there are deer and other wild life, but the greatest fascination is to see the herd of wild blackfaced goats, magnificent creatures with huge black horns and light grey shaggy coats. They are descendants of a herd which were presented to Sir John Bagot by King Richard II after he had enjoyed some hunting in Bagot's Park—the only herd of their kind in this country. . . .

MRS. L. HUSSELBEE, Abbots Bromley

🌹 "HER RAREST GIFT— A SINGLE, COLD, CAT'S KISS"

For me, the enduring fascination of the cat lies in its ability, when necessity arises, to do without the human race. Minette, my Siamese queen, is, on those rare occasions when we fall out, a past mistress of the art of sending me to Coventry.

I am stared through, non-existent, a ghost. All attempts to make conversation are met with a blue, basilisk stare; and, as the hours pass, it becomes increasingly difficult for either side to make an overture without losing face.

"Two can play at that game," I think, after suffering a morning of humiliation. I pass and repass as close as I can to her nose, brushing her whiskers and flapping a duster round her head as I tackle the chores, and even succeed for the first and, no doubt the last, time in my life in producing a piercing, taxi-whistle an inch away from her ear. Not a muscle moves.

She has refused all food, and I decide as a final gesture to produce that favourite delicacy—a dry, flaky biscuit cast nonchalantly on the hearth rug, to be stolen, rather than eaten in a civilised manner from a dish. (In such a crisis I would not insult a Siamese with fish.) I change the drinking water, that neglected necessity for all cats, after thoroughly cleaning the bowl.

Passing under the kitchen window a few minutes later I see my adversary tucking in with relish; but on entering the room again she is already sitting exactly where I left her. Only a single crumb on the tip of her nose gives the show away.

With appalling lack of manners I burst out laughing.

Minette rises to her feet and with incomparable dignity stalks across the room to leap lightly to the top of the open window. (The effect of this being slightly marred by the fact that the window slides down under her weight.) With a squawk of indignation, the only sound she has uttered during the entire day, she disappears, smelling strongly of Chanel No. 5, into the dusk.

I know now that within three yards of the front door she has entered that jungle of her own making where I, for all the love she shows me, no longer count. She will, like all her race, leave a warm hearth and a feast of rabbit to sit on a stone wall in an east wind or fish with a delicate paw for a herring head in the nearest dustbin.

Listening, as I lie sleepless, to the sounds of darkness, the hoot of an owl and those sudden, mysterious, never-repeated cries from the moorland to the east; I hear a rustle of leaves in the pear tree trained against the house.

For a moment my erring friend deliberates; silhouetted against the sky in the open window, poised, ready for flight.

I hear a soft thud and, shamming sleep, wait for her rarest

301

gift—a single, cold, cat's kiss against my face. I stretch out my warm hand and feel her cool, soft fur as she settles down, purring, against my arm.

Minette and I have many faults, but we can never let the moon go down on our wrath.

KAY HILL

NOT WORTH A 6d. SHOT

Perhaps if I cared more for the taste of pigeon I would sympathise more with the whole-hearted passion with which my family pursues them. But every time I am presented with an armful of the birds I can't help wishing they were something worthier of the time and electricity spent on them. A pheasant or a hare instead of those nasty little iron-clad gobbets of flesh prettily camouflaged in jackets of soft grey feathers.

To look at them you'd think their sleek topcoats and downy breasts covered the most succulent of game birds until you try, in all innocence, to treat them as such.

Breast upwards in the baking tin with a rasher of bacon tucked under its chin, a pigeon looks potentially as much a delicacy as its little brown cousin the partridge. Even in the serving dish its glistening juicy look misleads you until you start to carve it. And then you realise you might just as well make an attack on a bedspring with a butterknife for all the goodness you extract from its miserable frame.

It would be as well to grasp the fact that a pigeon has grey feathers because it's born old, and the only way to digest anything so ancient is to pulverise its bones by slow cooking totally submerged in a liquid which has taken all your ingenuity to concoct. This way a pigeon, or for that matter cotton-wool, can taste as tolerable as anything else whose essential substance is disguised by these methods.

As far as I'm concerned if the pigeon suddenly became extinct, which is not likely, however many of our husbands expend their cartridges on them, I would miss it no less than

the rat, dead or alive. Not so with other vermin—the squirrel or the rabbit, for instance. The woods have never been the same since their disappearance though I know I'm not supposed to think it.

The pigeon is a strangely bloodless bird. I once kept a wounded one in a cage for the children's sake and I was never really sure that it wasn't some sort of animated toy, with its beady red-rimmed eye and its mechanical pecking movement.

There's no earthly need for the Ministry of Agriculture to send round appeals for pigeon-shooters in this district. From the moment the cold weather starts father and son in this family put on what I call their pigeon eyes and scan the fields, trees and horizon for the first flocks. The moment there's a sign of any number of them, telephone calls are made, the uniform is donned and the necessary paraphernalia collected. Pigeon paraphernalia is perhaps worth a little further discussion, for never do I cease to be amazed by the elaborate lengths to which the passionate pigeon-shooter will go to lure these birds from the skies.

Some men, I believe, merely take the gun off the rack of an afternoon and go out and shoot pigeons. Not so mine; they pack a kind of trunkload of things and deck themselves in the strangest assortment of garments so that when the party foregathers outside this house, they look like an army of brigands about to make an armed assault on the nearest manor house.

Ex-paratrooper smocks seem the favourite top garment at the moment, plus little khaki-coloured veils which they tie over their hats with tapes. Father has a hole in the bottom half of his to smoke his pipe through.

There's been a discussion lately about hands—it's just possible that the odd pigeon may be put off by a few square inches of pink flesh; so, mut that I am, I have agreed to dye some old gardening gloves dark green. This will be child's play after the last job I undertook for them in the cause of this sport, which was sewing inch-long brown ribbons all over a tweed hat so that wisps of grass and twigs could be tied on to prove to the pigeon that you were not a man with a gun but just part of the landscape.

There are other ways of fooling the pigeon besides making a fool of yourself, though why one goes to all the trouble of merging oneself into the background with such subtleties as grassy hats, green gloves and khaki veils if a bird can't distinguish between its own pals and a lot of wooden imitations pegged out on the plough, I'll never understand.

We probably have every type of pigeon decoy ever invented here in this house. The first ones were cut out of some old lino and painted grey and the children had great fun putting in the eyes and the beaks.

Then we graduated to wooden ones with an arrangement in their tummies which, when you pegged them in the ground, made them move up and down in the wind as if they were pecking.

One step farther or backwards, nobody can decide, in the art of decoying are the rubber ones with wings outstretched. But these take quite a bit of time and patience for they have to be fixed at the right angle with guys of thin wire.

Having so far managed to outwit the poor bird brain by such devious methods, you'd think the human brain would now take a rest and just leave it at that. But not a bit of it. There are other forms of delusion which must be tried in order that yet another inedible contribution be added to the pot.

Nobody could say that the fervent pigeon-shooter spares himself where his sport is concerned. For weeks my persuasive powers have failed to achieve the transport of a couple of clothes-line props from the wood, where they lie ready cut, to the garden. But two Saturdays running man and boy have managed to stride comfortably up the hill with what looks like a bell tent and a chimney sweep's entire equipment.

The "sweep's brushes" are the means by which a wooden pigeon known as a "lofter" is shoved up about twenty feet into a tree to lure some wretched bird who may think he is about to join a pal for a quiet gossip among the branches.

These particular decoys are easier put up than brought down, so that when darkness falls and the sportsmen pack up their paraphernalia to return home they often have to be left up in the trees with the top section of the pole broken and hanging out of reach. Next morning the most junior of the party has to climb for it.

The "bell-tent" turns out to be nothing so cumbersome and, when erected, resembles more the sort of primitive concealment that can be seen at point-to-points and fair-grounds for the convenience of men visitors.

These "hides", as they are known, are basically of the same construction and vary only in the materials of which they are made.

We have two sorts here and a third in the making. The first consists of old sacks and deck-chair canvas held together at intervals with bamboo canes. The second—a roll of wire netting looped all over with stripes of old khaki shirting. Rag-bag, attic and surplus stores were ransacked for old and out-worn army clothing, the result of which is that I have cut enough khaki buttons off them to furnish a regiment.

For the third and latest "hide" they are making a patch-work quilt in which I have made myself become involved merely to keep the thing from being stuck to the floor or my best carpet.

I must say it's a work of art, which I only hope the pigeons will appreciate in the manner for which it is intended. Every evening the men's "needlework", as I call it, is brought out of the cupboard and a few more patches stuck on the sacks with glue. The bits that don't fit are reserved for more loops for the other "hide".

I am now waiting to see whether the next one in the series will be done in Italian quilting or needlepoint.

BARBARA HARGREAVES

 THE MAGIC POND

The Dew Pond goes back to the dawn of time. It is undoubt-edly the oldest example of the reservoir in the history of water engineering. In all probability some of the dew ponds flanking the older tracks that criss-cross the country date from Neo-lithic times, and it is probable that even further back Man knew that a dew pond would provide his wants in water no matter how dry the summer.

During the serious drought of 1921, many a dew pond retained water long after wells and streams had dried up; and last summer when there was concern about falling levels in our reservoirs cattle stood hock-high in the muddy depths of dew ponds.

The cattle of many a hill-farm rely almost entirely on dew ponds for their water. But the magic pond has uses far removed from those of agriculture. It is widely used in zoos; for example, in Whipsnade, where some forty of the larger ponds are of the variety which Neolithic Man made. The same principle is used in the making of ornamental ponds, fish pools—and even bathing pools.

How does it work? The answer is that it reflects the fundamental laws governing condensation, and at the same time the making of a dew pond is childishly simple.

Some years ago in Whitwell, Herts, I met an old fellow named Tom Smith who up to then had made more than 1,000 dew ponds and carefully following the rules he outlined, I made a pond that, with the same magic at which Early Man must have marvelled, kept itself well filled even during the hottest weather.

The first thing is to dig the hollow that is to become a pond. The usual size is about forty feet across by five or six feet deep in the centre. The hollow can be twice this size. For instance, the great lake in the Marquess of Salisbury's Hatfield House estate is really a dew pond. On the other hand the initial hollow can be much smaller than that of an average farm pond.

The secret of construction is less in the size of the hollow, than in how one lines it. "First," said old Tom Smith, "you stamps down the earth and strew straw on it. Then you puddle some clay and lay it good and thick over the straw—six inches or so."

This is where one must show extreme care. First of all, choose a warm day with no likelihood of a night frost for the clay-spreading, for otherwise your pond will not hold water. Second, and for the same reason, make sure that not so much as an inch of straw penetrates the surface of the puddled clay, which should not be too "wet".

And then? Prime your pond with water while the clay is still moist and go home in the certainty that the dew of the nights will fill your pond—and keep it filled! Indeed, it is

nothing uncommon for the level to rise as much as two inches in a single night without the aid of one drop of rain!

The magic in this is just that, chilled by contact with the clay the dew of the night turns into water, the clay and straw bed forming, not only a con-conductor of heat, but a retaining cup through which water cannot percolate so long as its surface is unbroken.

A well made dew pond will last almost indefinitely. But the straw-and-clay bed must be at least two feet deep in ponds to be used for watering cattle, as a safeguard against cloven hooves breaking through it. As for worms, attracted by the moisture, they bore up from the ground, and a few holes through to the water are enough to drain a pond. Perhaps the best way of defeating the worm is to mix lime with the puddled clay. But whatever the reason for the water draining away, the bed must be most carefully repaired and primed before it dries if the dew is to keep it filled.

The invention of Ancient Man, the dew pond has still an

important place in the civilisation of the twentieth century. In Britain the magic pond is used not only for the watering of cattle and in the construction of ornamental ponds but as a source of water for camping and caravanning sites.

In Europe it is widely used in the breeding of edible fish for commercial purposes, as it was in Britain in the days when almost every monastery had its "stew pond".

In Kenya and Basutoland, African herdsmen are being taught how to make dew ponds. Properly made, the magic pond will remain a brimfull monument to its maker, and carefully repaired, it will remain full for centuries, for there are undoubtedly many in Britain that date from the days when men wore skins.

JAMES FINDLAY

❧ SUFFOLK

. . . It was at this farm that one could see the true serenity of this little village, with the mist creeping over the marshes, from the sea, and mingling with the smoke from the chimneys of the little houses near by. Dunwich itself is so full of legend that books have already been written about it. . . .

MR. B. BLUNDELL, *Selby*, *Yorks*

❧ MOUNTS AND MAGIC

In this remote Welsh hill country where there is only one metalled road, few well-used tracks, fewer signposts and a maze of sheep paths, man's route is indicated by rocks, by wind-stunted trees and by the hill gates which lead out of small, walled fields on to the rough slopes of mountains.

The big and curiously-shaped rocks all have names. It had

always puzzled me why the frost-flaked slab at the foot of my neighbour's rhiw—the path leading up the mountain flank from his farm—should have been called The Stone Stallion. Admittedly it was as big as a horse, and in a hill mist its angular shape might conceivably be mistaken for a petrified stallion. But that didn't seem to be sufficient explanation, so I asked my neighbour.

"You breedin' hosses here and you don't know?" he asked incredulously.

I shook my head.

"Well, if you've got a mare what's barren, like, you ties her to the rock on a night of a full moon and leaves here there 'til dawn. She'll be in foal afore the year's out."

Only a complete stranger to these hills would have considered himself the victim of a leg-pull on hearing this.

In an island where authentic wild country diminishes yearly under bulldozer and playfield, where the countryside is becoming merely the tame garden-playground of an urban nation this high, empty mountain world jars the spirit with its total detachment from the time and purposes of life outside it. Things linger on up here—thoughts, customs, antique rituals— long after they have disappeared from less remote farming communities.

Wild horses ranged over these bleak mountains before Wales was even a nation. For centuries before the earliest Celtic saints, the horse had been a part of the landscape and a part of the vital spirit world of the Celtic pastoralists.

Now, as a result of the startling growth of interest in riding, the number of breeding animals is increasing again and there remains among their owners more than a remnant of what must be called either superstition or belief in extra-sensory perception, depending on your viewpoint, and perhaps on your heredity.

Trefor Evans—that isn't his name, but it will do—has a farmstead jutting out of a wall of mountain a thousand feet up. It is the usual kind of lean, austere hill holding, crouched bare-fanged to wind and mists like a gaunt greyhound. The thin, rain-soured grasses on the upper slopes are high enough to taste the salt on the breath of westerlies blowing in from the nearby sea. Trefor lives alone: half my hill-farming neighbours seem to be bachelors. He's a man well into his sixties, tall, withered as a galetorn rowan, with brown skin stretched over his sharp bones like thin, creased packing paper. His untidy thatch of grey hair billows smokily from under a sweat-stained cap, which he wears everywhere including, it is rumoured, in bed.

He farms about sixty acres with a hill right, keeps some surprisingly good Herefords, a score of pony mares and a mountain flock. When he's not herding them on his grey cob he walks with that curiously slow, sliding stride of men who spend their lives on the mist-embittered slopes of a lonely sheep range.

Hill people are no less sensitive to ridicule than anyone else in a world which grows increasingly unsympathetic to the supernatural, they are understandably reticent about their relationship to it.

That is why it was some time before I discovered that not only was Trefor Evans a horse charmer, but one who was by no means without clients even in this age of unbelief. Though he will use his mystic craft in the cure of warts on cattle, gid in sheep, and human toothache, it is for horses that his aid is usually sought.

An elderly hill farmer, riding across the mountains, cantered into some jagged bracken-smothered rock. He was unable to staunch the blood from a gashed fetlock. "I asked Trefor to have a look at it," the old man related to me afterwards. "He touched the mare on her withers and she grew all tense-like. He stood there for a moment, as if he were thinkin' hard. When he turned round his face was fair floodin' with sweat. 'Her'll be all right,' he says, and—dang me—when I comes to look at her I sees the bleedin' has stopped. . . ."

Trefor will treat any horse, except one which bears a star so small that it can be covered by his horny thumb. Such a mark is a portent of evil and the charmer will have nothing to do with it.

Not all charmers' treatments consist of magic, of course. There is much of what is traditional horse lore, sound horse-mastership and medicinal prescriptions acquired from gypsies. And not always have the efforts of the charmer been sought for healing purposes; in the not too distant past—perhaps even occasionally today—hill men have believed that their animals

311

have been injured by a bitter neighbour through the medium of a charmer.

Back in the winter of 1936 a farmer in my part of the hills lost eight mares and a shed of beef stores from some mysterious disease. There were no identifiable symptoms and no clues from a post-mortem. Recent veterinary developments might have provided an answer but at that time it was an enigma which, for the unfortunate owner, could have only one possible explanation: a neighbour with whom he had been having a feud over grazing rights had become the client of a charmer who was not nearly as particular as Trefor Evans in adopting unethical practices in his profession. That farmer still believes this was the answer and so do many other local hillmen.

There has been black as well as white magic in the hills.

Before the autumn and spring horse fairs we are kept busy breaking our young animals. When riding a raw horse for the first time many of our neighbours prefer to handle the brawling, raging creature, fresh from the mountain, in the steep-sided lane on a dark night. But rarely is a blue-eyed animal ridden at night in any place other than in the low-beamed stable, for a blue-eyed mountain horse has the peculiar gift of being able to detect immediately any supernatural being. Such horses have bolted in terror, it is said, after seeing what their riders could not see.

"I were comin' over the hill when the mist caught me," a young neighbour told me, "and I sees the light which I reck'ns is the farm. I tries to follow it, but my gelding wouldn't have it. I gets off the hoss and tries to lead him, but he wouldn't lead. So I unsaddles him and turns him loose and I begins to walk towards the light. I went about four paces—and then I stuck my boot in the edge of the worst bog in these parts. I knew then where I were, miles from home."

"The light?" I asked.

"Jack o' lanterns, Will o' Wisps—whatever you likes to call it. The old hoss knew, but I didn't."

Almost every hillman claims to have seen these mysterious lights at some time, and many believe they will deliberately lead a man into danger.

Then there are the phantom stallions. Some are never seen

312

at all, only the nightly thud of their hooves is heard. Whole families will relate their experiences of them. Or they will tell how, on a certain day in each year (the festival of some forgotten saint, perhaps) a stallion will lead his ghostly herd down one mountain track and up another, always taking the same route. They will tell, too, of the nights when they heard a stallion's pounding hooves as it galloped through certain meadows in the first hour of a new day and of the charmers, long ago, who could control these phantom horses.

In this wilderness region, where the old stony bones of the mountain jut up into the mists and where a family's occupation of a farm is counted not in years but in centuries, it is understandable that certain things are more enduring, more resistant to change than elsewhere.

Many of the ancient horse customs are admittedly fading— few men now nail the caul of a newborn foal over the stable door for good fortune, fewer still immerse strands of hair from a black mane in water collected from the roof of a church, believing that the hair will come alive and develop into an eel or snake. Nor any longer do they take their mares to our pebble-shaped lake in the evening, when it is a great yellow eye of the mountain blinking in the brittle sun—hoping that if they bathed the horse in the ice-chill, glittering water she would bear a golden foal the following spring.

But despite radio, the weekly trip to market, the AEC, the NFU, FW, and the occasional visit of an English duchess or American millionaire in search of a palomino, hill people are still quietly certain that there is more in life than what you can touch with your hands—and a few would say that there was more to a mountain horse than just the wind in his wild mane.

HUW MEREDITH

✿ SNAKES ALIVE

My garden writhes with snakes, and not just in the usual places. They leer at me from drainpipes; they swim around the water butts. They're draped on all the trees and trellises. Perhaps the word that I should use is "drips"?

Don't think because I play with words to find the one that fits I like these reptiles. The first time that I saw one I turned tail and ran. I didn't stop till I ran out of breath. The second time was when a lengthy serpent leapt out from a pile of muck that I was spreading with a rotavator. That time I shook and trembled for a week. Since then, by seeing them in almost every spot and by surviving the experience of having one sent to me in a parcel through the post, I have acquired an outward, unconvincing, altogether unreliable, false air of confidence.

I thought, to come back to my truthful feelings, that fear or loathing was a general reaction. I am surprised when people tell me that I shouldn't kill "my" snakes. I was astounded when, a few weekends ago, my snakes became a real "attraction".

A small boy arrived who really seems to love them. He'd heard that I had almost every kind there is, and he was out to get an adder.

I fortified myself with bottled, adult courage. Then, with teeth chattering just short of cracking point, I joined him on the hunt.

We didn't go into it unprotected. We were fully armed, and dressed, with spades, forks, gloves, rakes, Wellingtons and tongs. The devil of it was, that though we drew in all the likely covers, the one time we found the tong grip hadn't been perfected, so we lost. His Operation Snake was well worked out. The adder was to be (1) Caught; (2) Caged. Ploy three was taking adder to the London zoo and there demanding that it should be "milked". "After that," he said, "my dentist will pull out its fangs."

Obviously no other reptile could be fitted into such a careful scheme. I found him toads and frogs. We startled shoals of lizards (and most of the flowers) along the sunniest flower bed.

He rejected every one of them, and, very disappointed, left. As soon as he had gone we came across the right-shaped quarry.

After trying to be brave before a child, I must have felt that I could well relax, for I shrieked very noisily. I think my shriek was "SLOW-WORM". The other shriek was "ADDER". The serpent lay there looking startled. Only when hysteria was unified to "KILL IT", did it decide to leave the scene.

Given calm it isn't very difficult to distinguish adders from the other harmless snakes. The calm is necessary, for the easiest way to find out if the snake is a *Vipera berus berus* (adder—the one poisonous serpent in the British Isles) is to look it in the eye. The pupils of the adder's eyes are elliptic—like a cat's. The Ringed Snake (common grass-snake) and the Smooth Snake (very rare) have round pupils similar to man's. The Slow-Worm, which is not a snake at all—it is a lizard—has a half-shut, sleepy eye, and scales so smooth they look as if they have been polished.

A grass-snake (Ringed Snake, *natrix natrix helvetica*) is nearly always vividly coloured. Greeny-brown, or green-grey, or a bright green with black spots along its back, a yellowish checked belly and, the most distinctive mark, a yellow, orange, white or pinkish collar which doesn't as a rule quite meet behind its head. It is quite harmless, though, if frightened, it can give off a fearful stink.

In colour, adders show tremendous variation. It isn't safe to reckon, just because you cannot see a zig-zag stripe along the middle of its back (the most general characteristic), that "that snake isn't poisonous". The streak can look more like a heavy line or a continuous stripe, or may not be apparent to a casual look. Though most adders have the black zig-zag mark and most are grey or brownish, their colour range goes through the creams, yellows, silvers, greens, reds, browns, slaty-blues and black.

Those who want to read up this snake and reptile subject, should get a book called *British Amphibians and Reptiles* (Collins).

What should one do if one gets bitten?

Suck the bite, tie something around the limb above the bite, and make for the nearest hospital or doctor. If you have a knife immediately available, it may help to scrape the wound between the first and second suck. On the way to hospital the ligature should be undone and reapplied at intervals, so that the limb does not go "dead". If kept too tight and constantly in place, the chances are the ligature may be more damaging than viper poison.

Sometimes symptoms of snake-bite appear without the victim knowing that he has been bitten. The usual symptoms are both pain and swelling round the bite which can spread to the body. The victim may feel only slightly ill, or may collapse. He may be sick, have diarrhoea, or feel giddy. Reaction to a viper bite depends upon the dose of poison and upon the victim's size and health. One doesn't necessarily with every bite get every drop of poison that a viper has to give.

A child is much more likely to react severely than an adult. But while treating adder-bite—its chances and its possible effect—with great respect, it is important to remember that not only do most people not get bitten, but in common with the victims of bee, wasp and other insect stings, nearly every victim of an adder bite recovers. One authority on British snakes has stated that in the fifty years preceding 1945, only seven fatal cases were recorded.

MORAG WILLIAMS

✿ HAMPSHIRE

. . . In no other county do you find the variety that there is in Hampshire. The great rolling Downs of the north, stretching from Alton and Liphook across to Kingsclere (with that lovely home of Gilbert White—Selborne—nestling in them), and the heather and forest of the New Forest, are both so satisfying in their different ways. It is so easy to get right away from civilisation—a thing difficult to do in Sussex, beautiful as it is . . .

MRS. V. BERKLEY, Arundel, Sussex

✿ PEACE OF MIND

Sometimes when my mind is full of a confusion of thoughts and I've had an extra busy week, I make my way to the National Gallery and sit for a while opposite this picture. For me there is no landscape, no evening sky, no person, or object, to compare with the beauty of it.

Several years ago, you may remember, this picture hung in one of the smaller rooms in the gallery, lacking the brightness that it now has. But it was just as beautiful in its dim mellow colourings and when I heard it was to be cleaned my heart sank for fear my picture would be spoiled.

But I should have known it wasn't possible to spoil this artist's work and what the portrait lost a little in mystery it gained in a renewed depth of colour.

The Virgin and Child have been painted by every well-known artist at one time or another and each has painted his own interpretation of the Mother's character. There are smiling Madonnas, solid Madonnas, Madonnas with sorrowful faces and Madonnas with an impish look, but this Madonna of Leonardo da Vinci's has the face of a woman with a peaceful mind.

I don't know the history of "The Virgin of the Rocks" or

how Leonardo came to paint the scene this way. I have never tried to find out whether it has even been recorded. I like to imagine his intentions for myself.

Like all Italian masterpieces of those days, there is a certain amount of symbolism in the picture. The rocks for instance, there's nothing here that suggests the stable at Nazareth. But I always feel the artist liked this grotto setting not only for the background colour and shapes, but for the way the jagged edges of the rocks gave emphasis to the roundness of the Babies' limbs, the delicate curves of the Virgin's face and the whole quiet serenity of the scene. An inner world of calm within the outer world of storm.

It is said that when Handel finished writing *The Messiah* he fell on the floor and wept—wept with the joy of having written something so beautiful.

I wonder what were Leonardo's feelings when he put the last stroke of his brush on this painting.

Just look at the details in this picture. An artist of skill, perhaps, could paint limbs as beautifully, but it takes a genius to compose those lines, that flow of movement in the Virgin's arms. And notice how he has put a protective human mother's arm around the mortal child and the upraised worshipping hand above the head of the Infant Jesus. There, in a single gesture, the artist has not only portrayed the relationship of the Mother and Child, but has made the Child the centre of the group.

When we were children, one of the excitements of Christmas was visiting the crib in our village church. And, like all things in a child's memory, it's the atmosphere and happenings which surround an event as much as the event itself which are important.

We always used to make this visit after tea and oh the excitement of going out of the house after dark and the little shivers of expectancy which murmured through my small frame as we entered the church door and tip-toed across the stone floor to where the crib was arranged in the corner.

There it was, those little figures grouped round the inch-high doll lying in its little matchbox-sized crib. This tiny figure representing the Man who was to make men and women of us all.

Now, when I look at this picture, I recall the feelings of those after-tea visits, and though now I can express my thoughts a little more clearly the magic and majesty of it still remain.

What emerges more clearly as one stands before this painting is the Mother's peace of mind—strange that so nebulous a quality should shine out so distinctly. For her it was a peace of mind which came from having achieved so richly that for which she was chosen. For us it is strangely the same, for Peace of Mind is an achievement in itself. It is a philosophy of life born along the road to maturity. A state of mind achieved out of the guts of experience.

Then when you believe that you have found contentment in the way you live your life, a pride in your family and friends and no lasting envy of others, then peace of mind becomes the bridge over the gap between youthfulness and maturity which, when you cross it, makes you stronger and braver than the young.

The truth of this shines through the face of the Virgin in the picture and as one quietly gazes on this family group one begins to know the meaning of that Peace which Passeth all Understanding.

BARBARA HARGREAVES

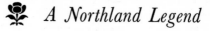 *A Northland Legend*

A Northland legend quotes—that on the Day
When ice and snow and all else melt away,
The Great White Chief (around whose hoary head
Flicker the Lights) shall judge both quick and dead.
He will be just, and little will he need
Men's vain excuses in that hour of need,
But seek the truth from those who cannot lie—
"Summon your dogs! Lo, they shall testify!"

JOE WALKER
from "That Day of Mine".

. . . But seek the truth from those who cannot lie—

Puss in Boot

THE SHEPHERD
OF RHYNNON PASS

Across the foot of the remote Rhynnon Valley, behind which the mountains rise, ridge upon ridge, to Plynlimmon under its cap of snow, there now runs a fine new motor road which sweeps to the top of the Pass, and then corkscrews down to join the main Aberystwyth road.

All that is left of the old road is a stony track which winds beside the River Rhynnon and leads to the tiny hamlet of Llanfitrion with its few white-washed cottages and the shop and post office, kept by Dai Howell and his wife. With them lived Dai's mother, old granny Howell, and on long winter evenings, many were the tales of her father, Idris the Shepherd, that she would tell to her grandson Glyn. For folk still speak of old Idris Pugh, and his skill and uncanny knowledge of the weather, though he has been dead these fifty years, and his cottage long ago fallen to ruin.

As eager to listen to her tales as Glyn was his cousin Barry, who had come on an unexpected visit, one cold February, to convalesce after an attack of bronchitis.

Despite the cold northerly winds which howled and swirled through the valley, bringing flurries of snow, and making spring seem like a distant dream, Barry grew stronger daily; and one still clear morning he begged his aunt to let him go with Glyn to the farm in the next valley where he worked.

She shook her head, saying that it would be too long a day for him, but promised that if it kept fine he should walk over with his dinner, and have it with Glyn.

So finally, muffled up well, Barry set off to climb the steep craggy ridge which stretched between the two valleys.

He found Glyn mending a dry stone wall near the farm, and in a sheltered corner they sat and ate their dinner.

They had nearly finished when the farmer's young son came to call Glyn to unload some straw into the barn. Glyn shouted that he would come at once, and getting up, turned to Barry—

"Best you go back home now, Barry," he said. "It may be late we shall be, and the wind has changed, I'm thinking; it

has swung to the west now, and 'tis raining it may be before dark."

"Can't I come and help, Glyn?" Barry asked, disappointed.

But Glyn shook his head. "No, indeed, not today; and what will mother be saying if you are coming home cold and wet perhaps? Best you go back by the road now and you not knowing the hill too well from this side. I'll see you later now, so long then."

With a grin, he was off round the corner of the barn, and Barry stood looking after him, undecided.

The way back by the road was nearly three miles longer, and though it was true that he didn't know this side of the hill very well, he didn't want to walk back along the road by himself. He looked at the sky, it was grey and overcast, and the wind seemed to be hovering uncertainly among the spruce trees farther down the valley. Still, there should be at least two more hours of daylight; and he made up his mind that he would take the shorter way over the hills.

He struck off quickly along the rough track behind the barn and climbed on steadily till the track petered out by the last stone wall on the hillside.

322

Here he stopped for breath, and taking off his scarf, bundled it into his pocket. He looked back over the little valley lying silent beneath him: away to the north Plynlimmon was invisible behind the dull grey haze. Looking up every now and again at the outline of the ridge still two hundred feet or so above him, he went on, half scrambling over the dark clumps of heather and jutting rocks.

He was over the last shoulder before the summit, when, despite the heat of his body from the climb, he felt a sudden chill like a cold hand closing over him, and starting erect, he turned about.

He looked straight into a rolling grey bank of mist that came swirling up at him, silvering his hair, and wreathing over him like a cold damp veil.

He gave a little gasp of alarm, looking desperately round him in all directions seeking some gap in the insubstantial vapour which had suddenly blotted out his world. But he could see nothing and once more stood, undecided, fighting back his panic.

Should he go back down the hill and try to find the farm again, or try to get back across the summit and down the more familiar side of the mountain?

If he went back, he might well miss the farm, and if he reached it Glyn would not be too pleased that he had gone up the track instead of by the road.

Barry decided to go on, up the mountain. There was a little cairn of stones on top of the ridge. If he could find them he might be able to get his direction for the descent. He scrambled on, knowing only that he was going up. Then at last the ground seemed to level out and he stopped and stood still, listening, for he could see nothing.

The silence was eerie and complete, save for the beating of his own heart, and the squeak of a heather twig under his boot. He seemed to have been suddenly wrapped and shut into silence. He started forward, groping and stumbling, but before many minutes he knew it was hopeless.

The summit was deceptive, not a clean-cut top as it looked from below, but a rambling, uneven plateau of some extent, and his chances of finding the cairn of stones or anything to guide him to the eastern slope were remote in that thick mist.

If only some familiar sound or sight would penetrate the uncanny, clinging twilight, he would feel better. If he could hear old Idris call to his flock, or see a bird flutter from the heather, he would not feel so utterly alone.

As he stood hesitating, the drops from his hair trickled coldly down his face and neck, his ears straining for the tiniest sound, he thought he heard over on his right, a sudden rap, like a hoof on a pebble. With arms outstretched before him, he groped towards the sound; it came again, but this time to the left. He swung round and out of the corner of his eye half saw a blurred shape in the mist. He lunged after it, but it was gone; then, almost beside him, he heard a sudden snuffle, and bending over, caught the rank, tallowy smell of a sheep. Thrusting down both hands, they closed on something wet and yielding, but not as deadly cold as the dripping heather around.

It was the fleece of a large sheep and as his fingers clutched a hold, it gave a sudden bound, and nearly got away from him, but he hung on desperately. Panting, its breath steaming up into the cold mist, the sheep leapt and bounded over the clumps of heather, twisting from side to side, so that Barry was hard put to it to keep his feet, but running and leaping beside it, he held on grimly.

Then, suddenly, they were going downhill, and the sheep slackened its pace and seemed now to be pattering quietly along a known path. Once it turned its curved black nose and looked at Barry out of strange yellow eyes. Then it plunged on downwards.

Barry stumbled on beside it, over loose stones and spikes of bog myrtle, going ever downwards, intent only on the guiding sheep and his hold upon it. His world shrunk to a tiny core of effort pulsing against the ancient power and terror of the hills.

Now there came to Barry's ears the distant sound of rushing water and he knew that it was the Rhynnon tumbling over its stony course far below. Now, too, the mist seemed to be thinning out and it was not long before Barry caught glimpses of the narrow trail that twisted before them, the heather gave way to tufted grass and bracken, and then at last they were on level ground. Above the murmur of water Barry seemed to hear the patter of many hooves and the quick breaths from little jostling bodies; then all was still.

As Barry stood there, the mist rolled away in front of him and he saw that he was standing by the ruined wall of the old sheep pen and before him stood the forlorn outline of old Idris Pugh's cottage.

The sheep had vanished. Barry gazed about him with a gulp of relief, then, suddenly light of heart and foot, he ran swiftly down the valley beside the river, clambered up the bank, across the main road, and down the lane to the Howells' cottage.

Lifting the latch, he let himself into the small kitchen. Its only occupant was old granny Howell, swaying gently back and forth in her rocking-chair by the fire, her small blue-veined hands folded on her apron. She looked up as Barry came in, and peering in the failing light, spoke in Welsh:

"There you are now, Dai bach, 'tis your tea you'll be wanting now, is it?"

Barry came slowly into the room and knelt on the hearth beside her chair, gazing at the glowing bars of the fire.

"Gran," he said, "is it a long time since Grandad Idris lived in his cottage?"

Granny Howell looked at him with her faded blue eyes, but she did not really seem to see him, and she went on rocking for several moments before replying; then she began speaking in a low sing-song voice and Barry had to listen closely to catch what she said.

"Fifty years ago, it is, Dai bach," she said, "fifty years to the very day, and snowing it was, snowing since noon, and your grandad away on the mountain, after the sheep. Turned eighty he was, but stepping as light as a cat; and not worrying I was—but listening and waiting, for didn't he always bring them safe back?

"And hearing the shuffle of their feet I was, and running to the door, see, to do the counting in the pen with him. All safely gathered in they was, not one lost.

"And there on the snow, peaceful like, an' his eyes closed, was your grandad, and beside him, Dilly, the old ram standing, and his hand in the fleece still. Failed on the hill he had, see, and took a hold of Dilly to bring him safe home. No need to be fretting at all, Dai bach, all safe home they was—not a one lost. . . ."

Her voice trailed away, but Barry said nothing. He was staring down at a little tuft of grey sheep's wool still clutched between his fingers.

M. TYNDALE-BISCOE

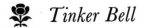 *Tinker Bell*

Tinker Bell is a tortoiseshell cat,
She's really the belle of the farm,
Sleek and poised, where the rest are fat
And fully aware of her charm.

Most of the day she sleeps in a chair,
Which no-one dares to disturb,
When we sweep underneath, with utmost care,
She glowers (if that's the right verb).

Just when it suits her, she stretches and yawns,
Thinks she will sally forth,
Casts an expert eye o'er the birds on the lawn,
Then sets her course for the north.

Here by the haystack, she takes up her stand,
Confident, patient and neat,
And in no time at all a half-grown rat
Lies warm, but still at her feet.

Bearing her trophy, she passes old Smut,
Who has toiled on all day on the stubble,
She has waited, alone, unblinking and damp,
And caught not a mouse for her trouble.

Tinker Bell airily places the corpse
Right in front of the door,
Resumes her place on the best armchair,
Lazily licking a paw.

B. M. UPTON

❧ SWANS—THEY'RE A MENACE

There is an old saying to the effect that one can have too much of a good thing. In human life that is generally true, especially with reference to agriculture. For example, at times one can have too much rain or too much sunshine, both good things in the right amounts but both bad things when in too lavish or too long-drawn-out supply.

But what brought this old saying to my mind recently was not a climatic condition but a bird—a lovely bird, a graceful bird, a bird that everybody admires; to give its correct name, the mute swan. On those counts, then, definitely a good thing, but today we are having too much of that good thing—here in Wiltshire, much too much.

During recent years—say, the previous dozen to fifteen—this variety of bird has increased in numbers to such an extent that it is now a definite nuisance, not merely to fishermen and those who wish to shoot wild duck, but also very harmful to the farming of the district. A nesting pair of mute swans every ten miles was a pleasing feature in the countryside, but a pair plus their cygnets every quarter-mile of chalk stream, approximately the present density, makes the mute swan a farming pest almost as bad as the wood pigeon.

It may be that the weather in early 1962 has been partially responsible, but what most of us regarded as a steadily increasing nuisance has now become a serious financial handicap. I don't know the correct comparison between a dairy cow's and a mute swan's consumption of grass, but my estimate would be that the latter's, plus what it spoils by paddling and messing, would amount to the needs of one cow. For argument's sake I'll put it at half a cow, and then remember those sixty swans I recently saw in a water-meadow. That tells me the size of today's swan trouble.

Of course, it is obvious that swans will feed on the grassland near the river and that was their habit until recently. But this year from the north of Wiltshire I have received accounts of flocks of sixty swans or more journeying daily to feed on and spoil crops of new clover and rye-grass and even winter cereals on arable land. Which isn't funny for the man who owns such crops. Then why doesn't he do something about it?.

The answer to that one is that the mute swan is deemed to be a wild bird and so is protected under the 1954 Act, which lays it down that it is illegal to kill such a bird or to take or destroy its eggs. So what? The prevailing habit of the country-man is to ignore the law when he considers its rulings to be absurd. For instance, in my opinion any buzzard, again a protected bird, which presents itself within range during the shooting season is practically committing suicide; yes, even if the carrier of the gun be possibly a magistrate or even a Lord Lieutenant.

But, by comparison with a buzzard even, a swan has valuable natural protection in addition to the legal one. This is because of its size and colour. I have always understood one of the principal deterrents to murder to be the difficulty of disposing of or even concealing the body of the victim.

So it is with swans. The carcass is not only large but also white, which means that someone is certain to witness either the actual crime or the attempts to destroy or conceal the evidence. For example, a dead pigeon or hare on the highway becomes a pinch of feathers or a twist of fur in next to no time; but in similar circumstances a dead swan is large enough to upset a small car, and glaring enough to make most cars pull up.

That is probably the principal reason why the legal protection of swans has managed to increase their numbers so rapidly; but I have it on good authority that there is another, partly responsible. The other day when I asked a farm-worker friend why we were now overrun with swans, he said it was because the habits of the average boy had changed so markedly.

"When I was a boy," he said, "a swan's nest was a challenge to us. We watched it built, waited for the first egg, and continued to take the eggs as long as they were fresh. Jolly good to eat they were—rich, better'n ducks'." According to him the modern village boy now buys records, and watches television. Anyway, he certainly doesn't keep down local swans to a bearable number.

What then is the aggrieved farmer's remedy? As far as I can find out the 1954 Act provides it, or rather a workable defence for contravening it. First the farmer kills a swan. Within thirty seconds at least three of his neighbours, usually women, will report his dastardly crime to the local police. They, in duty bound, must prosecute, and the farmer gets off on the grounds that he shot the bird to protect his crops.

Everyone must admit that the foregoing is a very unsatisfactory way of dealing with this problem. Accordingly, the Wiltshire N.F.U. have been making representations to the Ministry of Agriculture that in this county, anyway, swans are now so numerous as to be a damaging pest to farming. For it appears that under certain circumstances protected birds may be killed with the approval of the Minister of Agriculture.

I understand that the N.F.U. is now asking for the Ministry to authorise the pest officers of the Agricultural Executive Committee to take the necessary steps to reduce the present swan nuisance to more reasonable proportions. With that reasonable request I most certainly agree, for nobody wants to see dead swans lying about all over the countryside, nor swan-shooting being carried on at will by any and every farmer and gamekeeper in the district.

Incidentally, here is something that puzzles me greatly.

A few years ago at some function I attended I saw on the cold table a cold roast swan lying next to a boar's head. As far as I can remember nobody found the bird worth eating, but I cannot help wondering whether it is possible to purchase such a dish from a London caterer today. If so, would it be imported or the result of some criminal action here at home?

A. G. STREET

🌺 CAT ON HOT WOODEN SLATS

Yesterday afternoon I went to a very dear friend's wedding. I have been decidedly sentimental about the whole affair. I am fond of her—very fond, and Heaven be praised I like the man she married. So you see, the whole of yesterday was charged with feeling for me as much as for them. I don't mind telling you I abandoned myself that afternoon to a full set of emotions.

In church I sang all the hymns with choir-boy lungs; and cried when they walked down the aisle to the *Wedding March*. At the reception, well, I drank their health more than once. And not in iced coffee.

Getting through today's work was an effort. I can't have been very stoic about it either, for by teatime I was the possessor of a number of infallible remedies, from strong tea to Worcester sauce. I was about to leave for home when somebody said, "What you need, you know, is a Sauna bath." Which is how I landed up this evening at 6.30 in the basement of Finland House, Haymarket, London. An hour and a half later—now—I am sitting writing this and feeling fit enough to walk at least a hundred miles to watch another hundred people get married.

It is three years since I had, and swore never to have again, a Turkish bath, when I sweltered in a Congo heat and waited for the crocodiles to come at me through a haze of steam. Torture.

The Finnish bath (Sauna) is different. You get the heat; but not the humidity. The Sauna—pronounced Sow-ner—in Finland is not only more important than a wash-house or a bathroom is to us, but more important than a house. They say the Finns build their Sauna first and then the house. It's usually a hut in the garden made of birch logs.

Heat is produced by heating piles of stones and the Finns beat themselves with birch twigs and then go and roll in the snow outside.

In the London Sauna the same conditions were achieved

with electricity and a cold shower. They don't have the snow, but they do have the birch twigs.

I was shown into a cubicle and given an armful of whiter than whitest bath towels. I wrapped myself up like a Sultan and moved as I was bid to the next room. It's so restful sometimes to be ordered about.

In the corner was a half-open door. The little Finnish attendant pushed it wide open. "This is the Sauna," she said with rather the same sort of pride one shows off a well-stocked linen cupboard.

I stepped in rather cautiously and stepped out like a scalded cat. It was as hot as the No. 2 oven in the Aga, complete with two rows of shelves. The attendant suggested I had a cold shower then try the bottom shelf for a start.

I stood under that icy fountain as if these were to be my last moments on this side of hell.

I stretched myself out on the bottom shelf of the oven. It was just bearable and after a few minutes even actually enjoyable. Then I noticed the temperature dial. Nonsense, it couldn't possibly be 120. I reduce potatoes from rock hard to floury soft in a couple of hours with my oven at that temperature.

The attendant put her head round the door. "Comfy?" she said. "I think I shut the door now you are more used to it."

The moment the door was closed I began to feel uneasy. Suppose the door stuck. Suppose it got hotter and hotter— Yorkshire pudding temperature. I couldn't get that oven out of my mind.

I jumped off my shelf and opened the door. That was better. I lay back and tried to concentrate on my surroundings. It wasn't like an oven at all really, it was more like an airing cupboard with its wood-lined walls and slatted wooden shelves.

The girl returned with a bucket of water. I hoped she was going to pour it over me but instead she pulled out of it a big bundle of branches tied together with string. These were the famous birch twigs. She laid them on the hot pipes hissing and spluttering. "Smell them," she said, holding them under my nose, "aren't they divine?" I didn't tell her, but to me they smelt like senna pods. Anyway, the whole business seemed horribly like a hangman showing the victim the rope.

Under the shower she ordered me. You're not supposed to feel the cold after all that heat but I can tell you that first stream of water was like a butcher's knife. And there was more torment to come. There I stood as pink as a peeled prawn while she bashed me all over with the besom. Then more icy water. After all that scolding back to the hot shelf for more scalding.

I went home lightweight, light-hearted and certainly less light-headed than the night before. But there were some awkward questions asked when a shower of birch leaves fell out of my blouse when I got ready for bed.

BARBARA HARGREAVES

🌹 CUMBERLAND

. . . Keswick and Derwentwater, where the stone bridges straddle the streams like some plump child making a "back" for leapfrog. Surely it is a British Isles in miniature with its lakes, fells, valleys, coast-line, forest, rivers, waterfalls, towns and villages. . . . Oh, to be able, once again, to climb a fell on a Sunday morning and hear the distant church bells, and see below the sparkling blue lake, with, from the height, all the shaded blues showing up the currents, and the seemingly toy steamer with the white froth in its wake. Days like this always reminded us of the two hymn lines:

> "Oh quiet restly Gal
> Oh calm of hills beyond."

In autumn, heather carpets the slopes, and bracken and leaves set the countryside aflame; "apple pie" adds its spiky pink glow, and the cattle disappear from the fields as they are taken into their warm byres for the winter. The same freakish playful wind that scares the wits out of late holidaymakers by blowing up a sudden storm, just when they've taken out a boat for an hour's quiet fishing, covers the head of the fells with clouds, like a night-cap on an old man's head. Wind-driven clouds cast strange, fleeting shadows on the fells, and the same gusts hustle through fields of corn, making all the red poppies, blue cornflowers and white daisies dance like a proudly fluttering Union Flag above the rippling grain. . . .

MRS. M. S. LITCHFIELD, *Newborough, Staffs*

You've all heard of my county now, if you hadn't before—we are unique in having, I suppose, the only supply in this country of that rare substance which can raise mankind's hopes of a better life, or can damn us all to an awful, fearful destruction. . . .

Naturally, Windscale is not why I prefer "canny" Cumberland to all the rest of England's green and pleasant land, but isn't it strange how such occurrences can focus the mind more sharply on the great beauties of our land?

. . . I love Cumberland best because from my kitchen window I can see right down to Solway and beyond to Criffell, twenty-five miles away. On a good day we can see the separate fields with always the majestic blue height beyond and the silver ribbon this side. . . .

. . . Our own particular bit of this country is known as John Peel country and from the "garth" we see his Ruthwaite home. . . .

. . . The girls are lovely and the men most handsome. Nowhere else have I seen the roses and cream complexions and the straight bright eyes as in Cumberland. Just listen to their "crack" in strong and splendid vowels "Hoo is ter?" or "Who's ter ga-en?" (Who are you? Where are you going?). . . . Splendid hunting ground for language lovers. For food, too, none can surpass us. Have you tasted rum butter or Cumberland ham? Have you seen the "sets out" made at WI birthday parties? Scrumptious! The shepherds hold their "meets" to find the owners of stray sheep, and that is an occasion—with tatie-pots and local songs by local talent and many a swapping of tale and joke. . . .

MRS. H. M. PARK, *Ireby, Carlisle*

335

♣ Winter's Scene

No warmth, no cheerfulness, no healthful ease
No comfortable feel in any member—
No shade, no shine, no butterflies, no bees,
No fruits, no flowers, no leaves, no birds—
      November!

Winter Scene

The principal part of faith is patience

George Macdonald

✿ POLITICS APART

Last night for the first time since the Coronation I was glad of my television set. Being able to see the old man as he spoke was worth a century of bad programmes.

It was a very touching scene to see him standing there facing us all, and I agreed with him when he said that he was glad that modern science had enabled him to talk to us in this way.

It's not given to the British people to feel great emotion about their politicians or statesmen. Certainly whatever emotion one might expect to have of awe, perhaps of respect or admiration, affection wouldn't be among them. And yet I can truly say I do have a great affection for the old man. The term "old man", which is how so many people refer to him, is in itself a term of affection. The French equivalent, "mon vieux" does, in fact, mean old friend.

I remember one afternoon during the war I was having a cup of tea in a cafe in Woking when Churchill came over the radio and announced the sinking of our two biggest battleships. After he had spoken, there was a click and a silence, and then whatever programme had been on before was resumed. I looked round the cafe, everyone looked startled, it's true, but not scared out of their wits, which is certainly what we might have been since the news was a catastrophe of the first order.

But the old man had announced it and, like everything else he told us in the war—grim or gay—he managed to convey to our very souls the fact that Britain could never be beaten.

I've often wondered, since the war, if we should have felt so confident—put such a calm face on things—if we had had a man of lesser fibre than Churchill to lead us. I think if anyone but he had made that announcement in the cafe, for instance, there would have been a lot more shuffling and scraping of chairs.

It was stimulating then, as it is now, to hear Churchill interpret the country's whole sense of trying to do the right thing, of endeavouring to put the finer touch to an action or a motive. He spoke in words that nobody else has used, he spoke sitting and through his words the nation did the deeds. That's what he meant last night when he said that the nation was resolute, he was lucky enough to have the lion's roar.

As he talked last night I noticed how he moved his hands in gestures familiar to us in still pictures, but which I had never had an opportunity to see in movement before. They are not the gestures of the proverbial orator—indeed, they reminded me of my father when he used to stand with his back to the fire talking to us children after supper. Perhaps that is why we have this affection for the old man because he is the Father of the Nation, which is why, whatever Government is in power, he does not lose his place in our hearts.

No wonder he has been one of the greatest statesmen we have ever had for he is a leader without being a Dictator, and a politician with a broad sense of humour, who tells jokes against himself and the country. He is also a man who is damned whether he'll allow Britain to go to the dogs. All the characteristics of guts and go which we hope belong to this country are expressed in his every gesture and every phrase.

He is not only our country's ambassador but the ambassador of the British spirit. Just as a poet can convey the meaning of a whole philosophy in a few lines, so this old man can do the same with speech—politics apart.

He is the answer to vegetarianism, teetotalism and to those people who believe in Yogi and early bed as a means of living to a ripe old age or earning immortality.

BARBARA HARGREAVES

❧ OVERTURE TO A WHIST DRIVE

"Good evening, Mrs. B., I'll start at this table with you and your husband, shall I? So nice and near the fire; not that there is much fire, is there, really they ought to light the stove in the afternoon to get the room warm for us, but people never think of these things do they? and of course one stove isn't enough to heat a big place like this, there should be at least three, I told the Women's Institute so the other day.

"My dear, who is that little man on the door? I'm sure I've seen him somewhere but I can't quite—Oh? Oh, of course—but he looks so different doesn't he, quite smart; clothes do make such a difference, don't they?

"Goodness, there's that Mrs. A. and her daughter coming in. I should have thought she'd have had the decency to stay away from our whist drives in future.

"But really, didn't you hear, I actually caught her cheating at one the other week—she trumped my ace of spades and then a couple of tricks later she actually led a spade! She pretended of course that it was all a mistake and that two cards had got stuck together; and then she had the impudence to say: 'But why didn't you tell me at the time, Mrs. F., you had a good look at my hand before we started to play.' My dear, as if I should dream of looking at anyone else's cards!

"Of course one does get an accidental peep sometimes—people are so careless how they hold their cards, aren't they—but to suggest that I actually looked! All I can say is that I shall keep a close watch on her tonight. After all, as I always say, what does it matter who wins? I come for the game and it doesn't matter to me whether I win or not.

"Oh bother, aren't they going to start yet, really you might think they could get started on time. They said 7.30 and I came prompt at a quarter to eight so that I shouldn't have so sit about waiting, and here it is, nearly eight o'clock. Ah—here comes Mr. J., quite a good M.C., but of course not the authority that dear Mr. D. used to have—it needs someone firm to stop all the chattering and get things organised. Anyone would think people just came here to gossip! Another gentleman here, Mr. J. . . . ! Really, why won't he listen—oh, here comes that nice Mr. H., such a pleasant man. Come and be my partner, Mr. H.! Well, did you see—ignored me completely and has gone to sit with that M. woman!

"What did you say, Mrs. B.? Pretty? Oh, well, I suppose she is if you like that type; but after all, we're here to play cards, aren't we. Dear me, all the tables seem to be full now except ours—Mr. J., Mr. J., you've forgotten us! What did he say, dear? I didn't quite catch. Oh, I see, he's coming here himself, I didn't realise. I always think it holds the game up so if the M.C. plays himself—however! And he isn't a terribly good player, you know—he lost me three tricks once, right on the last hand, and I missed first prize because of it, so annoying—they were quite good prizes that night, and I always thought it rather an odd coincidence that Mrs. Y. should have been the winner. Mr. J. is rather a friend of hers, I believe, though, of course, I don't listen to gossip—not like some people I could mention.

"Ah, here comes Mr. J. at last, now we are going to start. Thank goodness everyone is quiet now, I can't concentrate with people talking all round me—after all, whist is supposed to be a quiet game, isn't it? . . ."

E. S. BROWN

🌹 *One Day Only*

Her skirts were green,
Her heart was sound,
She sat demure in her piece of ground,
A dewdrop glinted clear and bright
Where the morn had kissed her late last night.
Now, in the sun's adoring ray
She settled down to enjoy the day
A day's a long time in the life of a lettuce!

Her heart was white, as a girl's should be,
Not worn outside for the world to see,
But the sun had a warm and joyous mirth
To tempt a girl from her bit of earth
And she felt the naughty familiar thrill,
Of turbulence in her chlorophyll.
A day's a long time in the life of a lettuce!

Now a lettuce must think in a cellular way
How to make most of her stationary day,
For though one is green, firm hearted and hard,
There isn't much fun in a single square yard!
One must give thought to moments so great,
It's best for a girl to envisage her fate.
A day's a long time in the life of a lettuce!

Her root tips twitched with a vulgar ease,
The sun was warm with desire to please,
But a lettuce is coy, if she's properly bred,
So she tightened her leaves around her head,
But couldn't ignore the plasmodic throes
That deep from her vascular bundles rose.
A day's a long time in the life of a lettuce!

Her skirts spread wide as the sun rose high
Alas and alack the soil was dry,
And a lettuce can only look her best
If the tips of her toes in moisture rest.
By hot midday this wilted girl
Had softened her heart and lost her curl.
A day's too long for a full-grown lettuce!

MISS D. A. BRUNNING

341

🌹 HEREFORDSHIRE

. . . Herefordshire: I don't think the trees are as large or as green anywhere else. Then there is the wood smoke. Whenever I smell wood smoke, I think of the clean perfumed air of the country in the evening when the cottage fires are lit and the walks along the lanes at dusk. . . .

. . . As one drives through the county the sign-posts point to such places as Much Birch and Little Birch. Much Marcle, Lugwardine and Stretton Sugwas. I wonder who thought of these names?

There is the May Fair which is held in the High Town along the streets of Hereford. . . . We used to throw paper streamers and confetti.

. . . I mustn't forget the Hereford cattle with their white faces which always look to me like human faces in the dark. I have run across a field in the dark more than once because I thought someone was there. I could go on for ever about the thatched cottages with the geraniums flowering on the wide window-sills and a cat sleeping in the middle of the pots. . . .

MRS. K. SARGESON, *Rossington, Yorks*

342

✿ CLARENCE

Clarence is a mouse and I sincerely hope I was right in assuming that he is a boy and not a girl. If I am wrong I can foresee serious trouble shortly because Clarence has taken up residence in my car. Recently he has started to take little bits of the stuffing from the back seat for purposes best known to himself. I trust I am not misplacing my confidence. One mouse is quite enough in a car.

Clarence joined me about two months ago and has lived with me ever since. He was one of a very large family which had been living in a pile of sacks which a farmer placed in the boot of the car. As each sack was lifted and shaken, showers of mice of all ages fell out, and scurried to safety. Something must have been going on in the bags judging by the number present. It may have been a political meeting or a celebration of some kind. Anyway, Clarence was not shaken out and became the inhabitant of the boot of the car.

I was driving in the city when I first noticed my uninvited passenger. Out of my eye corner I noticed something like a piece of string hanging from the left-hand glove pocket of the car. Glancing quickly I saw the string move and go into the hole. At first I thought little of this but later I realised that pieces of string could not fall upwards. The next day I saw Clarence. As I was driving he appeared from under the seat, walked slowly across the floor of the car and then leisurely climbed up the side and entered his hole. I knew then that the piece of string belonged to Clarence—it was his tail.

My next stop was at a farm. I mentioned Clarence. The farmer produced a screw-driver and we took off the piece of cardboard through which Clarence had disappeared. We peered inside. All we could see was the windscreen wiper motor and a further space which would admit Clarence behind the dashboard. Short of dismantling the car there was no hope of apprehending him.

The farmer's wife, who was an interested spectator, suggested using some of her mouse bait which, she said, would put an end to Clarence. Accepting her offer, I placed a match-

box containing the powder in the glove pocket and left it for the mouse to eat.

Some time later I felt that this was not a happy solution to the problem. It was not remorse that made me throw the bait away but the thought that Clarence might expire in a most inaccessible place and then smell as he slowly decayed. I decided to wait for some other decision.

I tried a trap baited with a very nice piece of cheese. Clar-

ence showed no interest. All that happened was that I caught my finger in the trap and had to drive with one hand until I disentangled the thing without letting my wife know—she does not like mice. Clarence was quite satisfied with the samples of corn provided. I contemplated leaving him a saucer of water well laced with gin in the hope that he might be found drunk in charge but I discarded the idea as not being quite fair.

Once I left him nothing to eat but after he had peered at me from his hole with a rather reproachful look in his eyes, I replaced my corn samples in the car and tried to think of some other way.

I had hoped that Clarence would put on weight and be unable to get into his hole but that has not happened yet. As several people have reminded me of the possibility of Clarence being mis-named and the significance of his extracting the stuffing from the back seat I have now decided to harden my heart. I am faced with two alternatives.

Either Clarence must be eliminated or I shall sell the car complete with mouse and all. I dislike both. If I poison Clarence I feel I shall have him on my conscience. If I sell the car without telling him I feel it would not be quite fair. I feel that I shall soon have my mind made up for me. Some more stuffing has gone. If Clarence has misled me and abused my confidence he is on his—or her—way out.

G. A. LLOYD

🌹 A SHAGGY DOG STORY

The other night, driving home from the office through one of London's back streets, I hit a dog. Wham—with the right wing of my car. It was a dark, wet night, and it ran out from a crowd of children on the pavement, right in front of me. As I slowed down to stop I looked in my rear view mirror expecting to see a motionless lump or a wriggling heap in the middle of the road. There was neither. But as I backed the car up the road I heard screams coming from the children who were now huddled in the shadow of the houses.

I suppose the wretched animal must have crawled back to its owner. Oh, why hadn't I killed it outright.

Pain in an animal is a fearful thing to watch. A human being is so frustrated by the impossibility of explaining the situation to the poor beast, and one feels that in its animal subconscious it imagines you've done this on purpose. You, who have nurtured the creature from a pup, cub or kitten, have suddenly become its predator.

As I walked towards the group of children I suddenly realised that the screaming was not coming from the dog but from a small girl with straight yellow hair who was rocking backwards and forwards on her knees with her fists pressed into her eyes. The dog was nowhere to be seen.

A woman with her sleeves rolled up and her coat over her shoulders came up and said to me almost apologetically: "You see, they've got no mother, and Doris thinks the world of that dog. He's a bit wild—it's only young, you see."

"But where is the dog?" I asked her, completely bewildered. I put my hand on the screaming child's shoulder. "Was it your dog?" She didn't answer but screamed all the more.

A man joined the group. "'ere," he said to one of the small boys who was just gaping along with the others. "Fetch a torch, and see if 'e's in the 'ouse somewhere."

With this the whole group seemed to come to life. Other people seemed to appear and in a moment we were all running upstairs and looking into rooms, the men were whistling and calling "Mickie, Mick".

Despite my anxiety about the dog I couldn't help noticing

things about this house. It was obviously lived in by quite a number of different families each of whom appeared to have a room or a couple of rooms. By the way we all barged into the rooms whistling and shouting the families were obviously all on very neighbourly terms.

Here in this house where once one family lived well (it was that kind of building) were now living probably six families. There was no bath and no electric light—hence the torch.

The people weren't really poor in the sense of old days "poor", for their clothes were good and I noticed newly bought toys lying about on the floors of some of the rooms. They were simply without homes of their own. The tragedy of the housing shortage had never really meant anything to me before I entered this house on a cold wet night in late October.

We found Micky in the cellar curled up on the seat of a tattered old Victorian horse-hair chair. He was trembling and when he saw us in the light of the torch his ears went back and his eyes showed more than a crescent of white. The look you get from an animal caught in a trap.

I picked him up. He was only just not a puppy with awkard limbs and a coat which had the harshness of newly matured hair. He didn't wince, he only shook. So no bones broken. He had blood on his nose and when I opened his mouth there was the reason. One of his brand new grown-up teeth were missing. He was just a big frightened baby.

I put him back in the chair and went to find the little yellow-haired girl.

Her eyes were bulgy with crying and tears broke out afresh when I told her we'd found Micky.

"But don't you want to see him?" I said. She nodded her head violently from side to side. I began to get impatient. This wasn't the way one was brought up to face trouble—even at ten.

Then I remembered. Doris hadn't been brought up. She had no mother, and here she was faced with the possibility of her beloved Micky being hurt beyond her help. A neighbour chipped in. "She comes home from school in her lunch hour to take it out, you know, Mam."

I went and fetched Micky. "Look," I said to her, "he needs

347

you." And having recovered some of his guts, Micky gave his tail a feeble wag. That did it. She bent down and buried her face in his fur.

Going home—very slowly, keeping a look out for more silly "Mickies"—I pondered on that word "need". It's probably the most meaningful word in the language.

BARBARA HARGREAVES

A Twentieth Century Drinking Song

Each Thursday I've to market, marked
Me beast and made me bid.
In twenty years I've not misjudged,
Noe never once been did.
So it's hard to know they're jeering. Mates.
And dealer-lads be glad
That woman's beat me "know how"
I reckon I've been did.

Two years ago come Michaelmas
I saw a fitting wench,
With body strong as cart horse.
And brawny arms could wrench
Two charging bulls asunder. So
I put it to her Dad
And took the girl in wedlock.
But I reckon I've been had.

She looked like being a doer. Sleek
And plump and fond of work
Till she read some damn fool magazine
Writ for them who's time to shirk
Then she starts to moan and worry
'Bout her size and how she's clad
And what the newest "Look" was.
Then I guessed as I'd been had.

You should see the meals she dishes!
Bits of nothing dressed up fine.
And me money's spent like water
On queer foods and foreign wine.
And half of her just isn't!
Ah, it makes a fellow mad
When he think's he's got a bargain
Then finds that he's been had.

349

Yet I'd let her think I liked it
If she's not disgraced my name
By starving down to skin and bone
In the fashion crazy game!
Eight score five of a lass I bought there,
And they'll think me feelings bad
Now she's naught but skin and scrag end.
There's no doubt that I've been had.

S. D. S.

WAY OF THE WEASEL

Weasels are nearly always coupled with their larger relatives, the stoats. Admittedly, the weasel and the stoat are of the same family, the *mustelidae*, but there the similarity ends. There is much in the old saw that "the stoat is stoatally different from the weasel which is weasely distinguished from it".

The stoat is much the larger animal. He has a decided white belly in summer pelage and a number of stoats change to all-white in winter whereas weasels in this country do not. Weasels do not have a black tip to their tails as the stoat does. Stoats breed once a year, weasels will breed two or three times. When travelling, weasels appear to slither, stoats, on the other hand, have an undulating action. There are other differences, of course, such as cranial structure, but these are few.

Weasels, the smallest of the *mustelidae*, are fascinating creatures and a good deal of myth and conjecture still surround their habits. This aura of mystery has been augmented from time to time by some quite remarkable reports on the behaviour and actions of individuals as well as chimes of weasels —"chime" is the term used to describe a pack or family. At the same time, there is still a lot we do not know about weasels and their ways and to the naturalist these creatures can provide a most interesting field of study.

In the past, there were believed to be two kinds of weasel— the big brown weasel and the mouse weasel. Even today, in certain parts of the country, particularly in Scotland, you occasionally still hear this distinction. The fact that the male and female weasel can vary appreciably in size may well have been the basic cause for this belief.

Weasels, like the majority of wild carnivorous animals, spend a good deal of their time in the education of their young and an almost inevitable corollary to this instruction is play. It is difficult to set a fine line of demarcation between work and sport.

After teaching young weasels to hunt, and perhaps killing their first prey for them, the adult, or adults, may well join in playing with the dead victim be it mouse, bird or reptile. During this period of relaxation, weasels will indulge in the most remarkable acrobatics. Whether these evolutions are also performed as a part of the young's education is not known, but there is no doubt that weasels engage in the art of "fascination".

Many observers have witnessed a weasel perform in front of an intended victim. The dance of a weasel before a bird or small mammal is a remarkable performance, full of the most grotesque gyrations, jumps, tumbles and cartwheels. I doubt whether the weasel always actually kills after he has succeeded in mesmerising his quarry with these astonishing evolutions. If he is already satiated, he may tire of his exertions and just go away.

J. G. Millais, in his massive work on the British mammals, has described a remarkable performance by a weasel in front of a presumably enraptured audience of birds which consisted of wrens, robins, chaffinches and blackbirds!

There is no doubt that, at times, weasels hunt in packs. The packs, or chimes, are frequently a family party perhaps under instruction and sometimes families join up—as many as thirty weasels have been known to hunt together. They always hunt by scent, like a pack of miniature foxhounds—never by sight.

Compared with the stoat, the weasel is a prolific creature having, as the females do, two or three litters a year averaging four to six young at each birth so that such large gatherings are easily achieved. Legends contain many tales of packs of these little animals hunting hares by night and even attacking humans.

Possibly, due to their early education as well as their inheritance, all weasels like to play with their dead quarry and this practice also extends to the deceased of their own kind. Recently I came across an account of the alleged burial ceremony of a so-called "king" weasel by a number of its kind. This description detailed a near military funeral where the corpse of a particularly large weasel was carried to interment by a pack.

There is no doubt that weasels are attracted by their own dead. The gamekeeper knows this only too well and in the days of the gin trap it was a common device to bait a trap with a corpse. This is still done when the legal tunnel trap is used.

Weasels will sometimes make caches of food in holes in stone walls or old trees. This habit of secreting their belongings may well be akin to their concealment of their own dead. I have seen an adult weasel cross the road carrying the body of another almost as large as itself. They can drag immense weights compared to their own—a near-adult rabbit is not beyond their capabilities.

At one time, the weasel was almost universally destroyed by man as an undesirable wild animal and keepers, in particular, endeavoured to eliminate these animals from their territories. But for some time now, prominent sportsmen have strongly advocated a partial preservation of the weasel in the interests of game rearing, for the animal is a far more efficient destructor of rats—a menace on any game property—than mankind.

I have read a report of a weasel attacking a rabbit by leaping upon its back and loosely holding the rabbit with its teeth. The weasel then wriggled around and put its anal orifice against the rabbit's nose. He did this several times until the rabbit appeared to become completely stupefied. The witness of this incident said he was able to rescue the rabbit who appeared none the worse for its horrible experience!

HENRY TEGNER

🌹 CORNWALL

... About twelve miles away lies a much loved haunt of mine, Tintagel, where I've spent many enchanted hours gazing out over the Atlantic's blue-green waters, or watching the seals flashing their delightful whiskery faces in and out of the surf....

... I even enjoy the winter here when the icy winds sweep down from the snow-capped hills and the curlew's plaintive cry echoes on the air....

MRS. J. SHOVELL, *Launceston*

. . . Cornwall, of the hidden valleys, like the Glyn, little used lanes and apple country, even a pack horse bridge around Withel way, creeks and estuaries where yachts ride at anchor, salmon trout in the Camel; hills and dales where firs and spruces abound, heather wild of the moors—Bodmin, Goss, the Down country, Carnon, Blackdown, and the glimpse of Atlantic and Channel from high clay mounds and wind-swept tin-mine shafts. . . .

MRS. D. FOGG, St. Austell

. . . Cornwall of the grey rocks and wild seas, where jewel-bright anemones are as big round as breakfast cups, and the very place names are music: Lostwithiel, Minions, Lerryn Zennor, Marazion and the rest. . . .

MRS. M. COLEMAN, Bletchley, Bucks

TEST OF FRIENDSHIP

I'm devoted to my old school friend Cynthia, in spite of the way she brings up her children. Most of the year what she does or doesn't do with her children is of no concern of mine, since we live at opposite ends of England and our only communication with each other is by post, telephone and the occasional gossipy lunch in town on one of her rare days off.

But for two weeks of the summer she brings her family to stay with us and then our long friendship undergoes a pretty severe strain. By the time she departs Cynthia and I are being so jolly polite to each other you'd think we'd only recently met, instead of having been receivers of each others joys and sorrows for the past twenty years or so.

If my child insisted on chalking all over the kitchen lino, I would gently but firmly remove it and the chalk to somewhere where it could pursue its artistic inclinations and where the rain eventually did the job on which dear Cynthia would spend a devoted hour with the scrubbing-brush.

Neither am I so attached to my offspring (on second

thoughts perhaps I'm more attached) that I could encourage individuality, initiative, or what you will, to the point where I was able to sit at lunch unmoved by the sight of my youngest peeling an apple with a newly-sharpened bread knife.

Perhaps if someone were to convince me that such free enterprise would turn toddlers into men of iron, I might sacrifice enjoyment of my adult life and give myself up to scrubbing chalk off floors, scribbles off walls, gluing together bits of broken china and chairs and being told by my son, aged four, that I didn't know what the heck I was talking about. "Silly old Mummy."

But I'm not convinced and until such time as I am converted I shall remain faithful to my highly untheoretical methods of using good old common sense as my guide to bringing up the young.

Pet theories, like ideologies, are all right if you practise them on home ground, but it seems to me to be the height of selfishness to impose them on your relatives and friends. For a vegetarian, for instance, to insist on your cooking him a nut cutlet when you're roasting a darn great joint for everyone else seems about as unreasonable and as unsociable a request as allowing your child to pour sand down the lavatory or cut the heads off your pinks with a pair of nail scissors (yours) are unsociable acts.

Apart from the rights and wrongs of this sort of upbringing, it seems to me to be a lot too much like hard work for both the child and parent. By the time Cynthia's children have been allowed to "express their feelings" all day they're ready to collapse with exhaustion by evening.

As for Cynthia, by the time she's finally got the children to agree to that bed, even if it is a conventional place to spend the night, is really more comfortable than the back seat of the car in which Daddy had decided to drive to the pub for a well-earned pint, she has to be revived with something pretty strong in the drink line herself.

Our house is not large and by a fairly simple rearrangement can accommodate quite a few extra. Cynthia's husband, however, is the only member of the family who ever sleeps in the house when they come to stay. The eldest child insists on sleeping in a tent on the lawn, the second on a camp bed in

355

the tool shed, "just like my own little house," she purrs and Cynthia—well this year she's sleeping in the stable with the youngest because he's pretending to be a horse. Last year it was the loft and he was "ever such a big rat".

As I said before, I'm fond of Cynthia and when she comes to stay I do my best to make it as much a holiday for her as she'll allow herself to have. But my, its hard work. Not the cooking/washing-up part of it, that's easy, but controlling the urge to cuff the little monster nearest to hand. This demands patience of the very highest order.

I don't really mind awfully being woken at 5.30 in the morning by a shrieking band of Red Indians. I'm not all that perturbed by a couple of the little darlings pretending to navigate the Niagara Falls in the bathroom as I'm about to take my longed for and much needed evening bath, but I find it difficult not to show some irritation when our evening meal is disturbed.

We sit down to supper with all the promise of peace. The little dreadnoughts, if not exactly tucked into their alfresco beds, are at least safely out of the house. Cynthia has been revived with a stiff gin and tonic. Her husband and mine have returned from a visit to the pub just as the coast is clear. And I with what water was left over from the Niagara expedition have had a reasonable bath and am just about in my right mind.

Half-way through the soup Cynthia's head suddenly goes up and she sniffs the air like a stag disturbed at its grazing. We all stop and listen with our spoons poised in mid-air. We hear nothing.

"It's Drusilla," Cynthia screams jumping to her feet, and dashes out of the house.

(You must have guessed by now that Cynthia was bound to have children with names like this!)

I put her soup back in the saucepan and we continue without her.

"Poor darling had a nightmare," says Cynthia sitting down at the table once more.

Just as I am putting a really superbly cooked chop in front of Cynthia the most blood-curdling shrieks reach us from the direction of the tool shed. This time both Cynthia and her husband dash from the table.

"That'll be Drusilla carving up Jason with the hedge clippers," I remark to the family as I put both chops back in the oven to spoil. They return just as we finish ours.

"Would you believe it," says Cynthia, "the naughty boy had crept into Drusilla's tent and broken her biscuit in half."

I decided that the nine o'clock news switched on full pitch to deafen outside noises might allow us to have our coffee in peace and, with luck, together. But Sunday was to be the real test of our friendship.

Just as we had arranged tea in the garden two of my spinster aunts rang up to say that as they were motoring in the district, could they call in and see us.

Impeccably laundered, straw-hatted and sensibly shod they arrived looking the epitome of respectable auntiness and settled down on our only two deckchairs as if they intended to make an afternoon of it.

Cynthia had taken the children swimming before they arrived and when I heard their returning screams and cries I became increasingly uneasy for Cynthia had the same lack of inhibitions about her children's clothes as she had about their general behaviour.

If Jason, Drusilla or Araminta, for instance, want to pretend they are Ancient Britons, Cynthia would be the last person to dissuade them from disrobing and the first to help them mix up woad from one of their paint boxes.

Similarly, she's not the sort of person who would insist on their putting on any clothes if one morning they woke up and decided they didn't want to dress that day. These are Cynthia's freedom-of-movement and no-restriction-of-limbs theories.

I've never considered myself a severe moralist where these matters are concerned. Personally I think tiny children happen to look sweeter and more comfortable in a pair of pants than in the nude, but, in any case wearing clothes or not wearing clothes had been up to that moment the least of my bothers where C's children were concerned.

However, I am anxious not to embarrass older and more sensitive people in these things, and so I hoped for once, as I sat gabbling away to the aunts, that Cynthia would rise to the occasion just once and put something—if only a hanky—on those dear little bottom halves.

357

I am afraid she did not.

It would not have been so bad if they had all scattered round the lawn. At least I could have diverted the aunts' gaze by handing cups of tea and plates of sandwiches, and with any luck their Victorian outlook would have been appeased on the what-a-jolly-lot-of-little-Cupids basis.

Of course, I hadn't reckoned on the fact that these children of nature were just as awe-struck by the aunts' clothes as the aunts' were horror-struck by the children's lack of them. And so for what seemed an interminable length of time they stood, one or other of them in their nudity, and gazed and gazed at the aunts with their mouths open. And the aunts, with their tea-cups poised between lap and lip, gazed back at them in unbelieving speechlessness.

Drusilla was the first to speak.

"Oh, Mummy, what a funny hat."

"Oh funny bunny hat, funny bunny hat," joined in Jason.

"Two funny hats, two funny hats, two funny hats," chorused the baby jumping up and down.

Nobody, nothing. Not even a thunder-storm came to my rescue.

BARBARA HARGREAVES

🌹 FACT OF LIFE

While taking her turn with dinner duty in a small country school, a young teacher noticed a small boy nudge the little girl next to him, and pointing to a bottle of A.1 sauce he exclaimed, "Don't have any of that or you will have a baby calf."

MRS. R. A. NORRIS

❧ FLASH POINTS

Our hottest areas have the greatest number of thunder-storms. Most of Lincolnshire experiences just over twenty days of thunder every year, while Leicestershire, west Yorkshire, Essex and the mid-Thames Valley are next in line with between fifteen and twenty days. Western and north-western districts of Britain are the least thundery regions, particularly Scotland, and south and east Ireland. In the Shetlands there are only about two days of thunder a year.

Between December and April thunder-storms are infrequent everywhere in Britain. Between May and August there are generally five thundery days in East Anglia, London, the Midlands and the Welsh Border counties, for every one or two in the west and south-west. Then, by the autumn, there is a marked change as south-west England becomes more thundery than anywhere else.

Dartmoor at this time is four times as vulnerable as any eastern area. Thunder-storms can be a real menace on the farm, and seeing that animals will insist on sheltering under lone trees or by isolated hedges or thickets the comparatively small cost of insuring them against this risk is well worth while.

According to statistics recently made available, the oak suffers more from lightning than any other tree. Next in order come the elm and ash and last of all, the beech. We should keep away from outbuildings, wire fences, single trees and all high ground during thunder-storms. Rivers and lakes should also be avoided.

Some idea of the nearness of a storm can be obtained by counting the number of seconds between each lightning flash and the resulting thunder. A five-second interval shows that the storm is a mile away, ten seconds that it is two miles away, and so on in that proportion. A flash from a storm immediately overhead comes simultaneously with the thunder, which, in the experience of most of us (at one time or another) resembles the smashing of several tons of plate glass.

In recent years there has been some confusion about the value of lightning conductors. They are necessary on tall buildings, and even on small buildings which stand on relatively high ground. They are also desirable on large or small buildings which stand singly on level ground and are not protected by nearby trees. However, except on very slim, steeple-like buildings, one conductor is seldom adequate, as it will protect only a small zone of the building. Houses having several chimneys, or which have a broad expanse of roof, invariably need several conductors. To install them is no job for the amateur handyman, and the cost of a large installation could be quite considerable in view of the large amount of copper rod that is used.

Chimneys, of course, are particularly vulnerable, since the lining of carbon inside the stack makes an excellent conductor for lightning in the immediate vicinity.

People sometimes wonder what to do if they are caught in a thunder-storm when driving. The answer here is not to rush out of the car, for a saloon car with metal roof will (according to laboratory tests) give complete protection to those inside. If the car is struck—and this, as it happens, is very rare—the lightning charge will be conducted through the car to the metal hubs and from there will jump to the ground.

Probably the most dangerous place of all in a thunder-storm is a golf course—the metal tip of a swinging golf club acts as a perfect conductor! Make for shelter as soon as possible, and, in this regard, I am bound to say that a wooden golf pavilion offers less protection against lightning than the underside of a cliff (should one be handy). The object is to get away from the highest ground in the vicinity, if possible.

Quite apart from casualties and damage to property, we suffer a loss of thousands of pounds worth of milk every year during thundery weather, due to the great number of temperature fluctuations (not always felt by human beings) that are associated with it. Winter thunder-storms, however, can be ignored in this respect, since temperature fluctuations have little effect when they are below about 60° Fahrenheit.

Meteorologists have long argued about whether there is such a thing as "ball" lightning. Due to the numerous reports of it, and even photographs, the old theory that it is simply an image in the eye of an observer (temporarily blinded by forked lightning) is not very convincing. But its exact composition remains a mystery. Nor is it known how it is formed. According to photographs, it varies in size and occasionally reaches the proportion of a football. It appears to have the habit of drifting through open windows and then exploding.

A single thunder-storm can be roughly compared to an atomic bomb explosion in slow motion. It contains winds that are vicious enough to tear an aircraft apart. A large thunderstorm would have the energy of at least one hydrogen bomb and enough electricity, if harnessed, to light a moderate-sized town for at least a week.

Conditions favourable for the development are to some extent predictable. The best guide is to go by the local indications. Turreting clouds top through the distant haze, a slight fall in barometer level after a very hot spell, or a slight fall of the barometer accompanied by unusually oppressive atmospheric conditions: these are all signs that we should be on the alert.

Don't blame the forecaster too much if he gives the alert, and no storm materialises. For though thundery weather can be general over a wide area it need not affect the whole of the area at the same time, the point being that slight shift of wind here or there can make all the difference to where the lightning will strike and the rain fall.

Can lightning strike twice in the same place? Most certainly it can—and will. The Empire State Building in New York was struck a dozen times within fifteen minutes!

DAVID BOWEN

Thoughts on a May Morning

You need to be young to smell daisies,
  Or tell what the whitethroat sings.
You need to be young to catch sunbeams,
  Or soar on the skylark's wings.

You need to be young to taste hawthorne,
  Or hear how the bluebell rings.
You need to be young to count swallows,
  Or know what the cuckoo brings.

You need to be young to seek rainbows
  Or notice the tiny things.
You need to be young to know wonder,
  —Young as a million springs!

BERYL M. RALPH

🌹 HAT PHOBIA

I never wear a hat. Except to church, and very formal functions. For these, I possess one summer hat and one winter hat; both of which I've had for years and owe absolutely nothing to current fashion.

I never really feel happy in a hat. Which is perhaps why I've never been interested in them. It may be something to do with my hair. Hats don't settle down on a mop like mine and by the end of an afternoon if I don't do a bit of adjusting my whole head is apt to look like a bucket on top of some rather forceful rhubarb.

Buying hats for me is a nightmare. I start the day in a mood of desperation; confident I'm never going to find something suitable. There always seem to be hundreds just right for every sort and kind of occasion, any of which would look wonderful on anyone else but me.

Maybe I'll pick a couple of possibles from a pile on the counter and put one on my head. While I'm gazing in the mirror wondering whether to die of laughing or burst into tears of frustration, an assistant comes up behind me.

"Moddom should wear it like this," she says, tilting it down over my nose.

I look up from under it and then I really do have a good laugh. I look exactly like Old Mother Riley.

The menfolk in my family make up for my attitude to hats. Whereas I have an obvious allergy, they have a positive mania for them. Not, I might say, for putting the finishing touch to formal suit or rugged tweed. Nor to enhance the qualities of a shooting or fishing jacket. The mania lies not so much in wearing the unsuitable but in the completely eccentric.

You should see our lobby. Fritz (our artist) once drew a picture of it—perhaps you remember. It is a complete saga of the family's hats, going back to the tartan tammy shanter bought for five-year-old Bay to keep her head warm.

On these pegs, for instance, I can trace the evolution of "the perfect shooting hat" from an old knitted balaclava complete with camouflage net sewn curtainwise on the front, to a doggy tweed object on which I once had to sew all over it one-inch pieces of khaki ribbon for securing pieces of bracken and grass for pigeon-hide shooting.

There are caps of all styles and stuffs. Even a Soviet work-man's cap I brought back from Russia, alongside a Yankee soldier's denim one. Also berets—someone had a theory they were the most comfortable headgear until it was discovered the rain ran down the back of their necks. Even a couple of bowlers, not there, by the way, in case of a formal Hunt or a town wedding but for skiffle group parties and homely jazz festivals.

I can't count the number of rain-sodden old head protect-
ors— you couldn't call them hats—which are stuck on pegs
either under, over or in between a pile of coats and macs. No
hat is considered worthy of its name until it's been "broken in"
by a good two years' drenching.

"At last this thing's wearable," says a voice from under a
dark brown cabbage leaf.

Since Simon's been studying for exams he's even taken to
wearing a hat in the house. Keeps his hair out of his eyes, he
says, there's no time to get it cut. The other morning I found
him in an old straw boater of mine which I'd put out for the
jumble. Once my pride and joy with a tangerine ribbon round
the middle and one of the very few hats I liked. Now a real
Eliza Doolittle.

"Why that particular one in favour of any of your own?"
I asked him. "It lets the air in through the holes," he replied,
"and it's a bit hot working here in the kitchen."

And these guys have the audacity to criticise my hats on
occasions when I have to wear them. The very hat, in fact,
which I've just mentioned brought in its day some typical but
quite unjustified comments . . . "Jolly boating weather,"
"Where's your punt?" and similar pungent witticisms.

The trouble is I can never think at the time of a suitable
comment to make about their get-ups. Never mind, I've written
this instead!

BARBARA HARGREAVES

NICKNAMES

I wonder if the nicknames are as colourful in the South as they are in the North?

How do you like these examples. . . . Shippon Jack, Hop-a-dill-Dock and Tommy Hoss Muck? They are even passed down from one generation to another. I have a friend who is called Young Sitacock because his grandfather once put a sitting of eggs under a broody cockerel to the great amusement of the neighbouring farmers.

MRS. R. OWEN-ROBERTS

"I COULD SCREAM . . ."

A woman with a baby in her arms was standing at the counter where I was buying stockings, and carrying on an animated conversation with her friend. The small boy at her side—his head barely reached the counter—kept tugging at her skirt to attract her attention.

But the two women were indulging in one of those conversations which was every bit as important to them as a discussion between two politicians on an issue of government policy. Even if it did only consist of the various reasons why Mrs. So-and-so from across the way had failed to catch the early bus.

And as the chatter relentlessly continued with no obvious signs of abatement, small Harry suddenly stopped tugging and let out a howl.

Such a howl. It contained all the frustrations, misery and helpless rage of all mankind from the beginning of his existence on earth.

Organised into action, this "howl" through the decades had stormed citadels and attacked the enemy. But more often it was the agonised cry of someone from whom the "enemy" has flown. Or as in the case of small Harry, the mother whom you worship had forsaken you for baby brother, auntie and nylon stockings.

The first tug at her skirt had been to tell her the fascinating fact that the Lady over there had a dog just like your Wog. The second was to ask if you could have one of those lovely big oranges on the next counter. And then you suddenly felt thirsty and tugged again.

If only you were nearer, like Billy up there in her arms, you could make her hear. Why did auntie have to come shopping too. Oh, if only he could have an orange. . . .

From the midst of all these ifs and buts emerged the howl which signified the awful possibility that perhaps he, Harry, didn't matter any more.

The howl had reached that hiccuping hysterical stage before mum became irritable enough to give Harry a friendly cuff over the ear. Whereupon Harry let forth further squeals and sobs of rage and had to be hurried out of the shop.

But even if Harry's mother had picked him up in her arms and given him a hug it wouldn't at that moment have made any difference. That little spring which lies coiled within and gives us the bounce and confidence had been slowly uncoiled. It would take more than a quick hug to recover the spring.

Was I, too, a little sad that morning that my heart went out to Harry, not as a mother towards a pathetic child, but as his equal. For as I listened to those screams I could gauge the exact depths of his anguish.

How many times have you wanted to scream your head off with frustration? Not over big difficulties where something definite must be done, but over the multitude of little things. Trivial things, each one of which could never be responsible for an outburst, but coming together from different directions converge on our sensibilities all at one time.

This moment can be a breaking point when we say beastly things we don't mean, think up even beastlier things and threaten to pack up and leave home.

Oh, don't say you've never felt like this. There are moments in every woman's life, however ideally happy and well adjusted she may be, when she feels, just like small Harry, that the whole world is momentarily against her.

These moments have small beginnings. Maybe we get no response to some request. No reaction to a special idea we feel strongly about. From there it's easy enough to feel you don't count and from there that you're not loved or even much needed.

And what do you do? Instead of screaming like small Harry, which is what you feel like doing, you behave like a perfect B. or go away and brood.

There are three possible short cuts to repairing the damage. Dig, laugh or pray. In that order. For if you dig the ground really hard, like a man, with the tears of rage pouring down your face, you'll end up by laughing at yourself and after that you can thank God for a return to sanity.

No good reading poetry or listening to music or anything like that. You've got to remember it was comparatively a short time ago that we were shooting arrows at people we didn't like, and we don't get rid of those primitive instincts in a thousand odd years or so, however Christian our outlook. So it's a good idea to think of something harmless which approximates to violence and does nobody any harm.

Well, you can't throw a lot of plates around because that's expensive and childish, and there isn't always a shooting gallery near where you can go and aim at a lot of ping-pong balls with a fairground rifle.

But you can carve somebody up quite harmlessly with a spade on a plot of ground and get a bit of gardening done at the same time.

An old gardener once said to me; "Nothing like getting close to the earth, Mam, for peace of mind." Well, you can put it his way if you like. Doesn't matter as long as peace of mind's the result.

BARBARA HARGREAVES

❧ MONSTER IN THE KITCHEN

For a year now I have shared my kitchen with a Monster; a temperamental tyrant who has ruled over me, and the

kitchen, with a rod of iron. There is no escape, and he knows it. He is Master.

Of course, I knew when we moved to a cottage without "power" that I should miss my electric cooker, but I resolved to make the best of a bad job. I was entirely innocent as to how bad a job would be the rusty, black range which glowered sullenly at me from the corner of the kitchen.

At first I felt sorry for him. He looked so rusty and neglected as he tottered rather pathetically on his gammy leg. I would give him a liquid shampoo, like the advertisements said, to cheer him up, but this wasn't a very great success. The resultant streaky mess did nothing to improve either the Monster's general appearance, or my own temper when he subsequently dabbed me with patches of black whenever I ventured too near. The only things successfully and indelibly shampooed were my own hands, which for days would have been more at home on a Kentucky Minstrel.

It was soon apparent that, once alight, the Monster was boss; a creature of vile moods, more temperamental than any film star. At times he would be in a scarlet frenzy, red-eyed and roaring defiance at me; burning and scorching anything within striking distance. At other times he would be in a dark and sullen mood, gloomily refusing to respond to my coaxing. In vain would I feed him succulent morsels of wood and coal.

I discovered, to my cost, that he was particularly allergic to sponge cakes. They seemed to bring out all that is worst in him, which is quite something. Small cakes or biscuits he might, when in favourable frame of mind and with considerable persuasion from me, bake to reasonable standards. But show him a sponge cake! Of course, I never antagonise him now by even attempting such a thing; not after the sad efforts which emerged, either charred to a cinder or like chewed leather discs. We live on small cakes now which require a minimum of time for his evil work.

"Come, Monster," I say encouragingly, "let's do some baking today." And I feed his ever-hungry jowl with more coal. He leers at me, drooling ash into a broken ash pan in obviously unco-operative mood. We do not bake today! Or else, with terrifying roar and the red of his eye glowing evilly, he will demand more and more coal, at the same time contriving to send his heat anywhere but into the oven.

I have further offended the brute by washing him! This indignity does at least reduce his capacity for smearing me and everything else in range with black marks. It doesn't improve his appearance of course. It does spur him on to more furious efforts, though, to frustrate my every attempt to do anything more than fry or boil!

"If this were my house," I threaten, "you would be my first contribution to the scrap-iron drive."

"But it isn't your house, is it?" he leers at me, and glowers across at the electric cooker, spending its days in idleness. I retire defeated, and he continues his Iron Rule.

But at last there is Hope on the Horizon! Even yet I may escape from this Black Tyranny. Power, that magic open sesame, is on the way, and already the poles and wires are comfortingly in place along the lane.

Soon I shall brush the dust from the electric cooker, which I begin to prize as highly as the Crown Jewels. Never again will I complain that it takes a long time to heat up; that it is extravagant! I shall remember the Monster! His shall be the final indignity of spending his days behind a curtain which is all ready to draw over his ugly form.

DIANA BERLOW

🌺 THE HAPPY PLAN

I am owned, or rather ruled, by two blue-eyed Siamese tyrants. As I watched all hope of yet another summer holiday receding into the distance, I thought it time to take stock of the situation and see how it came about.

Do not for one moment imagine that I wait hand and foot on two exotics too delicate and pampered to be let out of my sight. On the contrary, it is their appalling vitality, the rip-roaring lives they lead, on and around the farm, the hours they keep, and their voracious demands for this and that, which have reduced me to this abject state of slavery.

In the winter, things are comparatively quiet, except that no night is too cold, no wind, rain, or hail too violent to put a stop to their excursions around the buildings outside. This, of course, means that my bedroom window must be kept open—and wide open—to let them in. Unfortunately for me, a large tree is trained against the wall of the house and its highest branches are parallel with my room. Doors may be left temptingly open downstairs, a small window opens into the scullery, but these hold no fascination compared with the pear tree.

My room is small and narrow; if I close the window just enough to stop driving rain from hitting the opposite wall, I may be sure that a plaintive call will drag me out of bed to open it still wider.

Here again, with appalling subtlety, they lower my defences. Not for one moment would Simon dream of jumping, in a wet and dirty condition, on to my bed. He meticulously cleans his feet and has a lengthy wash and brush up before offering himself for a general rub down, at which he grumbles unceasingly and yet complains if it is neglected.

Then there is the food question. They do not eat what they ought to eat and they like entirely different dishes. Simon turns up his nose at liver, Minette sings its praise; even when the week's offal ration is smuggled into the house under layers of parcels. Minette likes cod roe, Simon detests it. He, on the other hand, would eat too many cornflakes; Minette will not touch them, or brown bread—she prefers dry cheese and unsweetened biscuits.

Both drink quantities of water. Simon begs for yeast tablets. Minette glares at me if I offer them to her. Rabbit, game and chicken provoke such deafening cries that they are hardly worth the agony of cooking. If I buy a "shop" cake, tasting strongly of baking powder and starch, a sooty paw is laid on my arm, weighing down every effort to get a slice into my mouth.

They both like to curl up on my knee together, settling happily down at the exact moment when the telephone bell rings, or I am hoping to sew or write.

As spring draws near the tempo increases. There is usually a noisy honeymoon followed by comparative quiet. Several weeks later every cupboard and drawer in the house is inspected, with a view to the nursery, by Minette (although she knows perfectly well exactly where her kittens will be born). She tears up newspapers and lines various unlikely sites with them; at the last moment she dashes to the box prepared by me and demands that I stay with her. If I move, or try to leave, she howls on a peculiar note heard on no other occasion.

When all is over, there are a few weeks of peace. Suddenly I realise that I now have five more minute, but terrible, tyrants. There are five little mugs to be smeared with milky mixture and taught how to lap; five creatures who are left by their mother on the wrong sides of doors and returned to at odd and unaccountable times; presently, five explorers who penetrate into every hole and corner of the house, like the fifth column before an advancing army; and, finally, five devils who find their way up the pear tree.

All through the cares of parenthood Minette and Simon never lose their affection for each other. She, like certain modern beauties, seldom washes her face. Simon does it for her. She greets him on his return from hunting with a peculiar trilling call. He, even when occupied with younger, more ravishing brides, hurries up to her and offers the daily courtesy of the beauty parlour.

As the kittens grow older, he proudly sleeps with them, washes them, and teaches them, by example, his own faultless manners in the house. Minette leaves this last duty to him; she is far too busy hunting at nights to bother with domestic details. She staggers across the lawn in the early mornings carrying rabbits bigger than herself. Rats of revolting size are laid tenderly among the astonished kittens.

One night, of terrible memory, she came up the tree and on to my bed. I stirred and spoke to her, but she did not answer. Struggling out of sleep, a little alarmed at her silence, I heard a choking. Sitting up in terror in the dark, I stretched out my hand to touch her. She was cold, wet, and somehow small. I grovelled under my pillow for the electric torch and shone it on to my free hand, which was tenderly stroking a large, dead rat clenched in the dreadful grip of Minette's jaws.

But the frenzied hunting dies down and all is quiet—too quiet. The five have gone, one by one, to carefully chosen homes. And yet, with each departure, at the sight of the agonized blue eyes, the desperately clutching claws, I ask myself: is this a betrayal?

I go sadly back into the empty house. The children have gone out into the world and it is time for the old people to settle down again together. I look at the two, sleeping quietly together, paws entwined. They do not bother to open their eyes, but something tells me that it would be a waste of time to plan a summer holiday this year.

KAY HILL

🌹 *The Village Shop*

Under the frying-pans close to the cheese,
old Mrs. Oliphant
stores the split peas;
And down by the cabbages ranged on the floor
a battle-scarred tabby sits
guarding the door.
Bees-wax and turpentine vie for a place
next to the button thread,
hard by the lace,
Whilst tucked in a tin by the paraffin lamps
shrewd Mrs. Oliphant
hides all the stamps.
Method in madness was never more planned,
for just in a trice can she
lay a deft hand
Straight on the vinegar, mouse-traps, and glue,
or the jam which the Rector is
so partial to.
Dear Mrs. O. only once went away,
(off in a char-a-banc
just for a day);
But leaving the shop to a feather-brained niece
meant poor Mrs. Oliphant
suffered no peace.
For how was so green an apprentice to know
the time-honoured secrets
of wise Mrs. O.?
How could so youthful a relative hope
to find some good customer's
favourite soap?
So now Mrs. Oliphant stays on her guard
safely confined in a
single square yard,
And all's in its place, and the place for the peas
is under the frying-pans,
Close to the cheese.

PAMELA STREET

374

THE BUCKET DOWN THE WELL

You must not think that because we have a well in our front garden, we are all behind the times. Oh dear no! Years and years ago they had a scheme and brought the water along in pipes. Everybody in the village has a tap in the scullery and some houses have even got a bathroom.

The well in our garden complete with lid, roller and chain is supposed to be the best as well as the biggest anywhere round; "turn a waggon and horses at the bottom of that well," old Fred Mackay told me. I've never been down so I can't rightly say as to that.

When the dry spell had lasted long enough to be called a "drouth" they sent round a bit of a printed paper to ask us not to use the tap water for the gardens. I like to be patriotic. "Good," says I; "now is the time to use the well water."

A few windings and I became quite an expert or do I mean an adept? Clipping the bucket on with a big spring hook, giving the handle a flick and the bucket, safe on the end of the chain, would race down the well quite on its own. All I had to do was to wind it up, or as they say hereabouts, wind it in.

Then one night I sent if off too fast for its good, and when I wound in there was no bucket, it was down in the well!

What was to be done? The garden fairly crying out for water, and none could I get. Now I remembered seeing a contraption, a sort of four-hooked grapnel, at old Tom Grey's, with which I thought I could retrieve my bucket. So next day being Saturday and my day off, I went to see Tom. Tom is our local carpenter and wheelwright. I found him busy, with the aid of strong glasses and bright sunlight, sharpening a saw. "Morning, Tom," I says. He turned his wise, kind, old face toward me, "Morning, boy." I'm over fifty and my hair is getting grey but everybody under eighty is a "boy" to Tom.

"I've lost my bucket, down the well." He made a sound that was expressive of a certain contempt of me, and satisfaction with himself, took down the grappling irons and gave them to me saying: "A hundred and twenty year old these irons be, don't you lose 'em or . . ." The punishment was, I suppose, beyond expression.

I was making the iron fast to a stout line when Fred and his dog Tip came up. Fred is shepherd at the farm; he loves his sheep, but better still he loves a gossip and as he has spent the whole of a long life in the village he is a walking biography of the inhabitants.

"Bucket down the well, wot?"

"Yes, I'm going to get it up," I dropped the line a few jerks and pulls and I got a "bite", up came bucket. "That bain't your bucket," exclaimed Fred, "Why 'tis Betsy Newman's, that went down the well a long time afore you came about here. I knows it by the brass bands." And he carefully examined the old bucket as if hoping to find a hall-mark.

"If it was Betsy's bucket why didn't she get it up?"

"'Twas like this, Betsy, a red-haired lass with a bit of a temper, was going to be married. Alf Greenaway the chap was called, lived t'other side the village. He came over one evening and they went to the well to get a bucket of water (like Jack and Jill, I murmured, but he didn't know anything about Jack and Jill). Well, they started argyfying as to the right way to clip on the bucket, he said one thing and she another till they very nearly came to blows. Betsy dashed the bucket down the well, and it didn't come up. Alf, he went on at her worse than ever. She rushed home; a few days and we heard she had gone to a "place" in Lunnon. Alf, he joined up, and that were that."

During this narration I dropped the iron again. The "bite" came and I pulled up a yet more ancient bucket. Fred scratched his head, "Why," he said, his face lighting up, "that's Sam Carter's bucket, his did have a chin handle. Used to live across the road, died afore you came about here.

"That bucket did for Sam. Must abeen the Boer War, cause I was only a nipper when it happened. Sam came across for a bucket of water and was havin' a chin-wag with old Daddy Green, when somebody came tearing across. 'Here, Sam, quick, here's a telegramph to say as your boy was killed at Mafikin and your wife's gone off in a dead faint.'

"Well telling bad news like that Sam left go the handle, and rushed home. His wife were coming round, but he didn't see that, he only thought of Sam his bright lad—dead—out foreign. That were really the end of Sam, he never perked up again, just divined away."

Fred told his sad story so well I had stopped my operations. "Now," I said, "third time lucky." The irons caught again. "That's your bucket," said Fred as it came into view, "cause I don't know it." His tone was one of relief. Taking an old pipe from one pocket and a shiny brass bacca box from another and thinking perhaps his sheep should have some attention, he lit up and, calling his dog, moved off. Tip having driven our cat to the top of the apple tree, was engaged in hunting for a flea in his rear portion. He, like his master, liked a break in the daily round and common task.

I carried the irons back to Tom, thinking how the very heart of the village, with its comedy and tragedy, can come to light through losing a bucket down the well.

G. A. R.

🌹 ZEBRA IQ

With a litter of puppies, children, jackdaws, rabbits, and so on to feed and clean, I haven't been able to spend my usual two evenings in town. So during the past few weeks, I've done a lot of driving to and from the country to the office. And when you do a lot of driving you are apt to notice a lot of things you've never noticed before, however familiar your route may be.

For instance, I've discovered that lorry drivers are quite the best drivers on the road, that 'buses expect you to know their stops by heart, that the most infuriating people are the ones who drive at thirty miles an hour in the middle of the road and remain completely deaf to any hooter. They probably prefer to think there is nobody behind them since they usually obscure their back windows with little nodding birds which drive you into a stupor as you strive to get past them.

Then there's the driver who hates to be passed. He goes along at a steady forty, and if you so much as hint you are going to pass him he ups speed and from then on his whole aim in life is to keep ahead of you. If you do eventually succeed in getting by him, his next aim in life is to get back at you, and long after you've forgotten all about him you will find him pulling up next to you at the lights and fixing you with a "thought-you-could-get-away-with-it-did-you" gleam in the eye.

I could go on for ever with driving types but I won't because I want to tell you about what I have discovered are the most fascinating road types of all, the Zebra crossers. I have collected —and am still collecting—quite an album of these and I am sure they'll be familiar to you all. In fact you've probably got a better collection than mine.

The curious thing that strikes me about Zebras is that although the Minister of Transport says they were instituted for the sake of the lame, the old and the young, these seem to be the ones who use them least. All the people who have crossed in front of me during the past fortnight, and there have been thousands, appear to be quite the healthiest specimens of our race—the sort who look as if they had all day to walk about at the pace which suited them best. In fact, it occurred to me at one moment that perhaps some of them actually cross and re-cross Zebras just for fun, like children who go up and down escalators and lifts. But I admit this might be a bit of motoristic prejudice.

What is so particularly interesting is the way one can so easily categorise the types. There's not a bit odd this way or a bit odd that way about them; they are absolutely one thing or another. Each of its kind, whether he or she be crossing the Strand or a village street, behaves in his or her categorised manner. It's really fascinating.

There are, I think, broadly seven different sorts of Zebra types: The Hesitator, The Disbeliever, The Ambler, The Cavalier, The Dictator, The Apologiser and The Complete Idiot.

I haven't any special preferences—they all do a fairly wicked wear and tear job on one's nerves, brakes and shoe leather. It's really only a question of whether one prefers to be scared stiff quickly or slowly, or whether one's patience can stand stupidity better than subservience.

With The Hesitator, for instance, who steps on to the crossing then steps back, then steps on again, this becomes a kind of Nuts-and-May situation calculated to take some sixteenths of an inch off your tyres and the soles of your shoes.

The Disbeliever, though perhaps not so nerve-racking, leaves one with the uncomfortable feeling that he or she is not quite human. This is just a waiting as opposed to a jerking operation, and I suppose only occurs when one is in a more generous and less hurried frame of mind oneself. The Disbeliever is seen standing at the edge of the pavement looking into the distance across the white lines. You stop, you wait, they continue to stare.

It then occurs to you that perhaps they are waiting for someone and don't want to cross at all, so you accelerate forward. And if you look in the mirror a few yards on, there they will be, still staring across the road. I have found one or two of this sort to cross over the moment you accelerate, but this is exceptional.

The Ambler can be sub-divided into three types: the couple with a retinue of children, a pram and a dog, the two women who are continuing their tea-table gossip into the street, and the young man, usually with a cigarette out of the corner of his mouth, who believes that Zebras were invented for his express use and he's something or other blowed if he's going to hurry for any blooming motorist.

This type makes me fairly cross but there's another who makes me far crosser and that's The Dictator. He marches on to the Zebra with hand upraised and demands that you stop immediately, be it a wet or icy road. Sometimes this type carries a brief-case and umbrella which are raised also.

The Cavalier is less obnoxious but can be rather tiresome if you are not feeling in the same jaunty mood as he is. This sort motions to you with his eyes that he would like to cross if it would be all right with you, and when you stop he either gives you a military salute or takes off his hat and bows low. Sometimes I wonder if this sort really mean to be very insulting.

Since it's best to be brutally frank about oneself I will now tell you the type I am. The Apologiser. I am, or he or she is, apt to stand at a Zebra because it's just a convenient crossing with an island, and when a car looks like stopping to wave it on. If it should stop then I (and my type) dash across as if I had committed the most gross offence, not daring even to snatch a glance at the driver as I go.

The Complete Idiot—well there's one of these in each type I've mentioned, but there are more definite examples, like the sort who just close their eyes and walk across, or those who get half-way across then decide to go back again.

Before I discovered the fascination of making a collection of Zebra-ites I used to spend a whole journey muttering under my breath all kinds of oaths against them. Simon, who likes to work out mild engineering theories, invented a silly kind of megaphone which would work off the horn with buttons on the dashboard which one would push or twist at the appropriate types. He invented dozens of suitable phrases which would issue from this megaphone like, "Suppose you've never had a chance to drive a car," "Cissy boy can't cross the road without a Zebra," "Ever tried to pull up on a wet road?" "Take your time, ladies," "Why don't you put an L plate round your waist." All very third form, of course, but I can't say I wouldn't be tempted to use the odd one occasionally.

BARBARA HARGREAVES

🌻 THE CALF

Jim and Mrs. Green had bought the little farm two years before; he'd been trained as an engineer really and getting on well, but suddenly they'd felt they couldn't bear a town any longer, so they'd taken their little bit of capital out of its safe investment and borrowed a bit more and bought thirty acres with a plain little house tucked away in Sussex.

It had been a big change, of course, to no one more than the two boys, Robert and little Jim, nine and seven in years but much more, now, in experience, who'd forgotten that there was anything in the world except fields and hedges, stock to be looked after and two miles to walk to school. Robert loved it all, but Little Jim, well, Little Jim worshipped it with a passionate love that none of the others could have understood, even if they had wanted to try.

He would wake in the morning, and watch the sunlight dappling the white-washed ceiling of his little attic bedroom and hear the branch of the pear tree rasping very softly in the wind, against his window pane. And, wriggling his toes under the sheets he'd know, with a deep, almost sick satisfaction, that out there, the animals were waiting for him, two small calves, the littlest pigs, his own, very own ducks, and Greylegs the old, old pony they'd bought at a farm sale, for pulling the small cart. Greylegs . . . who, if they hadn't bought him, would have been sold for dog's meat. Jim shuddered at the thought and, to reassure himself, leapt out of bed and tore to the window, to see that, really, Greylegs and the farm were still there.

Slipping on his clothes the small boy raced downstairs and plunged out of the back door. Robert was out already, getting steadily through his allotted jobs before breakfast and school. Robert would always be early. Little Jim would always be late, but then Robert hadn't had to gaze out of the window to satisfy himself that the farm was still there; Robert took the farm for granted, loved it, certainly, but never woke in the night wondering what the world had been like before they had a farm, never went to bed to clutch his knees and murmur ecstatically to himself that, one day, he would be a farmer— a real farmer.

Their tasks over the two boys sat down to breakfast in the little brick-floored kitchen, where the sun slanted on to a checked tablecloth, and their mother poured cream on to porridge from a jug with a crinkled lip. Big Jim came in from outside and sat down at the table; he was a quiet, giant of a man with a way with animals, and he never ceased to bless the day they had taken their courage in both hands and left the town for the lonely countryside.

Little Jim finished first and went to fetch cap and books while Robert jeered, "You must want to get to school an awful lot to start so early!" But his mother silenced him. She knew that the smaller boy, as part of a solemn morning ritual, must lean on each gate, inspect each crop and study the stock in all the fields beside the road on his way to school. She pushed him gently through the door.

The first part of his way led past their own land . . . roots in the Valley field coming up well, the hay in Patch Pocket needed some more bottom to it, the grazing in Hilly Acre was running out. Next, their neighbour Farmer Goode, a difficult man, they never knew quite how he'd take things; sometimes everything was all right, sometimes all wrong. The boys had learnt to be wary of him. Jim looked over the first gate appraisingly. Hay . . . better than theirs, because it had had more fertiliser.

This time last year, he remembered, their young stock had broken into the field and done a lot of damage. His father had had to work for Mr. Goode to compensate him, because money had been short just then. There, down by the pond, was the gap they'd broken through, mended safely, now, of course . . . but no . . . the small boy gasped, it must have been made again, because there, on the edge of the pond, were some yearlings, two roan shorthorns and a red and white. He threw his books on to the grass and scrambled over the gate, then, carefully keeping to the hedge, he ran as fast as his short legs would carry him, round the field and down the boundary hedge.

Just as he reached the cattle he stopped, there were four of them, not three, two roans, a red and a red and white, and the red one was up to her neck in the mud at the edge of the pond. He plunged down the bank, his feet slipping and sliding on the dried leaves and cow pats. The little heifer was giving agonised cries, almost at the end of her strength. All her efforts had resulted only in her getting more firmly fixed in the mud. Now, resigned to her fate, she rolled her eyes despairingly. Jim clasped his arms round her neck and heaved, the mud sucked and gurgled, but the heifer stayed where she was. He heaved again, still no result.

Five minutes later, covered in mud himself, his small hands hot and sticky, his curly hair streaked over his forehead and tears pouring down his cheeks, the little boy sat back on the bank. "It's no good," he sobbed, jerkily, "I can't get her, I can't, she'll have to die." He looked again at the little red head and the liquid brown eyes. "You don't do anything to help," he stormed. "I can't get you out, it's no good, I'm not big enough . . . if only you'd push, or something. I'll go for help and tell someone, but you'll be dead before they get here, do you hear . . . it's your own fault." And he scrambled up the bank, and toiled back the way he had come, giving a last look at the heifer as he went.

Suddenly, something made him glance at the other field—their field—and there, grazing peacefully, were their own yearlings, two roans, a red and a white and red; then those others must be Farmer Goode's. He heaved a sigh of relief. It didn't matter then that the little red heifer was stuck in the mud, someone else could get her out. And as if to remind him of her plight the red heifer gave a feeble bellow. Jim's face grew little and white and, with a sick feeling at the bottom of himself, he knew he'd got to go back and get her out somehow, otherwise she'd die and it would be his fault.

He undid his belt and slid once more down the bank and studied the position. If he'd something to cling on to it would be easier. That stump was too far away, but if his belt was hooked round it, like that . . . and some branches to dig his feet into, like that. . . . The little red heifer watched him and while he worked he talked to her gently, confidingly, till at last he was ready. Then, arms round her neck once more and with every ounce of strength he possessed gathered together, gasping, straining, heaving and sobbing, the small boy worked to free the animal, regardless of his surroundings and unaware that help was near at hand.

Farmer Goode saw the two figures from the top hedge and in a moment he was down at the water level heaving at the little red heifer's flanks, easing her from her muddy prison. Jim and the calf flopped on to the bank together and, between them, the man and boy rubbed the animal dry and left her to recover. Then the farmer lifted the small boy on to his shoulder and took him home.

Back at the cottage, Jim was too tired to do more than drink the lemonade his mother gave him and listen dazedly to Farmer Goode's voice. "He's a brave little chap . . ." the voice was saying. ". . . must have seen the calf and gone to help it."

And suddenly Jim knew with awful certainty that that wasn't how it had happened and, more dreadful still, he'd have to tell them and lose this big man's good opinion. Still the voice went on, "Just the sort of smart lad I'm looking for to give my cowman a hand sometimes, in the holidays, say, and Saturday mornings."

Jim gave a loud gulp. "But it wasn't," he said, in an anguished voice, "I didn't go to help her. At least I did, but then I couldn't, and then I saw she was yours anyway so I thought I wouldn't bother, and I'd only gone because I thought they were our ones in your hay again and you'd be cross. . . ." After which confused explanation he flung himself at his mother and clung to her.

Farmer Goode scratched his head thoughtfully. "That's another thing as would have to be right about a smart lad working for me," he said. "He'd have to be one as didn't mind telling me a straight story, even if it did tell against him." Then he coughed. "Saturday, my cowman's going to market with two cows, he needs a smart lad to help him in the cattle truck. Like the job?"

CATHERINE DENT

🌹 KENT

. . . Go, as in pilgrimage, to Canterbury. The excitement of the cathedral sitting above the city never fails me; but to stand inside the cathedral gate and look up at the great West front fills me with a huge and simple peace, rarely found. . . .

MRS. J. B. THOMAS, Llandyssul, Cards

. . . I will take you with me through the marsh to the coast, to the inhospitable point of Dungeness, where great ships come close to the shore and the wind always blows and the same families have lived and fished for generations. But it is cold on the stony beach; farther east are sand dunes and warm ribbed sea sand to scuff our toes in. We will go round the coast past Dymchurch to the faded, calm gentility of Hythe and so to blustering Folkestone. . . .

. . . Let us go inland again to the rolling hills and views of Goudhurst, Cranbrook and Ashford, where the fields have tall secretive hedges and flimsy netted screens flung round them to protect the precious hops and orchards from the chill spring winds. Oast houses, their pointed white-painted steeples like weather cocks, turned to the wind.

MRS. G. TEBBUTT, East Grinstead, Sussex

 Child on a Gate

Child on a gate, so raptly gazing,
Across the green fields of your mind,
At ploughland and pasture, sheep calmly grazing.
What secret, wonderful things do you find?

Do you see Nancy, so peacefully chewing
The cud of contentment, there in the shade,
Or is she a lion, her quarry pursuing
Through sombre green ways of jungle shade?

Are the gnarled trunks of the ash and oak,
Giants with arms uplifted in might?
Does a witch lurk there, in tall hat and cloak,
Waiting to ride the wild wind at night?

Does the sunlight glint on gossamer wings,
As fairies flit from tree to tree?
Do elves dance when the missel thrush sings?
Rejoicing with them to be wild and free?

Cherish your fancies, child, while you may.
All too soon the enchantment dies,
And the dazzle of life's bright clear day
Will hide the dream world from your eyes.

MRS. MARGARET KIRKUP

🌹 LINCOLNSHIRE

. . . We who live in this fertile open county by the sea have the winds to put life and energy into us. True they are sometimes idle winds, as we say, and blow through instead of round you, but that only makes the blood run faster and makes you square your shoulders and step out to keep it doing so. . . .

MRS. E. HAND, *Alvingham, Louth, Lincs*

🌹 NORFOLK

. . . The people here are friendly folk. I have got used to their way of saying they are now going to do something. (I once overheard one lady say to another in the street, "I now told her what you then told me") and a grassy lane is a "loke", and thunderstorms are always "tempests". . . .

MRS. L. F. GOFF, *Brooke, Norwich*

🌹 MONEY FROM MONSTERS

"Come and see the smallest horse in the world—come and see Midget, the world's smallest quadruped; only sixpence to see the smallest horse in the world." The barker must have recently acquired the word "quadruped" for he used it often— with obvious relish, and emphasising the U so that at first hearing it was not easy to recognise the word.

Whether it was this, or the advertised attraction, he was drawing good business. The sixpences poured in, mostly from children who had come with their parents to the horse and cattle show at Bellingham in Northumberland.

Behind the screen of canvas was a tiny shetland foal—well worth paying sixpence to see, not only because of her size, but also because she was very young and obviously well-fed and contented in her warm, sheltered stall.

The smallest-horse-in-the-world is one of the showman's oldest exhibits. "Smallest" horses were shown by the Romans and the Greeks in their hey-days and, I have no doubt, the Egyptians before them. Another exhibit which seems to fetch the crowds at country fairs and shows, is the biggest-rat-in the-world. The biggest-rat, is as East Anglian readers will have guessed, the coypu. This is a beaver-like creature with a remarkable resemblance to a giant rat. The coypu, although firmly established today in Britain and increasing in numbers, was originally imported from South America.

In the past monstrosities were attractive to a considerable percentage of the population. Showmen were well aware of this fact and they went out of their way to cater for the public's curiosity. Malformed animals, such as five-legged horses, multi-headed chickens and Siamese twins of various sorts all had great pulling-powers. Not long before the 1939–45 war an alleged bird-woman was being exhibited at Olympia in one of the circus side-shows. This poor female—she was an Asiatic of some sort—had a profile which was decidedly bird-like, her nose looked like a curved beak and doubtless this prominent feature was nightly titivated to make it look more like a beak than it normally did. Almost chinless, she was not a pretty sight and, to me at least, a pathetic one. The size of the crowds, however, who paid to see her, showed her to have a powerful attraction.

Francis Buckland, a prolific writer on natural history subjects during the mid-nineteenth century, made a speciality of investigating, and personally examining, any curious exhibits he heard of. He has left, in his writings, some interesting material. At one time whales and mermaids were both good money-makers. Whales it was impossible to keep alive for exhibition purposes and so they were either stuffed or otherwise preserved, frequently, one gathers, most inadequately. Buckland comments feelingly on the strong odours of some of these specimens. The mermaids were mainly fabricated or mummified creatures consisting often of a monkey's upper-parts with a big fish's tail attached. The Japanese were clever manufacturers of mermaids.

Even today preserved whales and alleged mermaids may be seen. In a museum in the Swedish port of Gothenburg, there is a specimen of a great whale which occupies a long gallery; the whale has been preserved with a chemical of particularly odoriferous qualities. When I went to see this exhibit it happened to be a hot day; I was very nearly overcome by the fumes. What the old-time pickled show-pieces must have smelt like can well be imagined.

Recently in Antwerp I came across a mermaid. She was rather a nice creature, obviously very contented and healthy in her commodious bath. She would come to the steps, at the side of her tank, and take pieces of chopped chicory in her lips, with a kissing noise, from the mouth of her keeper. She was a manatee from tropical seas. The manatee and its near relative the dugong, of Australian waters, are by many writers considered to be the original mermaids, so that my Antwerp mermaid was not quite such a fake as one might be inclined to think.

Hybrids, largely because of their comparative rarity, have always had a certain power of attraction. Personally, I find unusual hybrids rather pathetic creatures. Such animals as ligons and tigons are certain attractions—the ligon is the result of a liaison between a lion and a tigress and the tigon vice versa. If anyone could discover a genuine fox-dog cross I am sure it would prove to be a gold-mine in the side shows. I have searched in many parts of the world for such a specimen and utterly without success. The fox-dog cross is an evergreen chimera with an extensive and credulous following.

It is, perhaps, interesting to note that even now an investigation is afoot to discover some of these unlikely hybrids.

At one time the money-making power of the unusual hybrid was so strong that even the famous German wild-animal breeder Hagenbeck took to trying to create curious creatures. Hagenbeck was a most unusual man and he undoubtedly had a remarkable way with wild animals. He was the first man to train a polar bear, a notoriously difficult animal to control. Hagenbeck dealt in wild beasts just as a cattle dealer does in domestic stock. Great wild, red deer stags from the Carpathians

were trapped and sold to deer-forest owners in Europe and Britain for stud purposes; there were few wild creatures that Hagenbeck could not supply, provided he was given sufficient notice. At the same time Hagenbeck was in many ways far in advance of his times for he was one of the first—if not the first man—to create the open-air zoo. Today the open-air zoo is accepted as the pleasantest possible solution for both the confined animals and their admiring public.

Today fewer people want to see pathetic abnormalities or outrageous creatures; they are not averse to a peep at the smallest-horse-in-the-world or the largest rat but five-legged horses and multi-limbed chickens are not the draws they used to be. And that can only be reckoned as a good thing.

HENRY TEGNER

 # NORTHUMBERLAND

. . . I can understand strangers looking over the misty fells and thinking life must be quiet and dull stuck out here, I know the other side. Inside those plain stone farmhouses on the hillsides are warmth and comfort, plenty of activity, lots of fun and a jolly good cook, so that on returning from the infrequent jaunt, I think, "Well, maybe there is no accounting for tastes, but this is what I like."

MRS. E. HUNTER, *Hexham*

 # 600 MILES TO MILK A COW

Many hundreds of animal lovers the world over admit to being hopelessly tied and ruled by their animals, but in most cases these animals are of the cat and dog species. I am hopelessly ruled by a cow!

Queenie started her life on the estate of a rich banker, her future looked assured. White-coated herdsmen tended her and the best of everything was hers to command. But Queenie's ancestors let her down, her yield of milk after giving birth to her first calf was disappointing to say the least of it, but her herdsmen decided to give Queenie a second chance, and his faith was justified—she doubled her yield.

Thus with high hopes of being a famous member of a famous herd Queenie calved her third heifer calf. This was thirteen years ago come New Year's Day, and in those days the use of penicillin was hardly known for cows, and Queenie contracted bad mastitis. The usual blowing up of her bag did not work well and she lost her milk-giving capabilities on that quarter, so Queenie was packed off without pedigree or warranty to the local market.

Used as she was to the warmth of luxury cowsheds she shivered in the icy wind of the market, her baby calf shivered even more. No one started the bidding and then it began unnoticed by me who was engaged in ardent conversation at the side of the ring with my husband. A silence and the auctioneer's voice brought me back to consciousness of the going's on with the words, "Your cow, Mrs. Woodhouse," and when I protested that I hadn't given a bid he said I had waved my hand every time he had asked for a bid, as indeed I probably had as I gesticulate when talking.

Thus started my slavery, for Queenie came to my home for the rest of her natural life. What has that meant to me and my family? It has meant that with the most loving care, Queenie recovered her health and her lost quarter. It meant she was top of the county milk yield for small herds for five years, it meant she and I loved each other so much that we were never parted. She went where I went, she even went to the seaside with the family rather than leave her to others to milk. It meant when I was lecturing in Barnsley I came three hundred miles by train that night to milk her and after the morning milking returned to Bradford to give another lecture that next day—six hundred miles to milk a cow.

It meant that one freezing Christmas when I had a temperature of 102° I stayed up all night with her and safely delivered her twins coming the wrong way. She trusted me to see her through. Appointments were made or broken on Queenie's behalf, people laughed rather witheringly when I put Queenie first.

When I bought her the vet gave her ten days to live, she was so ill with pneumonia, yet in four weeks' time Queenie will be seventeen years old, still bright of eye, milking well and with a coat of silk.

Fifteen times I brought her out of unconsciousness with milk fever after her last calf. She had a terrible calving and the fire brigade had to pull her out of the cowshed drain where she had rolled. Everyone but my family said end her life. But we won through. Summer sun made Queenie strong again. As she chews her cud and thinks of the films she has appeared in, of her daughter who starred with Douglas Fairbanks in "The Charm", as she muses over all the cows and calves she has trained on my small farm to recognise her as head of the herd her memories must be happy ones.

Everyone asks after Queenie—many say, "is she still alive," with obvious wonder in their minds. When her walk was painfully slow after her last illness at calving, heads wagged, tongues muttered "poor old girl, she's had her day," they did not reckon on Queenie's will-power.

Queenie makes my life a burden when I have to leave a party, or give up a television engagement because I have to milk her; is she worth it? Yes! A thousand times yes! Her milk has reared my children as well as her own, her cream has made countless business associates feel mellow after a good meal, her deep brown eyes full of adoration have made me realise just how much we owe to the animal world for their undying affection. Long live Queenie.

BARBARA WOODHOUSE

❧ COOL, COOL WATER

"Where should we go for our holidays?" a mother of two small children said to me some time ago. And my answer was almost anywhere so long as there's water. For not even the most sophisticated space-man toy will keep a child so happily employed for so many hours as a quantity of H_2O. I was going to say "any child up to fourteen" and then I realised that, in fact, we all go on loving it long after we've finished splashing in it.

Why do you think we love water? Why do so many people go to the sea for their holidays—surely not just to breathe the ozone? And why do we like to idle back in a punt on the river when a grassy bank would do as well? And why are people's first remarks when they visit our house, "Oh, how lovely; you live by a river!" House agents have told me, too, that if there's any water on a property they want to sell they always mention it first (water as opposed to damp, of course) and it never fails to bring dozens more people to see it.

When I was given my first bicycle, at the age of fourteen, I used to go exploring all round the country looking for a stream or a lake, somewhere where I could swim or even wade. But our part of Essex was clay soil and an absolute desert. Thunder-storms turned ditches into raging torrents overnight, which were gone by morning.

I did find water: two lakes and a disused gravel pit; all three made by man, and none of them turned out either peaceful, beautiful or amusing which is what any stretch of water should be. In the first lake I sank up to my knees in mud, in the second one I got tangled up in slimy weeds, and in the third, well, it was fine for swimming, but the scenery left much to be desired. Sunbathing on yellow gravel gazing at a rusty old elevator system rather spoilt the effect.

My mother and I dug what she called a splash pool and I called a bird bath, at the end of the garden in an effort to have some water about the place. It quickly filled up with newts and scum and provided a gorgeous love-nest for all the frogs in the district. Nobody would have put a toe in it, but Mother grew aubretias and lilies all round the edge; and at least it was big enough to hold the moon's reflection which provided a certain romantic atmosphere when we got to the boy-friend stage.

But the sea is a different kettle of fish! The waves breaking on a rocky shore, the blue of it in the sun, the grey angriness of it in a storm, its moody beauty stirs something deep within us, in a way no other stretch of water quite achieves.

People who dislike it say it's a waste of good space. Those who like it can't explain why. "I don't know what you see in all that water," they say. But I just end up talking romantic nonsense. It's rather like trying to explain why you like a clock ticking in a room.

I still get the same childish excitement when we get a mile away from the sea and I know we are soon to catch a glimpse of it. "The sea, the sea!" the children shout out, and I smile as I, too, shout the same to myself.

I am not, of course, talking about what the children call "the boring sea". Sea where the waves break drearily on a lot of mud or grey pebbles or when roused from a kind of glum inertia roar up and smack the face of its concrete promenade. I'm talking about the Cornish seas, the Welsh and Scottish seas, which are still carving out after millions of years their own beautiful landscape. Where gulls wheel in and out of the hollows in the cliffs and cormorants bob about on the water like toy boats. Where it's a relaxation (for me) to sit for hours on a grassy verge of a little cove and watch the spray leaping up as the waves drum, drum, drum on the crags. Sometimes an extra heavy wave will dash the spray in my face and I lick the salt off my lips like a cat washes the cream off its whiskers.

I remember a whitewashed farm on the Pembrokeshire coast overlooking a sandy bay. I used to have long talks with Mrs. Evans trying to discover what sort of farming head-aches she and her husband had. Surely, there must be some snags, I thought, to living in such a beautiful place. Apart from the storms and the rock in the ground, they didn't appear to have any more troubles than anyone else in the farming profession and they certainly managed to do very well without snow or frost.

I was quizzing with an ulterior motive, really, for it has always been a dream of mine that I'll land up, one of these days, living on a farm near a rocky coastline!

Meanwhile, we have our river running through the water meadows, which now are at their best with the meadow sweet, willow herb and tall lush reeds. It's lovely to run across the lawn and dangle my feet in the water for a few minutes when the kitchen gets hot.

The river, too, at this time of the year becomes the ideal host to people who visit us. Last weekend the children and their friends spent their entire time there. It obligingly swelled its banks to the size of the Amazon for the children to play at Indians, it became the Sargasso Sea for under-water shark fishing, it expanded into the broad Atlantic ocean where a dinghy full of shipwrecked sailors bobbed up and down shouting for help. Later that evening for the benefit of the grown-ups who drew deck-chairs up alongside, it provided the reflected moon, a willow with a nightingale and the music of its own voice running over stones.

Perhaps this unexplainable pleasure we get from lakes, rivers and the sea comes from the very depths of our sub-conscious from the times when so much of the world was submerged. After all, fairy tales and legends are merely symbolic picture stories of those urges and dreams that lie deep in our souls; remember the little mermaid in the fairy tale who thought she wanted to come up on land and marry a beautiful prince, but in the end forsook all for the sea she couldn't keep away from? And do you remember the story of Europa and the white bull? Is it possible that these tales come from the jelly souls which first squirmed out of the water billions of years ago?

You know the sort of quack doctor who puts every complaint you have down to one thing—your feet, your teeth, your spine, too much acid, not enough iodine. If I were to turn quack I might easily prescribe looking at water for the following troubles:

Insomnia: Sit by the river and gaze at the weed moving endlessly in the flow of the water and you will find your eyes beginning to close and your whole tension relax.

Anxious husbands: Borrow a fishing rod, light your pipe and sit by the river till dusk.

Obesity, Liver, Head-aches: Learn to swim.

Children round your feet on a hot day: Fill up a galvanised bath, put it out in the garden and let them dunk themselves in it all day—or get the hose going.

There's nothing one need hate about water except the following: Water on the knee, water on the brain, water running down the walls. Maybe you can think of some more.

BARBARA HARGREAVES

🌹 LEICESTERSHIRE

. . . the best picture you could get is to stand atop of the Beacon Hill on a clear day, with the woods of Swithland at your feet, a carpet of blue in the spring, and there you can take in, in one panoramic glance, the beauties of this, the heart of England. I, for one, hope to live nowhere else.

MRS. L. TOLLEY, *Shepshed, Leics*

🌹 THE TALL SHIPS

Sailing ships hold for the landsman the same romance that farming has for the town dweller. We see only the poetry of billowing sails and intricate rigging, strange names painted on bow and stern, and the heartbreaking smallness of the boats, pitting themselves against enormous distances and the hazards of weather and wind. But as farmers, we know a little of the fight against the weather, we know there must be more to sailing than leaning bare-chested over the rail, cap tilted over a weather-beaten face, or sitting in the peaceful sunshine splicing rope.

So that when I went to Dartmouth to see the ships that were to take part in the International Training Ships Race from Torbay to Lisbon, my mind saw more than my eyes.

My eyes saw *Sagres* the Portugueseman, the biggest ship in the race, and *Creole*, next to her in size, owned by Mr. Stavros Niarchos and by his generosity enabled to compete, Royal

Naval College, H.M.S. Conway, H.M.S. Worcester and the Nautical College, Pangbourne.

I saw, too, the *Christian Radich* and the *Sorlandet* from Norway, the *Falken* and the *Gladen* from Sweden, the *George Stag* from Denmark.

Each ship was dressed overall with bunting and flags, and from every vantage point faces grinned and caps were waved, blue caps with pompons, white caps with an impudent tilt, gold braided caps and a Turkish fez.

When we arrived races were going on between crews from the various ships, using the 27-foot whalers belonging to the Royal Naval College. And straight away you would have known the crews were Danes, Swedes and Norwegians by the strange noises emerging from the mouths of the coxes who stood at their tillers waving a windmill of arm and body to keep their five oars to time. Who won I couldn't tell you . . . it didn't seem to matter.

The tall ships had been putting into the harbour all the week and that Saturday was to see the start of the race. Eleven nations took part and during the week they were at Dartmouth an Inshore Regatta had been arranged, so that something always seemed to be going on, and boat-loads of cadets, midshipmen and apprentices sailed about the water like water beetles. And seldom, anywhere, have I seen a nicer looking crowd of boys.

One might ask, I suppose, what possible training can boys who expect to go into twentieth-century navies get, in nine-teenth-century sailing ships, and I think the answer can best be given by quoting from the Souvenir Booklet issued by the Committee. "Sailing . . ." they say, "is not always a matter of fair winds and azure seas, but the ability to keep going in the face of physical fatigue, sickness and mental fatigue is essential in the career in which they are embarking, and the young officers soon find out, sometimes to their own surprise, that they are capable of more than they would have imagined."

As well as the niceness of the boys, we were struck with their youngness; many of them seemed hardly old enough to have come away from their mothers. What a very good thing it is, that they had.

KATHLEEN THOMAS

🌹 THE ROEBUCK

He stood quite still on the far side of the field, the evening sun slanting red on his shining chocolate coat, his chiselled head and beautiful branching antlers silhouetted against the skyline. He sensed, rather than saw, the man waiting at the edge of the wood; until he saw the light glance on the barrel, and then without effort, and moving swiftly, he made a wide semi-circle, jumping gracefully over the wire to regain the shelter of the forest.

There he waited, hidden in the deep shadow of a giant beech. Someone else was approaching over the ride: he saw her climb the style and walk towards the man. Their voices came clear over the evening air.

"If I don't," he said defensively, "they'll come more and more and I shan't have any wheat left."

She pleaded, insistently, trying to keep her anger in check, knowing she would gain nothing by losing her temper.

"But they take very little—why, its the rabbits coming back that are doing the damage—all this land you cleared—" she waved her arm towards the rotting piles of scrub and tree trunks that lay at the side of the field, "there are dozens under there now—it's they that are nibbling your corn."

He looked down at her, shining fair hair hanging thickly to her shoulders, her eyes sparkling blue with anger. He grinned appreciatively.

"So you don't want me to shoot them?"

"Please," she said, "don't, I love them so, you see. I come up here such a lot to watch them. They are so beautiful. Soon, we shan't have anything like this left in England if everything has got to be sacrificed to efficiency—and making money."

He thought for a moment, watching her. Then he pushed his cap back and rubbed his forehead. "Tell you what," he said, "if you come up here every evening till harvest time, and keep them off—I won't try and shoot them—how's that?"

"Oh I will," she promised eagerly. "I work in Intbridge, and get home at five—so I could be up here each evening by seven, and I'll stay until it's dark.

He smiled. "Not nervous?"

"Good heavens no." She laughed at the thought. "I should think I know every owl for miles around, I'll come—I promise."

The roebuck turned away and walked deeper into the woods after his deer, his hooves crackling the twigs and dead leaves as he passed.

She was as good as her word. Each evening the buck saw her walking slowly up and down the ride, or sitting on the fence where the primroses made a yellow misty path at the end of the clearing. The wheat was growing fast now, green and tempting, and with the warmer weather the flies and midges came out in swarms under the trees, worrying him. But he did not dare bring his deer out with a human being there. Sometimes the evenings were cold, with a strong gusty rain blowing across from the hills, and the curlews crying weirdly as they swooped in front of it. But still she came, walking with her head bowed, and dripping oilskins rustling against her legs, watching the wet corn ripple like the waves on the sea.

And now the Land-Rover would drive up with the same man in who carried the gun, and she would stop and talk— for hours it seemed, they would talk together, and there was no argument now—but much laughter. After it had driven off she would lean against the big oak gazing after it, her eyes dreamy, and she would stay like this for a long, long time. This puzzled the buck; in his world one either slept or ate, one didn't stand or sit doing nothing, except making a strange humming sound sometimes—rather nice to hear.

Then one evening in July, when the wheat stood strong and fine and the ears were filled with a delicious sweet milk, he saw them both, the man and the girl, coming up the ride together. The man had his arm round the girl as though she could not walk alone and she had her head against his shoulder. They stood close together by the stile, and her arms were linked round the back of his neck. Then they lay down in the grass at the side of the ride, and their voices were low and soft.

The roebuck did not know what happiness was, but he was aware of peace, and a great contentment. Warily he kept down wind, and leapt the wire fence. The deer followed him, and

399

together they browsed appreciatively on the tender heads of corn, turning time and again to watch the silent figures lying so near, ready to fly at the slightest movement. But none came; and gradually the old buck felt in his bones that they were safe now in this spot—and for always.

MARGARET TURNER